NATIONAL SAFETY COUNCIL
INJURY FACTS®

2013 EDITION

FORMERLY
ACCIDENT FACTS®

The National Safety Council, chartered by an act of Congress, is a nongovernmental, not-for-profit, public service organization. The mission of the National Safety Council is to save lives by preventing injuries and deaths at work, in homes and communities, and on the roads through leadership, research, education, and advocacy.

Injury Facts®, the Council's annual statistical report on unintentional injuries and their characteristics and costs, was prepared by:

Research and Safety Management Solutions Group:
Terry Miller, Senior Director, Research and Safety Management Solutions
Kenneth P. Kolosh, Manager, Statistics Department
Kevin T. Fearn, Sr. Statistical Associate
Kathleen T. Porretta, Technical Editor

Publications Department:
Melissa J. Ruminski, Editor
Jennifer Yario, Managing Editor
Bryan O'Donnell, Copy Editor
Ian Palmer, Senior Graphic Designer
Joy Tan-Pipilas, Production Coordinator
Tracy Haas, Editorial Assistant

Questions or comments about the content of *Injury Facts* should be directed to the Research and Safety Management Solutions Group, National Safety Council, 1121 Spring Lake Drive, Itasca, IL, 60143, by phone at (630) 775-2322, fax at (630) 285-0242, or email *rssdept@nsc.org*.

For price and ordering information, visit *www.nsc.org* or write Customer Service, National Safety Council, 1121 Spring Lake Drive, Itasca, IL, 60143, call (800) 621-7619, or fax (630) 285-0797.

Acknowledgments
The information presented in *Injury Facts* was made possible by the cooperation of many organizations and individuals, including state vital and health statistics authorities, state traffic authorities, state workers' compensation authorities, trade associations, Bureau of the Census, Bureau of Labor Statistics, Consumer Product Safety Commission, Federal Highway Administration, Federal Railroad Administration, International Labour Organization, National Center for Health Statistics, National Fire Protection Association, National Highway Traffic Safety Administration, National Transportation Safety Board, National Weather Service, Mine Safety and Health Administration, and the World Health Organization. Specific contributions are acknowledged in footnotes and source notes throughout the book.

Visit the National Safety Council website:
nsc.org

Table of Contents

The year 2013 marks the National Safety Council's 100th anniversary as an organization dedicated to saving lives by preventing injuries and deaths at work, in homes and communities, and on the roads through leadership, research, education, and advocacy. During this milestone year, NSC is taking the time to celebrate the accomplishments of the past while also planning for the future. NSC is proud of the role it played in helping to cut the unintentional fatality rate in half over the past century. But as we plan for the future, it is clear that current trends are not acceptable. Since 1992, the unintentional fatality rate has increased 16%, erasing some of the gains achieved earlier in the century. Given these trends, it is clear that "business as usual" is not acceptable and not sufficient to address current and future safety challenges.

As the rate of change accelerates in our society, so must the rate of safety improvement. It is anticipated that by 2050, the United States will have a population of nearly 400 million. If the current fatality rate remains stable at 39.4 deaths per 100,000 population, by 2050 more than 157,000 people will die every year in the United States from unintentional injuries. This level of loss is equal to 34,000 additional people dying in 2050 than in 2011. To maintain the current number of unintentional fatalities each year, we will need to decrease the fatality rate by 22% to 30.7, the lowest rate in U.S. history. Although this rate of improvement is roughly equivalent to the average rate of improvement achieved over the past 100 years, is it adequate? Is it acceptable to set a goal for 4.8 million people to die between now and 2050, or must we find ways to do better?

As part of its 100th anniversary, NSC explored safety issues that are likely to impact society in the years to come. Through this process, NSC identified five strategic safety issues that have the potential for significantly improving safety in the United States:
- Improve workplace safety through a systematic approach known as the Journey to Safety Excellence.
- Enhance motor vehicle safety by decreasing distracted driving, with a focus on mobile technology while driving.
- Improve young driver safety through enhancing Graduated Driver Licensing programs, educating parents, and encouraging additional parental involvement.
- Decrease the number of prescription drug overdoses through community outreach, state coalitions, and advocacy for new laws and regulations.
- Expand the network of Safe Communities America, collaborations of community leaders and organizations, employers, and citizens to execute focused strategies to reduce injuries and fatalities in their communities.

NSC is spending its centennial year engaging stakeholders, identifying partners, and refining strategies to address these five strategic issues. Over the next several years, NSC will work with members, elected officials, safety advocacy groups, and community groups to improve safety associated with these five areas and start reversing the current negative safety trends.

Unfortunately, the latest estimates show a continuation of the recent negative trend with a 1.7% increase in unintentional-injury-related deaths in 2011 compared to the revised 2010 total. Unintentional-injury-related deaths were estimated to total 122,900 in 2011 and 120,859 in 2010.

The resident population of the United States was 311,591,000 in 2011, an increase of less than 1% from 2010. The unintentional death rate in 2011 was 39.4 per 100,000 population – up 1% from 2010 and 16% greater than the lowest rate on record, which was 34.0 in 1992.

The graph on page v shows the overall trends in the number of unintentional-injury-related deaths, the population, and the death rate per 100,000 population. A more complete summary of the situation in 2011 and recent trends is given on page 2.

Changes in the 2013 edition

New content for 2013 includes graphic displays of overall injury fatality data and workplace injury data. Additionally, look for new data on:
- Safety impact of OSHA inspections
- Workplace nature of injury and part of body injuries
- Motor vehicle crashes by time of day and day of week
- Childhood drownings
- Fireworks-related fires

and *updated or expanded* data on:
- General mortality
- Occupational injury and illness incidence rates by industry
- Forklift injury trends
- Workers' compensation claims and costs
- Disasters
- Comparing safety of transportation modes
- Traffic safety issues – alcohol, occupant protection, speeding, among others
- Consumer product-related injuries
- Accidental deaths by state

We also are still receiving questions regarding a change made two years ago. Editions of *Injury Facts* prior to 2011 included estimates of disabling injuries. Starting with the 2011 edition, NSC adopted the concept of "medically consulted injury" in place of "disabling injury." This new definition was adopted from the National Health Interview Survey, a household survey conducted by the National Center for Health Statistics (NCHS). A medically consulted injury, as defined by NCHS, is an injury serious enough that a medical professional was consulted. Moving *Injury Facts* estimates from disabling injuries to medically consulted injuries provides several advantages. However, the primary motivation is that a medically consulted injury is a more inclusive definition that allows for more comprehensive estimates of the true burden of unintentional injuries. For more information, please see the Technical Appendix.

For more information on *Injury Facts* and other products, visit the National Safety Council's website at *www.nsc.org*, call Customer Service at (800) 621-7619, or contact your local Council chapter.

Unintentional-injury-related deaths, death rates, and population, United States, 1903-2011

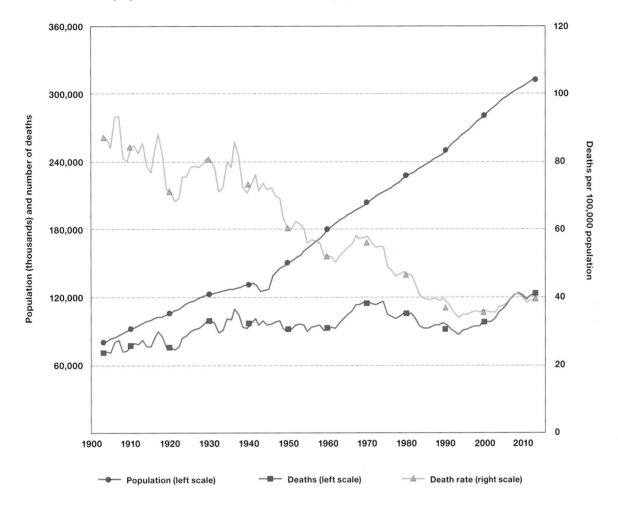

All Injuries

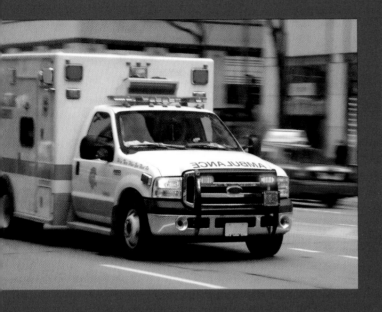

INJURY FACTS® 2013

Unintentional-injury-related deaths were up 1.7% in 2011, compared to the revised 2010 estimate. Unintentional-injury-related deaths were estimated to total 122,900 in 2011 and 120,859 in 2010. The 2011 estimate is 42% greater than the 1992 total of 86,777 (the lowest annual total since 1924).

The death rate in 2011 was 39.4 per 100,000 population – 16% greater than the lowest rate on record, which was 34.0 in 1992. The 2011 death rate was up 1% from the 2010 revised rate of 39.0.

Comparing 2011 to 2010, motor vehicle deaths decreased and home and public deaths increased, while work remained nearly steady. The population death rate for the motor vehicle class declined and the public and work rates stayed the same, while the home rate increased.

The motor vehicle death total was down 2.1% in 2011. The 2011 mileage death rate of 1.18 per 100,000,000 vehicle miles was down 1% from the revised 2010 rate of 1.19, and is the lowest on record. The 2011 rate is down 3% from the revised 2009 rate of 1.22.

According to the latest final data (2010), unintentional injuries continued to be the fifth leading cause of death, exceeded only by heart disease, cancer, stroke, and chronic lower respiratory diseases.

Nonfatal injuries also affect millions of Americans. In 2011, 37 million people – about 1 out of 8 – sought medical attention.

The economic impact of these fatal and nonfatal unintentional injuries amounted to $753.0 billion in 2011. This is equivalent to about $2,400 per capita, or about $6,300 per household. These are costs that every individual and household pays whether directly out of pocket, through higher prices for goods and services, or through higher taxes.

Between 1912 and 2011, unintentional-injury-related deaths per 100,000 population were reduced 50% (after adjusting for the classification change in 1948) from 82.5 to 39.4. The reduction in the overall rate during a period when the nation's population tripled has resulted in 5,900,000 fewer people being killed due to unintentional injuries than there would have been if the rate had not been reduced.

All unintentional injuries, 2011

Class	Deaths	Change from 2010	Deaths per 100,000 people	Medically consulted injuries[a]
All classes[b]	122,900	1.7%	39.4	37,000,000
Motor vehicle	34,600	-2%	11.1	3,700,000
Public nonwork	*32,797*			*3,600,000*
Work	*1,603*			*100,000*
Home	*200*			*(c)*
Work	3,909	<1%	1.3	5,000,000
Non-motor vehicle	*2,306*			*4,900,000*
Motor vehicle	*1,603*			*100,000*
Home	60,600	4%	19.4	18,800,000
Non-motor vehicle	*60,400*			*18,800,000*
Motor vehicle	*200*			*(c)*
Public	25,500	1%	8.2	9,700,000

Source: National Safety Council estimates (rounded) based on data from the National Center for Health Statistics (NCHS), state departments of health, and state traffic authorities, except for the work figures, which are from the Bureau of Labor Statistics Census of Fatal Occupational Injuries (CFOI). The National Safety Council adopted the CFOI count for work-related unintentional injuries beginning with 1992. See the Glossary for definitions and the Technical Appendix for estimating procedures. Beginning with 1999 data, deaths are classified according to the 10th revision of the International Classification of Diseases. Caution should be used in comparing data classified under the two systems.
[a]The totals shown are approximations based on the National Safety Council's analysis of National Health Interview Survey results that is conducted by NCHS. The totals are the best estimates for the current year. They should not, however, be compared with totals shown in previous editions of this book to indicate year-to-year changes or trends. See the Glossary for definitions and the Technical Appendix for estimating procedures.
[b]Deaths and injuries above for the four separate classes add to more than the "All classes" figures due to rounding and because some deaths and injuries are included in more than one class. For example, 1,603 work deaths involved motor vehicles and are in both the work and motor vehicle totals, and 200 motor vehicle deaths occurred on home premises and are in both home and motor vehicle. The total of such duplication amounted to about 1,803 deaths and 200,000 injuries in 2011.
[c]Less than 10,000.

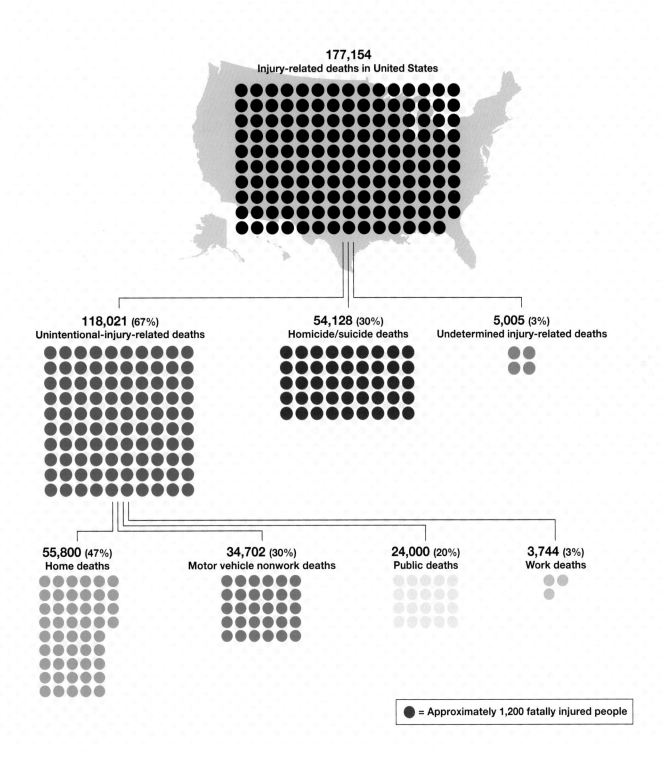

4,000,000
Injury-related deaths worldwide

177,154
Injury-related deaths in United States

118,021 (67%)
Unintentional-injury-related deaths

54,128 (30%)
Homicide/suicide deaths

5,005 (3%)
Undetermined injury-related deaths

55,800 (47%)
Home deaths

34,702 (30%)
Motor vehicle nonwork deaths

24,000 (20%)
Public deaths

3,744 (3%)
Work deaths

● = Approximately 1,200 fatally injured people

Unintentional-injury-related deaths by class, United States, 2011

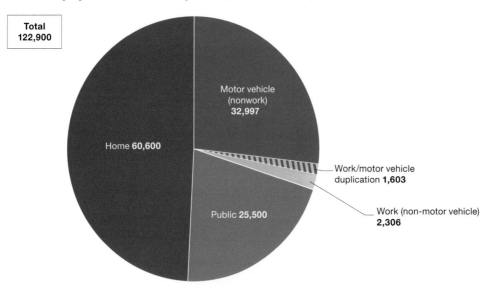

Total
122,900

Motor vehicle
(nonwork)
32,997

Home **60,600**

Work/motor vehicle
duplication **1,603**

Public **25,500**

Work (non-motor vehicle)
2,306

Unintentional medically consulted injuries by class, United States, 2011

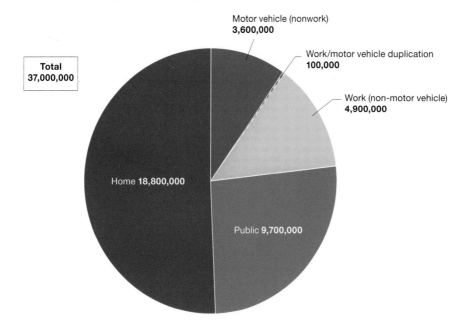

Motor vehicle (nonwork)
3,600,000

Work/motor vehicle duplication
100,000

Total
37,000,000

Work (non-motor vehicle)
4,900,000

Home **18,800,000**

Public **9,700,000**

In 1912, the First Cooperative Safety Congress met in Milwaukee. The meeting was attended by representatives of industry, government, insurance, and others. The most important result of this Congress was the decision to form a "permanent body devoted to the promotion of safety to human life in the industries of the U.S." One year later, during the Second Safety Congress, the National Safety Council was created. At this same time, unintentional-injury-related deaths were occurring at a staggering pace of 82.4 deaths per 100,000 population. Since then, the "safety movement" has contributed to the 50% reduction (after adjusting for the classification change in 1948) in the unintentional-injury rate to its current level of 39.4. The reduction in the overall rate during a period when the nation's population tripled has resulted in 5,900,000 fewer people being killed due to unintentional injuries than there would have been if the rate had not been reduced.

Lives saved from 1912 to 2011, United States

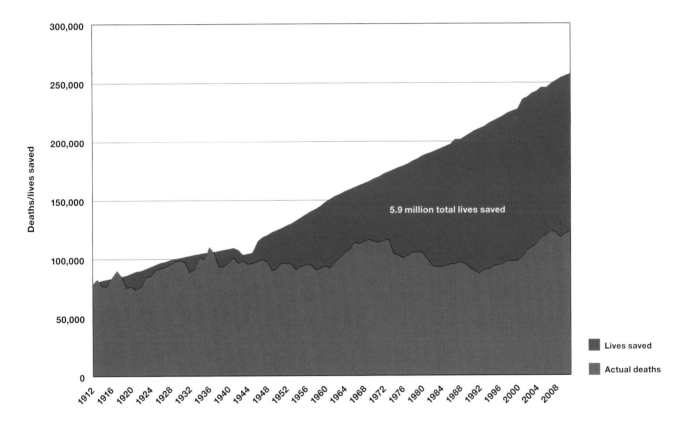

The total cost of unintentional injuries in 2011, $753 billion, includes estimates of economic costs of fatal and nonfatal unintentional injuries together with employers' uninsured costs, vehicle damage costs, and fire losses. Wage and productivity losses, medical expenses, administrative expenses, and employers' uninsured costs are included in all four classes of injuries. Cost components unique to each class are identified below.

Motor vehicle crash costs include property damage from motor vehicle incidents. Work costs include the value of property damage in on-the-job motor vehicle incidents and fires. Home and public costs include estimated fire losses, but do not include other property damage costs.

Besides the estimated $753 billion in economic losses from unintentional injuries in 2011, lost quality of life from those injuries is valued at an additional $3,611.5 billion, making the comprehensive cost $4,364.5 billion in 2011.

Several cost benchmarks were updated for the 2005-2006 edition of *Injury Facts*, making 2004 and later costs not comparable to previous years. The method for estimating the number of medically attended injuries by class was revised to use the latest National Health Interview Survey data. Estimated property damage costs in motor vehicle crashes were re-benchmarked using data from the National Highway Traffic Safety Administration. The value of a statistical life also was updated, which affects only the comprehensive cost mentioned in the paragraph above.

Certain costs of unintentional injuries by class, 2011 ($ billions)

Cost	Total[a]	Motor vehicle	Work	Home	Public non-motor vehicle
Total	$753.0	$263.8	$188.9	$206.7	$115.9
Wage and productivity losses	363.7	85.0	86.7	126.6	69.6
Medical expenses	197.9	57.7	52.3	56.4	34.7
Administrative expenses[b]	118.8	78.3	34.2	11.3	7.1
Motor vehicle damage	40.6	40.6	2.4	(c)	(c)
Employers' uninsured costs	20.3	2.2	10.5	5.1	2.9
Fire loss	11.7	(c)	2.8	7.3	1.6

Source: National Safety Council estimates. See the Technical Appendix. Cost-estimating procedures were revised extensively for the 1993 edition of Accident Facts. In general, cost estimates are not comparable from year to year. As additional data or new benchmarks become available, they are used from that point forward. Previously estimated figures are not revised.

[a]Duplication between work and motor vehicle, which amounted to $22.3 billion, was eliminated from the total.

[b]Home and public insurance administration costs may include costs of administering medical treatment claims for some motor vehicle injuries filed through health insurance plans.

[c]Not included, see comments above.

Costs of unintentional injuries by class, 2011

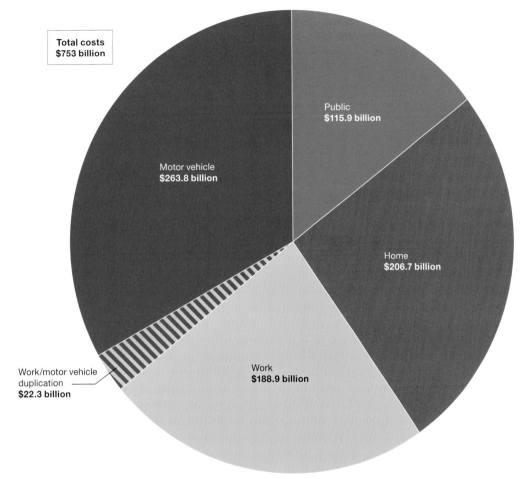

Total costs
$753 billion

Public
$115.9 billion

Motor vehicle
$263.8 billion

Home
$206.7 billion

Work/motor vehicle
duplication
$22.3 billion

Work
$188.9 billion

Wage and productivity losses

A person's contribution to the wealth of the nation usually is measured in terms of wages and household production. The total of wages and fringe benefits, together with an estimate of the replacement-cost value of household services, provides an estimate of this lost productivity. Also included is travel delay for motor vehicle incidents.

Medical expenses

Doctor fees; hospital charges; the cost of medicines; future medical costs; and ambulance, helicopter, and other emergency medical services are included.

Administrative expenses

Includes the administrative cost of public and private insurance, as well as police and legal costs. Private insurance administrative costs are the difference between premiums paid to insurance companies and claims paid out by them. It is their cost of doing business and a part of the cost total. Claims paid by insurance companies are not identified separately, as every claim is compensation for losses such as wages, medical expenses, property damage, etc.

Motor vehicle damage

Includes the value of damage to vehicles from motor vehicle crashes. The cost of normal wear and tear to vehicles is not included.

Employers' uninsured costs

This is an estimate of the uninsured costs incurred by employers, representing the dollar value of time lost by uninjured workers. It includes time spent investigating and reporting injuries, administering first aid, hiring and training replacement workers, and the extra cost of overtime for uninjured workers.

Fire loss

Includes losses from both structure fires and nonstructure fires, such as vehicles, outside storage, crops, and timber.

Work – motor vehicle duplication

The cost of motor vehicle crashes that involve people in the course of their work is included in both classes, but the duplication is eliminated from the total. The duplication in 2011 amounted to $22.3 billion and consists of $4.2 billion in wage and productivity losses, $3.2 billion in medical expenses, $12.1 billion in administrative expenses, $2.4 billion in vehicle damage, and $0.4 billion in employers' uninsured costs.

Costs of unintentional injuries by component, 2011

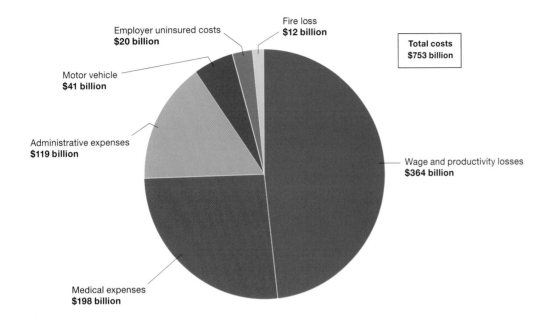

Fire loss
$12 billion

Employer uninsured costs
$20 billion

Motor vehicle
$41 billion

Administrative expenses
$119 billion

Total costs
$753 billion

Wage and productivity losses
$364 billion

Medical expenses
$198 billion

Cost Equivalents

The costs of unintentional injuries are immense – billions of dollars. Because figures this large can be difficult to comprehend, it is sometimes useful to reduce the numbers to a more understandable scale by relating them to quantities encountered in daily life. The table below shows how the costs of unintentional injuries compare to common quantities such as taxes, corporate profits, or stock dividends.

Cost equivalents, 2011

The cost of...	Is equivalent to...
...All injuries ($753.0 billion)	...70 cents of every dollar paid in federal personal income taxes, **or** ...51 cents of every dollar spent on food in the United States.
...Motor vehicle crashes ($263.8 billion)	...purchasing 300 gallons of gasoline for each registered vehicle in the United States, **or** ...more than $1,200 per licensed driver.
...Work injuries ($188.9 billion)	...23 cents of every dollar of corporate dividends to stockholders, **or** ...10 cents of every dollar of pre-tax corporate profits, **or** ...exceeds the combined profits reported by the 16 largest Fortune 500 companies.
...Home injuries ($206.7 billion)	...a $493,900 rebate on each new single-family home built, **or** ...47 cents of every dollar of property taxes paid.
...Public injuries ($115.9 billion)	...a $12.6 million grant to each public library in the United States, **or** ...a $103,100 bonus for each police officer and firefighter.

Source: National Safety Council estimates.

Type of event and age of victim

All unintentional injuries

The term "unintentional" covers most deaths from injury and poisoning. Excluded are homicides (including legal intervention), suicides, deaths for which none of these categories can be determined, and war deaths.

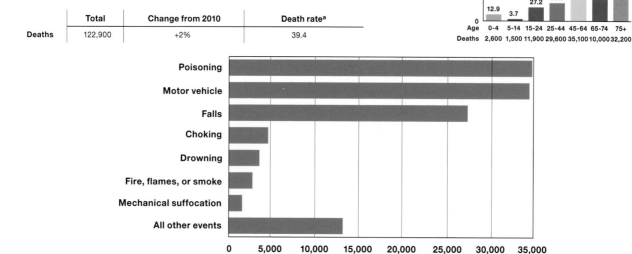

	Total	Change from 2010	Death rate[a]
Deaths	122,900	+2%	39.4

Poisoning

Includes deaths from drugs, medicines, other solid and liquid substances, and gases and vapors. Excludes poisonings from spoiled foods, *Salmonella*, etc., which are classified as disease deaths.

	Total	Change from 2010	Death rate[a]
Deaths	34,900	+6%	11.2

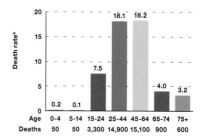

Motor vehicle incidents

Includes deaths involving mechanically or electrically powered highway-transport vehicles in motion (except those on rails), both on and off the highway or street.

	Total	Change from 2010	Death rate[a]
Deaths	34,600	-2%	11.1

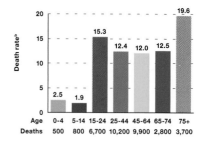

Falls

Includes deaths from falls from one level to another or on the same level. Excludes falls in or from transport vehicles, or while boarding or alighting from them.

	Total	Change from 2010	Death rate[a]
Deaths	27,500	+6%	8.8

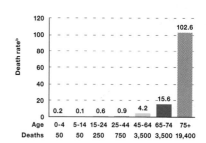

See footnotes on page 11.

Type of event and age of victim

Choking

Includes deaths from unintentional ingestion or inhalation of food or other objects resulting in the obstruction of respiratory passages.

	Total	Change from 2010	Death rate[a]
Deaths	4,600	+1%	1.5

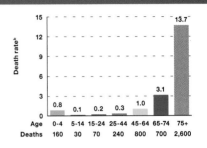

Drowning

Includes non-transport-related drownings such as those resulting from swimming, playing in the water, or falling in. Excludes drownings in floods and other cataclysms, which are classified to the cataclysm, and boating-related drownings.

	Total	Change from 2010	Death rate[a]
Deaths	3,600	-5%	1.2

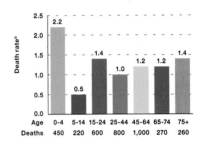

Fire, flames, or smoke

Includes deaths from exposure to fire, flames, or smoke, and from injuries in fires such as falls and struck by falling objects. Excludes burns from hot objects or liquids.

	Total	Change from 2010	Death rate[a]
Deaths	2,800	+1%	0.9

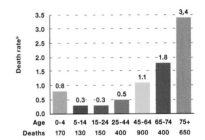

Mechanical suffocation

Includes deaths from hanging and strangulation, and suffocation in enclosed or confined spaces; cave-ins; or by bed clothes, plastic bags, or similar materials.

	Total	Change from 2010	Death rate[a]
Deaths	1,600	(c)	0.5

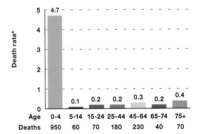

All other types

Most important types included are natural heat or cold; firearms; struck by or against object; machinery; electric current; and air, water, or rail transport.

	Total	Change from 2010	Death rate[a]
Deaths	13,300	-3%	4.3

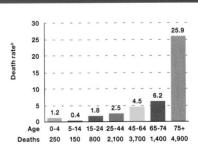

Note: Category descriptions have changed due to the adoption of the 10th revision of the International Classification of Diseases. See the Technical Appendix for comparability.
[a]*Deaths per 100,000 population.*
[b]*Deaths per 100,000 population in each age group.*
[c]*Change less than 0.5%.*

Unintentional injuries are the fifth leading cause of death overall and first among people ages 1 to 44. By single year of age, unintentional injuries are the leading cause of death from age 1 to 42.

Causes are ranked for both sexes combined. Some leading causes for males and females separately may not be shown. Beginning with 1999 data, deaths are classified according to the 10th revision of the *International Classification of Diseases*. See the Technical Appendix for comparability.

Deaths and death rates by age and sex, 2009

Cause	Number of deaths			Death rates[a]		
	Total	Male	Female	Total	Male	Female
All ages[b]						
All causes	**2,437,163**	**1,217,379**	**1,219,784**	**793.8**	**803.8**	**784.1**
Heart disease	599,413	307,225	292,188	195.2	202.9	187.8
Cancer (malignant neoplasms)	567,628	296,763	270,865	184.9	195.9	174.1
Chronic lower respiratory diseases	137,353	65,119	72,234	44.7	43.0	46.4
Stroke (cerebrovascular disease)	128,842	52,073	76,769	42.0	34.4	49.4
Unintentional injuries	**118,021**	**75,022**	**42,999**	**38.4**	**49.5**	**27.6**
Motor vehicle	36,216	25,430	10,786	11.8	16.8	6.9
Poisoning	31,758	20,577	11,181	10.3	13.6	7.2
Falls	24,792	12,724	12,068	8.1	8.4	7.8
Choking[c]	4,370	2,317	2,053	1.4	1.5	1.3
Drowning	3,517	2,724	793	1.1	1.8	0.5
All other unintentional injuries	17,368	11,250	6,118	5.7	7.4	3.9
Alzheimer's disease	79,003	23,900	55,103	25.7	15.8	35.4
Diabetes mellitus	68,705	35,054	33,651	22.4	23.1	21.6
Influenza or pneumonia	53,692	25,128	28,564	17.5	16.6	18.4
Nephritis or nephrosis	48,935	23,930	25,005	15.9	15.8	16.1
Suicide	36,909	29,089	7,820	12.0	19.2	5.0
Younger than 1						
All causes	**26,412**	**14,823**	**11,589**	**619.8**	**680.4**	**556.4**
Congenital anomalies	5,319	2,766	2,553	124.8	127.0	122.6
Short gestation or low birth weight, n.e.c.	4,538	2,547	1,991	106.5	116.9	95.6
Sudden infant death syndrome	2,226	1,304	922	52.2	59.9	44.3
Maternal complications of pregnancy	1,608	912	696	37.7	41.9	33.4
Unintentional injuries	**1,181**	**699**	**482**	**27.7**	**32.1**	**23.1**
Mechanical suffocation	853	511	342	20.0	23.5	16.4
Motor vehicle	95	54	41	2.2	2.5	2.0
Choking[c]	54	29	25	1.3	1.3	1.2
Drowning	45	25	20	1.1	1.1	1.0
Fire, flames, or smoke	24	14	10	0.6	0.6	0.5
All other unintentional injuries	110	66	44	2.6	3.0	2.1
Complications of placenta, cord, or membranes	1,064	573	491	25.0	26.3	23.6
Bacterial sepsis	652	368	284	15.3	16.9	13.6
Respiratory distress	595	352	243	14.0	16.2	11.7
Circulatory system disease	581	327	254	13.6	15.0	12.2
Neonatal hemorrhage	517	315	202	12.1	14.5	9.7
1-4 years						
All causes	**4,450**	**2,495**	**1,955**	**26.1**	**28.7**	**23.5**
Unintentional injuries	**1,466**	**925**	**541**	**8.6**	**10.6**	**6.5**
Motor vehicle	479	279	200	2.8	3.2	2.4
Drowning	450	298	152	2.6	3.4	1.8
Fire, flames, or smoke	167	104	63	1.0	1.2	0.8
Choking[c]	64	45	19	0.4	0.5	0.2
Mechanical suffocation	61	39	22	0.4	0.4	0.3
All other unintentional injuries	245	160	85	1.4	1.8	1.0
Congenital anomalies	464	230	234	2.7	2.6	2.8
Homicide	376	188	188	2.2	2.2	2.3
Cancer (malignant neoplasms)	350	180	170	2.1	2.1	2.0
Heart disease	154	77	77	0.9	0.9	0.9
Influenza or pneumonia	146	64	82	0.9	0.7	1.0
Septicemia	71	40	31	0.4	0.5	0.4
Chronic lower respiratory diseases	66	36	30	0.4	0.4	0.4
Perinatal period	58	33	25	0.3	0.4	0.3
Benign neoplasms	53	30	23	0.3	0.3	0.3

See source and footnotes on page 14.

Deaths and death rates by age and sex, 2009 (cont.)

Cause	Number of deaths			Death rates[a]		
	Total	Male	Female	Total	Male	Female
5-14 years						
All causes	**5,651**	**3,248**	**2,403**	**13.9**	**15.6**	**12.1**
Unintentional injuries	**1,689**	**1,052**	**637**	**4.2**	**5.1**	**3.2**
Motor vehicle	*974*	*571*	*403*	*2.4*	*2.8*	*2.0*
Drowning	*209*	*153*	*56*	*0.5*	*0.7*	*0.3*
Fire, flames, or smoke	*141*	*76*	*65*	*0.3*	*0.4*	*0.3*
Mechanical suffocation	*50*	*44*	*6*	*0.1*	*0.2*	*0.0*
Poisoning	*50*	*25*	*25*	*0.1*	*0.1*	*0.1*
All other unintentional injuries	*265*	*183*	*82*	*0.7*	*0.9*	*0.4*
Cancer (malignant neoplasms)	896	488	408	2.2	2.4	2.1
Congenital anomalies	364	206	158	0.9	1.0	0.8
Homicide	305	196	109	0.8	0.9	0.5
Suicide	265	175	90	0.7	0.8	0.5
Influenza or pneumonia	228	114	114	0.6	0.5	0.6
Heart disease	217	112	105	0.5	0.5	0.5
Chronic lower respiratory diseases	123	77	46	0.3	0.4	0.2
Benign neoplasms	85	51	34	0.2	0.2	0.2
Stroke (cerebrovascular disease)	74	45	29	0.2	0.2	0.1
15-24 years						
All causes	**30,416**	**22,312**	**8,104**	**70.6**	**100.8**	**38.7**
Unintentional injuries	**12,458**	**9,239**	**3,219**	**28.9**	**41.7**	**15.4**
Motor vehicle	*7,688*	*5,458*	*2,230*	*17.8*	*24.6*	*10.7*
Poisoning	*3,044*	*2,329*	*715*	*7.1*	*10.5*	*3.4*
Drowning	*548*	*490*	*58*	*1.3*	*2.2*	*0.3*
Falls	*192*	*173*	*19*	*0.4*	*0.8*	*0.1*
Fire, flames, or smoke	*142*	*87*	*55*	*0.3*	*0.4*	*0.3*
All other unintentional injuries	*844*	*702*	*142*	*2.0*	*3.2*	*0.7*
Homicide	4,862	4,205	657	11.3	19.0	3.1
Suicide	4,371	3,595	776	10.1	16.2	3.7
Cancer (malignant neoplasms)	1,636	993	643	3.8	4.5	3.1
Heart disease	1,035	687	348	2.4	3.1	1.7
Congenital anomalies	457	263	194	1.1	1.2	0.9
Influenza or pneumonia	418	224	194	1.0	1.0	0.9
Complicated pregnancy	227	0	227	0.5	0.0	1.1
Stroke (cerebrovascular disease)	193	108	85	0.4	0.5	0.4
Chronic lower respiratory diseases	187	108	79	0.4	0.5	0.4
25-34 years						
All causes	**42,502**	**29,199**	**13,303**	**102.3**	**137.6**	**65.4**
Unintentional injuries	**14,062**	**10,532**	**3,530**	**33.8**	**49.6**	**17.4**
Poisoning	*6,209*	*4,488*	*1,721*	*14.9*	*21.1*	*8.5*
Motor vehicle	*5,887*	*4,433*	*1,454*	*14.2*	*20.9*	*7.1*
Drowning	*396*	*331*	*65*	*1.0*	*1.6*	*0.3*
Falls	*302*	*253*	*49*	*0.7*	*1.2*	*0.2*
Fire, flames, or smoke	*200*	*135*	*65*	*0.5*	*0.6*	*0.3*
All other unintentional injuries	*1,068*	*892*	*176*	*2.6*	*4.2*	*0.9*
Suicide	5,320	4,293	1,027	12.8	20.2	5.0
Homicide	4,222	3,481	741	10.2	16.4	3.6
Cancer (malignant neoplasms)	3,659	1,807	1,852	8.8	8.5	9.1
Heart disease	3,174	2,164	1,010	7.6	10.2	5.0
Human immunodeficiency virus infection	881	561	320	2.1	2.6	1.6
Influenza or pneumonia	807	422	385	1.9	2.0	1.9
Diabetes mellitus	604	353	251	1.5	1.7	1.2
Stroke (cerebrovascular disease)	537	298	239	1.3	1.4	1.2
Chronic liver disease or cirrhosis	459	305	154	1.1	1.4	0.8
35-44 years						
All causes	**74,665**	**46,555**	**28,110**	**179.8**	**223.2**	**136.0**
Unintentional injuries	**15,102**	**10,649**	**4,453**	**36.4**	**51.1**	**21.5**
Poisoning	*7,388*	*4,788*	*2,600*	*17.8*	*23.0*	*12.6*
Motor vehicle	*5,066*	*3,767*	*1,299*	*12.2*	*18.1*	*6.3*
Falls	*551*	*438*	*113*	*1.3*	*2.1*	*0.5*
Drowning	*392*	*329*	*63*	*0.9*	*1.6*	*0.3*
Fire, flames, or smoke	*233*	*148*	*85*	*0.6*	*0.7*	*0.4*
All other unintentional injuries	*1,472*	*1,179*	*293*	*3.5*	*5.7*	*1.4*
Cancer (malignant neoplasms)	12,519	5,398	7,121	30.1	25.9	34.4
Heart disease	11,081	7,738	3,343	26.7	37.1	16.2
Suicide	6,677	5,142	1,535	16.1	24.7	7.4
Homicide	2,762	2,122	640	6.7	10.2	3.1
Chronic liver disease or cirrhosis	2,481	1,648	833	6.0	7.9	4.0
Human immunodeficiency virus infection	2,425	1,689	736	5.8	8.1	3.6
Stroke (cerebrovascular disease)	1,916	1,044	872	4.6	5.0	4.2
Diabetes mellitus	1,872	1,208	664	4.5	5.8	3.2
Influenza or pneumonia	1,314	732	582	3.2	3.5	2.8

See source and footnotes on page 14.

Deaths and death rates by age and sex, 2009 (cont.)

Cause	Number of deaths			Death rates[a]		
	Total	Male	Female	Total	Male	Female
45-54 years						
All causes	**187,568**	**114,820**	**72,748**	**420.6**	**522.5**	**321.6**
Cancer (malignant neoplasms)	50,616	25,447	25,169	113.5	115.8	111.3
Heart disease	36,927	26,432	10,495	82.8	120.3	46.4
Unintentional injuries	**19,974**	**13,454**	**6,520**	**44.8**	**61.2**	**28.8**
Poisoning	*9,675*	*5,791*	*3,884*	*21.7*	*26.4*	*17.2*
Motor vehicle	*5,695*	*4,186*	*1,509*	*12.8*	*19.1*	*6.7*
Falls	*1,341*	*987*	*354*	*3.0*	*4.5*	*1.6*
Drowning	*507*	*386*	*121*	*1.1*	*1.8*	*0.5*
Fire, flames, or smoke	*417*	*275*	*142*	*0.9*	*1.3*	*0.6*
All other unintentional injuries	*2,339*	*1,829*	*510*	*5.2*	*8.3*	*2.3*
Suicide	8,598	6,469	2,129	19.3	29.4	9.4
Chronic liver disease or cirrhosis	8,377	5,757	2,620	18.8	26.2	11.6
Stroke (cerebrovascular disease)	6,163	3,385	2,778	13.8	15.4	12.3
Diabetes mellitus	5,725	3,602	2,123	12.8	16.4	9.4
Chronic lower respiratory diseases	4,664	2,270	2,394	10.5	10.3	10.6
Human immunodeficiency virus infection	3,388	2,480	908	7.6	11.3	4.0
Influenza or pneumonia	2,918	1,558	1,360	6.5	7.1	6.0
55-64 years						
All causes	**303,307**	**184,142**	**119,165**	**871.9**	**1,097.3**	**661.8**
Cancer (malignant neoplasms)	106,829	59,058	47,771	307.1	351.9	265.3
Heart disease	67,261	46,802	20,459	193.4	278.9	113.6
Chronic lower respiratory diseases	14,160	7,354	6,806	40.7	43.8	37.8
Unintentional injuries	**12,933**	**8,960**	**3,973**	**37.2**	**53.4**	**22.1**
Motor vehicle	*4,082*	*2,933*	*1,149*	*11.7*	*17.5*	*6.4*
Poisoning	*3,913*	*2,426*	*1,487*	*11.2*	*14.5*	*8.3*
Falls	*1,888*	*1,322*	*566*	*5.4*	*7.9*	*3.1*
Choking[c]	*447*	*288*	*159*	*1.3*	*1.7*	*0.9*
Fire, flames, or smoke	*444*	*280*	*164*	*1.3*	*1.7*	*0.9*
All other unintentional injuries	*2,159*	*1,711*	*448*	*6.2*	*10.2*	*2.5*
Diabetes mellitus	11,361	6,837	4,524	32.7	40.7	25.1
Stroke (cerebrovascular disease)	10,523	5,977	4,546	30.2	35.6	25.2
Chronic liver disease or cirrhosis	9,154	6,474	2,680	26.3	38.6	14.9
Suicide	5,808	4,457	1,351	16.7	26.6	7.5
Nephritis or nephrosis	4,792	2,707	2,085	13.8	16.1	11.6
Septicemia	4,628	2,445	2,183	13.3	14.6	12.1
65-74 years						
All causes	**401,032**	**225,794**	**175,238**	**1,928.8**	**2,353.6**	**1,564.8**
Cancer (malignant neoplasms)	141,871	77,920	63,951	682.3	812.2	571.1
Heart disease	89,765	56,302	33,463	431.7	586.9	298.8
Chronic lower respiratory diseases	31,314	15,717	15,597	150.6	163.8	139.3
Stroke (cerebrovascular disease)	17,578	9,283	8,295	84.5	96.8	74.1
Diabetes mellitus	14,785	8,295	6,490	71.1	86.5	58.0
Unintentional injuries	**8,940**	**5,610**	**3,330**	**43.0**	**58.5**	**29.7**
Falls	*2,850*	*1,731*	*1,119*	*13.7*	*18.0*	*10.0*
Motor vehicle	*2,693*	*1,728*	*965*	*13.0*	*18.0*	*8.6*
Poisoning	*764*	*411*	*353*	*3.7*	*4.3*	*3.2*
Choking[c]	*635*	*360*	*275*	*3.1*	*3.8*	*2.5*
Fire, flames, or smoke	*386*	*214*	*172*	*1.9*	*2.2*	*1.5*
All other unintentional injuries	*1,612*	*1,166*	*446*	*7.8*	*12.2*	*4.0*
Nephritis or nephrosis	8,223	4,360	3,863	39.5	45.4	34.5
Septicemia	6,662	3,351	3,311	32.0	34.9	29.6
Influenza or pneumonia	6,259	3,465	2,794	30.1	36.1	24.9
Chronic liver disease or cirrhosis	5,383	3,330	2,053	25.9	34.7	18.3
75 and older[b]						
All causes	**1,361,160**	**573,991**	**787,169**	**7,248.5**	**7,938.8**	**6,816.3**
Heart disease	389,143	166,697	222,716	2,072.3	2,305.6	1,928.6
Cancer (malignant neoplasms)	249,178	125,428	123,750	1,326.9	1,734.8	1,071.6
Stroke (cerebrovascular disease)	91,664	31,820	59,844	488.1	440.1	518.2
Chronic lower respiratory diseases	85,786	39,041	46,745	456.8	540.0	404.8
Alzheimer's disease	74,059	21,697	52,362	394.4	300.1	453.4
Influenza or pneumonia	37,212	16,068	21,144	198.2	222.2	183.1
Diabetes mellitus	34,159	14,654	19,505	181.9	202.7	168.9
Nephritis or nephrosis	32,242	14,783	17,459	171.7	204.5	151.2
Unintentional injuries	**30,216**	**13,902**	**16,314**	**160.9**	**192.3**	**141.3**
Falls	*17,575*	*7,757*	*9,818*	*93.6*	*107.3*	*85.0*
Motor vehicle	*3,557*	*2,021*	*1,536*	*18.9*	*28.0*	*13.3*
Choking[c]	*2,522*	*1,200*	*1,322*	*13.4*	*16.6*	*11.4*
Poisoning	*656*	*286*	*370*	*3.5*	*4.0*	*3.2*
Fire, flames, or smoke	*602*	*319*	*283*	*3.2*	*4.4*	*2.5*
All other unintentional injuries	*5,304*	*2,319*	*2,985*	*28.2*	*32.1*	*25.8*
Septicemia	20,102	8,338	11,764	107.0	115.3	101.9

Source: National Safety Council analysis of National Center for Health Statistics (NCHS)–Mortality Data for 2009, as compiled from data provided by the 57 vital statistics jurisdictions through the Vital Statistics Cooperative Program. Rates are National Safety Council estimates based on data from NCHS and the U.S. Census Bureau.

[a]Deaths per 100,000 population in each age group.
[b]Includes 255 deaths where the age is unknown.
[c]Inhalation or ingestion of food or other objects.

The rank of unintentional injuries as a cause of death varies with race and Hispanic origin. While ranking fifth overall (following heart disease, cancer, stroke, and chronic lower respiratory diseases), unintentional injuries rank third for Hispanics after heart disease and cancer.

By race, unintentional injuries rank fifth for whites (after heart disease, cancer, stroke, and chronic lower respiratory diseases), and fourth for blacks, Asians, Pacific Islanders, American Indians, and Alaskan Natives.

Unintentional-injury-related deaths and death rates by race, Hispanic origin, and sex, United States, 2009

Race and sex	Total			Hispanic origin					
				Non-Hispanic			Hispanic		
	Rank	Number	Rate	Rank	Number	Rate	Rank	Number	Rate
All races	5	118,021	38.4	5	106,812	41.3	3	10,654	22.0
Males	3	75,022	49.5	3	66,791	52.8	3	7,841	31.3
Females	6	42,999	27.6	5	40,021	30.3	5	2,813	12.0
White	5	102,170	41.8	5	91,416	45.7	3	10,342	(b)
Males	3	64,501	53.2	4	56,804	57.9	3	7,894	(b)
Females	5	37,669	30.6	6	34,874	34.3	5	2,806	(b)
Black	4	12,074	30.5	5	11,810	31.3	3	139	(b)
Males	3	8,083	42.7	3	7,909	44.0	3	95	(b)
Females	7	3,991	19.3	7	3,931	19.9	4	46	(b)
Not white or black[a]	4	3,777	16.4	4	3,586	17.0	3	173	(b)
Males	3	2,438	21.6	3	2,324	22.7	3	134	(b)
Females	4	1,339	11.4	4	1,312	12.1	3	40	(b)

Source: National Safety Council analysis of National Center for Health Statistics (NCHS)–Mortality Data for 2009, as compiled from data provided by the 57 vital statistics jurisdictions through the Vital Statistics Cooperative Program. Rates are National Safety Council estimates based on data from NCHS and the U.S. Census Bureau.
Note: Rates are deaths per 100,000 population in each race/sex/Hispanic origin group. Total column includes 346 deaths for which Hispanic origin was not determined.
[a]*Includes American Indian, Alaskan Native, Asian, Native Hawaiian, and Pacific Islander.*
[b]*Race is not well-reported for persons of Hispanic origin. Population death rates are unreliable.*

Leading causes of unintentional-injury-related death by race, Hispanic origin, and sex, United States, 2009

Cause of death	All races			White			Black			Not white or black[a]		
	Both	Male	Female	Both	Male	Female	Both	Male	Female	Both	Male	Female
Total	118,021	75,022	42,999	102,170	64,501	37,669	12,074	8,083	3,991	3,777	2,438	1,339
Motor vehicle	36,216	25,430	10,786	30,081	21,176	8,905	4,667	3,331	1,336	1,468	923	545
Poisoning	31,758	20,577	11,181	28,019	18,104	9,915	2,951	1,928	1,023	788	545	243
Fall	24,792	12,724	12,068	22,934	11,653	11,281	1,173	683	490	685	388	297
Choking[b]	4,370	2,317	2,053	3,745	2,009	1,736	511	251	260	114	57	57
Drowning	3,517	2,724	793	2,789	2,136	653	525	433	92	203	155	48
Fire, flames, or smoke	2,756	1,652	1,104	2,044	1,233	811	635	374	261	77	45	32
Population (thousands)	*307,007*	*151,449*	*155,557*	*244,298*	*121,236*	*123,063*	*39,641*	*18,936*	*20,705*	*23,067*	*11,278*	*11,789*

Cause of death	Non-Hispanic			Hispanic			Unknown		
	Both	Male	Female	Both	Male	Female	Both	Male	Female
Total	106,812	66,791	40,021	10,654	7,841	2,813	555	390	165
Motor vehicle	31,251	21,745	9,506	4,789	3,553	1,236	176	132	44
Poisoning	28,979	18,476	10,503	2,584	1,969	615	195	132	63
Fall	23,480	11,901	11,579	1,242	782	460	70	41	29
Choking[b]	4,141	2,185	1,956	219	125	94	10	7	3
Drowning	2,993	2,304	689	505	406	99	19	14	5
Fire, flames, or smoke	2,580	1,529	1,051	156	110	46	20	13	7
Population (thousands)	*258,587*	*126,393*	*132,195*	*48,419*	*25,057*	*23,362*	*–*	*–*	*–*

Source: National Safety Council analysis of National Center for Health Statistics (NCHS)–Mortality Data for 2009, as compiled from data provided by the 57 vital statistics jurisdictions through the Vital Statistics Cooperative Program. Rates are National Safety Council estimates based on data from NCHS and the U.S. Census Bureau.
Note: Dashes (–) indicate not applicable.
[a]*Includes American Indian, Alaskan Native, Asian, Native Hawaiian, and Pacific Islander.*
[b]*Suffocation by inhalation or ingestion.*

Unintentional-injury-related deaths by age and event, United States, 2009

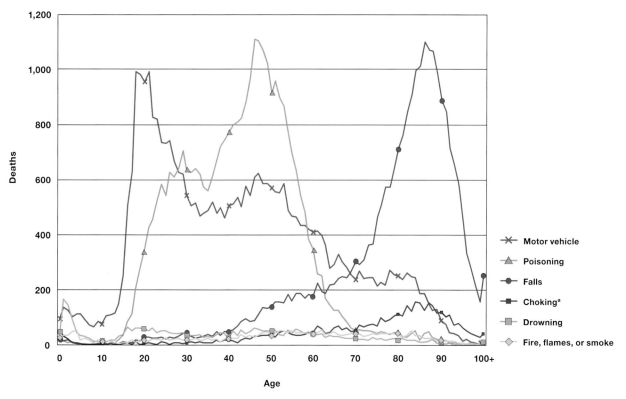

Motor vehicle crashes; poisonings; falls; choking (suffocation by inhalation or ingestion of food or other object); drownings; and fire, flames, or smoke were the six leading causes of unintentional-injury-related death in the United States in 2009. The graph above depicts the number of deaths attributed to the top six causes by age through age 99 and an aggregate age group of people 100 and older.

In 2009, motor vehicle crashes were the leading cause of unintentional-injury-related death for all ages combined and the leading cause of unintentional-injury-related death for each single year of age from 3 to 27, and from ages 59 to 68. Among infants younger than 1, motor vehicle deaths were second only to mechanical suffocation. Motor vehicle deaths also were the second leading cause of death among 1- and 2-year-olds, after drowning.

The distribution of 2009 motor vehicle fatalities shows a sharp increase during adolescence, rising to 993 for 18-year-olds from 250 for 15-year-olds. The greatest number of motor vehicle fatalities in 2009 occurred among people 18 years old.

The second leading cause of unintentional-injury-related death overall in 2009 was poisoning. Poisoning fatalities reached a high of 1,110 for 46-year-olds, and poisoning was the leading cause of unintentional-injury-related death for people ages 28-58. For these ages, motor vehicle deaths were the second leading cause of unintentional-injury-related death. Poisonings were the second most common cause for every single year of age from 16 to 27, and from ages 59 to 62.

Falls were the third leading cause of unintentional-injury-related death in the United States in 2009. Falls were the leading cause of unintentional-injury-related death of people age 69 and older and the second leading cause for ages 63-68 for each year of age; deaths resulting from falls peaked at 1,100 for individuals age 86.

The fourth leading cause of unintentional-injury-related death in 2009 was choking.[a] Choking deaths peaked at age 84 with 157 deaths. Choking was the second leading cause of unintentional-injury-related death for people ages 87-88 and 90 and older.

Drowning was the fifth leading cause of unintentional-injury-related death in 2009 and peaked at 167 fatalities for 1-year-olds, resulting in the leading cause of death for this age group as well as people age 2. Drownings were the second leading cause of unintentional-injury-related death for children age 3, ages 5-8, and ages 12-15 in 2009.

Fire, flames, or smoke were the sixth leading cause of unintentional-injury-related death in 2009. Fatalities due to fire, flames, or smoke were the second leading cause of death for people age 4 and peaked at 55 deaths among 62-year-olds.

Source: National Safety Council analysis of National Center for Health Statistics (NCHS)–Mortality Data for 2009, as compiled from data provided by the 57 vital statistics jurisdictions through the Vital Statistics Cooperative Program. Rates are National Safety Council estimates based on data from NCHS and the U.S. Census Bureau. See the Technical Appendix for the 10th revision of the International Classification of Diseases codes for the leading causes and comparability with prior years.
[a]Inhalation or ingestion of food or other objects.

Unintentional-injury-related deaths per 100,000 population by age and event, United States, 2009

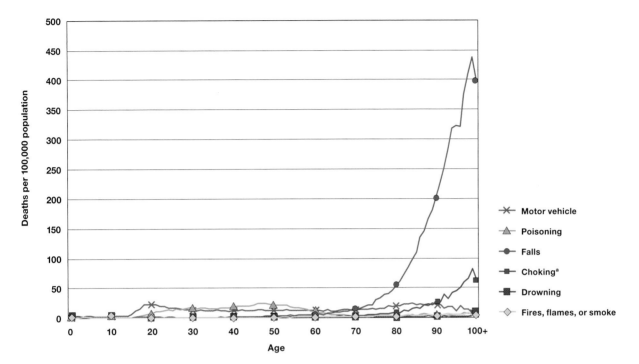

The graph above depicts U.S. death rates per 100,000 population for the six leading causes of unintentional-injury-related deaths in 2009 by age through age 99 and an aggregate age group of people 100 and older.

Unintentional motor vehicle fatalities had the highest overall death rate, with an average of 11.8 deaths per 100,000 population. Historically, motor vehicle death rates peak for people in the 18-20 age group. However, in 2009 the death rate was highest among people age 84, at a rate of 23.9. This peak rate is closely followed by a rate of 23.7 occurring at age 89, 23.1 for 21-year-olds, and 23.0 for both 83- and 86-year-olds.

Poisoning had the second highest overall death rate from unintentional injury in the United States, with an average rate of 10.3 deaths per 100,000 population. The poisoning death rate remained low until about age 18, when it started to increase steadily up to its peak rate of 24.5 at age 46 before it fell again.

While motor vehicle crashes are a significant problem for all ages, deaths resulting from falls for certain older ages had even higher death rates. Beginning at about age 68, the death rate from falls increased dramatically. At age 69, the falls death rate

surpassed that for motor vehicle, with the death rate continuing to rise steeply with increasing age, peaking at age 99 with a rate of 437.4. Based on 100,000 population, falls had an overall fatality rate of 8.1.

Death rates due to choking on inhaled or ingested food or other objects were quite low for most ages. Rates rise rapidly beginning at about age 71. While relatively stable and low for all ages, the death rates for drownings showed peaks in the first few years of life and again at some very old ages. Death rates for fire, flames, or smoke were only slightly elevated at very young ages and began to climb at about age 74. The overall death rates per 100,000 U.S. population for choking; drowning; and fire, flames, or smoke did not exceed 1.4.

Source: National Safety Council analysis of National Center for Health Statistics (NCHS)–Mortality Data for 2009, as compiled from data provided by the 57 vital statistics jurisdictions through the Vital Statistics Cooperative Program. Rates are National Safety Council estimates based on data from NCHS and the U.S. Census Bureau. See the Technical Appendix for the 10th revision of the International Classification of Diseases codes for the leading causes and comparability with prior years.
[a]*Inhalation or ingestion of food or other objects.*

Unintentional-injury-related deaths by sex and age, United States, 2009

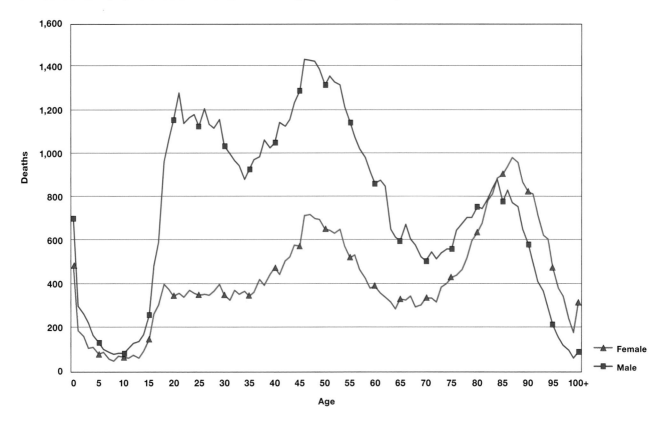

Males incurred more deaths due to unintentional injuries than females at all ages from birth to age 84 in 2009. The difference between the unintentional-injury-related death totals ranged from 13 more male deaths than female deaths at age 82 to 920 more deaths at age 21. The excess number of deaths for males compared to females was most evident from the late teen years to the mid-50s, when the gap begins to narrow. From age 84 on, deaths of females exceeded those of males by as little as four at age 84 to as much as 317 deaths nationwide at age 94.

Unintentional-injury-related deaths are at their lowest level for both sexes from about age 5 to about age 13. For males, the highest number of deaths (1,429) occurred at age 46, with high totals – including adjacent peaks of 1,424 deaths for people age 47 and 1,421 for people age 48 – occurring from the mid-teens until the late 50s. For females, however, the highest totals occurred among the elderly throughout the 80s and into the early 90s. The greatest number of female deaths (977) occurred at age 87.

The graph above shows the number of unintentional-injury-related deaths in the United States during 2009 for each sex by single year of age from younger than 1 to age 99 and an aggregate age group of people 100 and older. It is based on death certificate data from the National Center for Health Statistics.

Unintentional-injury-related deaths per 100,000 population by sex and age, United States, 2009

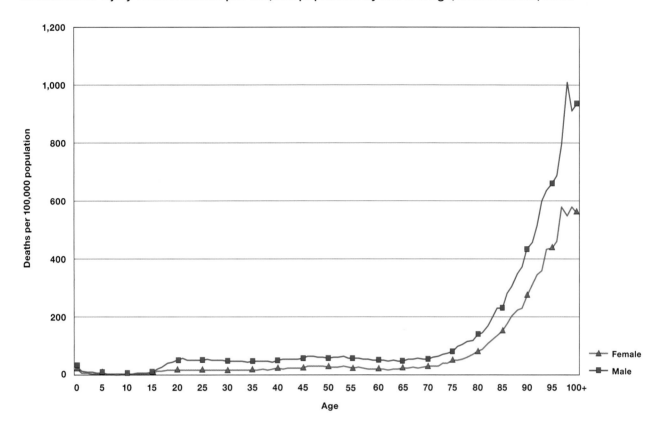

Males have greater unintentional-injury-related death rates for each year of age compared to females. The graph above shows the unintentional-injury-related death rates for males and females by single year of age from younger than 1 to age 99 and an aggregate age group of people 100 and older. It is based on National Center for Health Statistics mortality data and U.S. Census Bureau population data.

Death rates for both sexes are lowest from birth until the mid-teen years, where rates rise rapidly. Rates then remain fairly constant until the early 70s, where they again rise steadily with increasing age. Across all ages, males had an overall death rate of 49.5 unintentional-injury-related deaths per 100,000 males, while the rate among females in the United States was 27.6. The overall unintentional-injury-related death rate for all ages and both sexes was 38.4 deaths per 100,000 population.

Mortality by selected external causes, United States, 2007-2009

Type of accident or manner of injury	2009[a]	2008	2007
All external causes of mortality, V01-Y89, *U01, *U03[b]	179,770	183,816	185,076
Deaths due to unintentional (accidental) injuries, V01-X59, Y85-Y86	118,021	121,902	123,706
Transport accidents, V01-V99, Y85	39,031	42,709	46,844
Motor vehicle accidents, V02-V04, V09.0, V09.2, V12-V14, V19.0-V19.2, V19.4-V19.6, V20-V79, V80.3-V80.5, V81.0-V81.1, V82.0-V82.1, V83-V86, V87.0-V87.8, V88.0-V88.8, V89.0, V89.2	36,216	39,790	43,945
Pedestrian, V01-V09	5,219	5,578	5,958
Pedalcyclist, V10-V19	785	893	820
Motorcycle rider, V20-V29	4,310	5,143	5,024
Occupant of three-wheeled motor vehicle, V30-V39	12	12	10
Car occupant, V40-V49	9,415	10,629	12,772
Occupant of pick-up truck or van, V50-V59	2,449	2,386	3,100
Occupant of heavy transport vehicle, V60-V69	246	358	441
Bus occupant, V70-V79	22	63	43
Animal rider or occupant of animal-drawn vehicle, V80	118	103	101
Occupant of railway train or railway vehicle, V81	22	32	17
Occupant of streetcar, V82	2	3	2
Other and unspecified land transport accidents, V83-V89	14,649	15,730	16,740
Occupant of special industrial vehicle, V83	*14*	*11*	*14*
Occupant of special agricultural vehicle, V84	*87*	*124*	*148*
Occupant of special construction vehicle, V85	*21*	*21*	*26*
Occupant of all-terrain or other off-road motor vehicle, V86	*1,004*	*1,029*	*1,093*
Other and unspecified person, V87-V89	*13,523*	*14,545*	*15,459*
Water transport accidents, V90-V94	462	429	486
Drowning, V90, V92	*329*	*310*	*349*
Other and unspecified injuries, V91, V93-V94	*133*	*119*	*137*
Air and space transport accidents, V95-V97	541	545	550
Other and unspecified transport accidents and sequelae, V98-V99, Y85	779	805	780
Other specified transport accidents, V98	*1*	*0*	*0*
Unspecified transport accident, V99	*2*	*7*	*3*
Nontransport unintentional (accidental) injuries, W00-X59, Y86	78,990	79,193	76,862
Falls, W00-W19	24,792	24,013	22,631
Fall on same level from slipping, tripping, and stumbling, W01	*788*	*729*	*691*
Other fall on same level, W00, W02-W03, W18	*7,439*	*6,966*	*6,264*
Fall involving bed, chair, other furniture, W06-W08	*1,090*	*1,024*	*984*
Fall on and from stairs and steps, W10	*1,960*	*1,935*	*1,917*
Fall on and from ladder or scaffolding, W11-W12	*448*	*441*	*434*
Fall from out of or through building or structure, W13	*476*	*559*	*587*
Other fall from one level to another, W09, W14-W17	*635*	*686*	*695*
Other and unspecified fall, W04-W05, W19	*11,956*	*11,673*	*11,059*
Exposure to inanimate mechanical forces, W20-W49	2,353	2,596	2,591
Struck by or striking against object, W20-W22	*755*	*875*	*812*
Caught between objects, W23	*140*	*120*	*153*
Contact with machinery, W24, W30-W31	*608*	*693*	*659*
Contact with sharp objects, W25-W29	*121*	*81*	*104*
Firearms discharge, W32-W34	*554*	*592*	*613*
Explosion and rupture of pressurized devices, W35-W38	*29*	*23*	*39*
Fireworks discharge, W39	*4*	*6*	*10*
Explosion of other materials, W40	*78*	*131*	*111*
Foreign body entering through skin or natural orifice, W44-W45	*29*	*27*	*30*
Other and unspecified inanimate mechanical forces, W41-W43, W49	*35*	*47*	*60*
Exposure to animate mechanical forces, W50-W64	146	144	148
Struck by or against another person, W50-W52	*21*	*16*	*20*
Bitten or struck by dog, W54	*32*	*27*	*32*
Bitten or struck by other mammals, W53, W55	*68*	*75*	*76*
Bitten or stung by nonvenomous insect and other arthropods, W57	*10*	*12*	*11*
Bitten or crushed by other reptiles, W59	*0*	*0*	*0*
Other and unspecified animate mechanical forces, W56, W58, W60, W64	*15*	*14*	*9*
Accidental drowning and submersion, W65-W74	3,517	3,548	3,443
Drowning and submersion while in or falling into bathtub, W65-W66	*438*	*422*	*396*
Drowning and submersion while in or falling into swimming pool, W67-W68	*705*	*699*	*705*
Drowning and submersion while in or falling into natural water, W69-W70	*1,656*	*1,677*	*1,630*
Other and unspecified drowning and submersion, W73-W74	*718*	*750*	*712*
Other accidental threats to breathing, W75-W84	5,939	6,125	5,997
Accidental suffocation and strangulation in bed, W75	*717*	*809*	*741*
Other accidental hanging and strangulation, W76	*259*	*242*	*244*
Threat to breathing due to cave-in, falling earth and other substances, W77	*34*	*43*	*42*
Inhalation of gastric contents, W78	*264*	*322*	*315*
Inhalation and ingestion of food causing obstruction of respiratory tract, W79	*1,018*	*1,021*	*940*
Inhalation and ingestion of other objects causing obstruction of respiratory tract, W80	*3,088*	*3,023*	*3,089*
Confined to or trapped in a low-oxygen environment, W81	*6*	*8*	*25*
Other and unspecified threats to breathing, W83-W84	*553*	*657*	*601*

See source and footnotes on page 21.

Mortality by selected external causes, United States, 2007-2009

Type of accident or manner of injury	2009[a]	2008	2007
Exposure to electric current, radiation, temperature, or pressure, W85-W99	322	315	389
Electric transmission lines, W85	71	84	88
Other and unspecified electric current, W86-W87	232	215	281
Radiation, W88-W91	0	1	0
Excessive heat or cold of man-made origin, W92-W93	8	2	8
High and low air pressure or changes in air pressure, W94	11	13	12
Other and unspecified man-made environmental factors, W99	0	0	0
Exposure to smoke, fire, or flames, X00-X09	2,756	2,912	3,286
Uncontrolled fire in building or structure, X00	2,219	2,339	2,655
Uncontrolled fire not in building or structure, X01	52	48	65
Controlled fire in building or structure, X02	23	34	42
Controlled fire not in building or structure, X03	27	26	30
Ignition of highly flammable material, X04	39	54	59
Ignition or melting of nightwear, X05	5	4	3
Ignition or melting of other clothing or apparel, X06	97	97	113
Other and unspecified smoke, fire, and flames, X08-X09	294	310	319
Contact with heat or hot substances, X10-X19	67	80	89
Contact with hot tap water, X11	23	31	34
Other and unspecified heat and hot substances, X10, X12-X19	44	49	55
Contact with venomous animals and plants, X20-X29	80	71	73
Contact with venomous snakes and lizards, X20	5	4	7
Contact with venomous spiders, X21	6	5	8
Contact with hornets, wasps, and bees, X23	55	49	54
Contact with other and unspecified venomous animal or plant, X22, X24-X29	14	13	4
Exposure to forces of nature, X30-X39	1,084	1,167	1,217
Exposure to excessive natural heat, X30	352	296	309
Exposure to excessive natural cold, X31	616	641	711
Lightning, X33	31	29	46
Earthquake and other earth movements, X34-X36	19	40	26
Cataclysmic storm, X37	31	134	84
Flood, X38	15	7	22
Exposure to other and unspecified forces of nature, X32, X39	20	20	19
Accidental poisoning by or exposure to noxious substances, X40-X49	31,758	31,116	29,846
Nonopioid analgesics, antipyretics, and antirheumatics, X40	252	295	290
Antiepileptic, sedative-hypnotic, antiparkinsonism, or psychotropic drugs n.e.c., X41	1,681	1,557	1,545
Narcotics and psychodysleptics [hallucinogens] n.e.c., X42	12,458	12,762	13,030
Other and unspecified drugs, medicaments, and biologicals, X43-X44	14,363	13,557	12,793
Alcohol, X45	2,014	2,020	1,356
Gases and vapors, X46-X47	784	756	680
Other and unspecified chemicals or noxious substances, X48-X49	206	169	152
Overexertion, travel, and privation, X50-X57	28	35	20
Accidental exposure to other and unspecified factors or sequelae, X58-X59, Y86	6,148	7,071	7,132
Intentional self-harm, X60-X84, Y87.0, *U03	**36,909**	**36,035**	**34,598**
Intentional self-poisoning, X60-X69	6,398	6,442	6,358
Intentional self-harm by hanging, strangulation, and suffocation, X70	9,000	8,578	8,161
Intentional self-harm by firearm, X72-X74	18,735	18,223	17,352
Other and unspecified means and sequelae, X71, X75-X84, Y87.0	2,776	2,792	2,727
Terrorism, *U03	0	0	0
Assault, X85-Y09, Y87.1, *U01	**16,799**	**17,826**	**18,361**
Assault by firearm, X93-X95	11,493	12,179	12,632
Assault by sharp object, X99	1,874	2,043	1,981
Other and unspecified means and sequelae, X85-X92, X96-X98, Y00-Y09, Y87.1	3,432	3,604	3,748
Terrorism, *U01	0	0	0
Event of undetermined intent, Y10-Y34, Y87.2, Y89.9	**5,005**	**5,051**	**5,381**
Poisoning, Y10-Y19	3,349	3,421	3,770
Hanging, strangulation, and suffocation, Y20	163	169	135
Drowning and submersion, Y21	264	240	236
Firearm discharge, Y22-Y24	232	273	276
Exposure to smoke, fire, and flames, Y26	117	122	98
Falling, jumping, or pushed from a high place, Y30	67	78	66
Other and unspecified means and sequelae, Y25, Y27-Y29, Y31-Y34,Y87.2, Y89.9	813	748	800
Legal intervention, Y35, Y89.0	**395**	**381**	**412**
Legal intervention involving firearm discharge, Y35.0	333	326	351
Legal execution, Y35.5	49	35	40
Other and unspecified means and sequelae, Y35.1-Y35.4, Y35.6-Y35.7, Y89.0	13	20	21
Operations of war or sequelae, Y36, Y89.1	**25**	**31**	**21**
Complications of medical and surgical care and sequelae, Y40-Y84, Y88.0-Y88.3	**2,616**	**2,590**	**2,597**

Source: National Center for Health Statistics (NCHS)–Mortality Data for 2009, as compiled from data provided by the 57 vital statistics jurisdictions through the Vital
Statistics Cooperative Program. Deaths are classified on the basis of the 10th revision of the International Classification of Diseases (ICD-10), which became effective in 1999.
Note: "n.e.c." means not elsewhere classified.
[a]Latest official figures.
[b]Numbers following titles refer to external cause of injury and poisoning classifications in ICD-10.

Unintentional-injury-related deaths by age, sex, and type, United States, 2009[a]

Age and sex	Total[b]	Motor vehicle	Poisoning	Falls	Choking[c]	Drowning[d]	Fire, flames, or smoke	Mechanical suffocation	Natural heat or cold	All types Males	All types Females
Total	118,021	36,216	31,758	24,792	4,370	3,517	2,756	1,569	968	75,022	42,999
Younger than 5	2,647	574	59	65	118	495	191	914	32	1,624	1,023
5-14	1,689	974	50	28	17	209	141	50	6	1,052	637
15-24	12,458	7,688	3,044	192	56	548	142	75	36	9,239	3,219
25-44	29,164	10,953	13,597	853	214	788	433	195	150	21,181	7,983
45-64	32,907	9,777	13,588	3,229	808	925	861	229	340	22,414	10,493
65-74	8,940	2,693	764	2,850	635	247	386	38	98	5,610	3,330
75 and older	30,216	3,557	656	17,575	2,522	305	602	68	306	13,902	16,314
Males	75,022	25,430	20,577	12,724	2,317	2,724	1,652	1,060	655		
Females	42,999	10,786	11,181	12,068	2,053	793	1,104	509	313		

Source: National Safety Council analysis of National Center for Health Statistics (NCHS)–Mortality Data for 2009, as compiled from data provided by the 57 vital statistics jurisdictions through the Vital Statistics Cooperative Program.
[a]*Latest official figures.*
[b]*Includes types not shown separately.*
[c]*Inhalation or ingestion of food or other object obstructing breathing.*
[d]*Excludes transport drownings.*

Of the 118,021 unintentional-injury-related deaths in 2009, males accounted for 64% of all deaths. Females had the greatest share of deaths only in the 75 and older age group (54% female). For each type of incident listed above, males are disproportionably represented over females. The largest differences in the proportion of fatalities were drowning (77% male) and motor vehicle deaths (70% male). The smallest differences between the proportion of male and female fatalities were falls (51% male) and choking (53% male).

Unintentional-injury-related death rates by type and sex, United States, 2009[a]

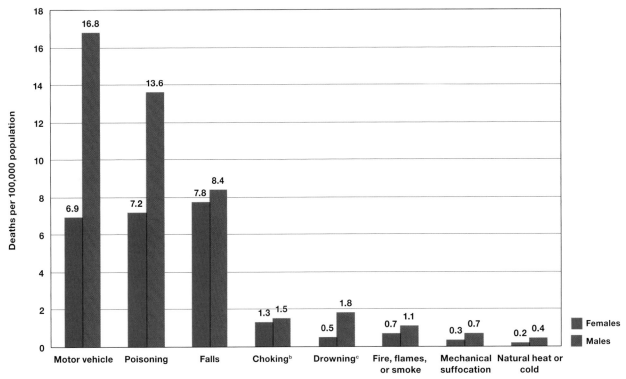

[a]*Latest official figures.*
[b]*Inhalation or ingestion of food or other objects.*
[c]*Excludes water transportation.*

Unintentional-injury-related deaths by month and type, United States, 2009[a]

Month	All types	Motor vehicle	Poisoning	Falls	Choking[b]	Drowning[c]	Fire, flames, or smoke	Mechanical suffocation	Natural heat or cold	Struck by or against	All other types
Total	118,021	36,216	31,758	24,792	4,370	3,517	2,756	1,569	968	755	11,320
January	9,972	2,820	2,811	2,128	400	101	398	136	172	75	931
February	8,933	2,481	2,611	1,912	391	134	287	93	89	59	876
March	9,840	2,833	2,788	2,202	391	204	295	136	76	59	856
April	9,620	3,019	2,558	2,024	345	251	243	133	34	69	944
May	10,120	3,272	2,702	1,972	365	382	209	141	27	60	990
June	10,055	3,216	2,474	1,984	362	552	170	127	119	58	993
July	10,473	3,326	2,605	2,073	351	616	149	133	98	79	1,043
August	10,272	3,353	2,625	2,074	314	498	123	131	73	61	1,020
September	9,541	3,077	2,522	1,998	335	274	138	138	31	70	958
October	9,795	3,087	2,658	2,144	348	194	200	136	30	52	946
November	9,484	2,984	2,606	2,002	358	167	225	134	48	67	893
December	9,916	2,748	2,798	2,279	410	144	319	131	171	46	870
Average	9,835	3,018	2,647	2,066	364	293	230	131	81	63	943

Source: National Safety Council analysis of National Center for Health Statistics (NCHS)–Mortality Data for 2009, as compiled from data provided by the 57 vital statistics jurisdictions through the Vital Statistics Cooperative Program.
[a]Latest official figures.
[b]Inhalation or ingestion of food or other object obstructing breathing.
[c]Excludes water transport drownings.

Unintentional-injury-related deaths by month and type, United States, 2009[a]

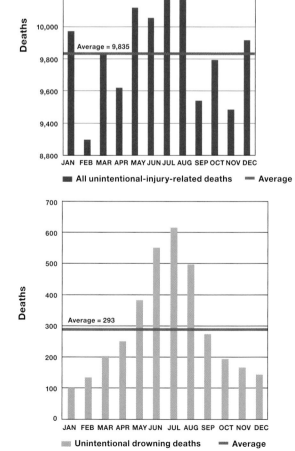

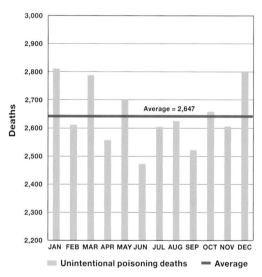

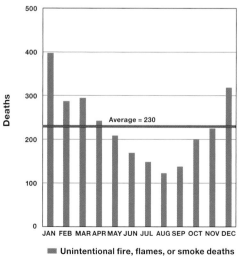

Cross-reference: See page 129 for motor vehicle deaths by month and page 165 for pedalcycle deaths by month.

The National Health Interview Survey (NHIS), conducted by the National Center for Health Statistics, is a continuous, personal-interview sampling of households to obtain information about the health status of household members, including injuries experienced during the five weeks prior to the interview.

Responsible family members residing in the household supplied the information found used in the survey. In 2010, interviews were completed for 89,976 people living in 34,329 households throughout the United States. See page 25 for definitions.

Number of leading external causes of medically consulted injury and poisoning episodes by age, United States, 2010

	Population[a] (000)	External cause of injury and poisoning (number in thousands)						
		Falls	Struck by or against person or object	Transportation[b]	Overexertion	Cutting-piercing instruments	Other injury causes[b]	Poisoning[b]
All ages	304,103	13,042	4,325	3,672	4,891	2,517	5,873	575[c]
Younger than 12	48,809	2,119	863	503[c]	191[c]	185[c]	632	[d]
12-17 years	25,170	1,485	917	343[c]	444[c]	283[c]	819	[d]
18-44 years	109,972	2,843	1,226	1,454	2,183	1,292	2,525	164[c]
45-64 years	80,972	3,420	898	931	1,725	602	1,447	[d]
65-74 years	21,629	1,162	266[c]	402[c]	[d]	[d]	234[c]	[d]
75 and older	17,551	2,013	[d]	[d]	301[c]	[d]	216[c]	0

[a]Civilian noninstitutionalized population.
[b]"Transportation" includes motor vehicle, bicycle, motorcycle, pedestrian, train, boat, or airplane. "Poisoning" does not include food poisoning or allergic reaction. "Other injury causes" includes fire/burn/scald-related, animal or insect bites, machinery, and unspecified causes.
[c]Estimate does not meet standard of reliability or precision and should be used with caution.
[d]Estimate is not shown because it does not meet standard of reliability or precision.

Leading external causes of injury and poisoning episodes by sex, United States, 2010

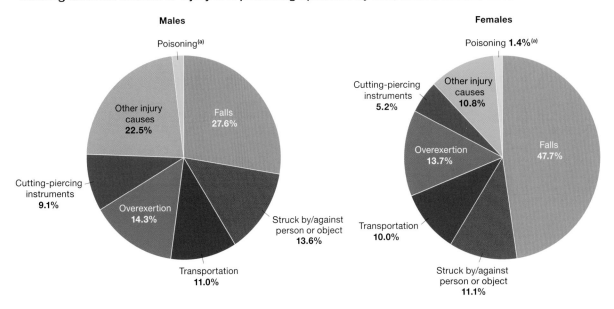

Males

Females

[a]The standard error of the poisoning estimate for males exceeds publication guidelines and the poisoning estimate for females does not meet standards of reliability or precision and should be used with caution.
Source: Adams, P.F., Martinez, M.E., Vickerie, J.L., & Kurzinger, W.K. (2011, December). Summary of health statistics for the U.S. population: National Health Interview Survey, 2010. National Center for Health Statistics. Vital and Health Statistics, Series 10 (No. 251).

In 2010, an estimated 34.9 million medically consulted injury and poisoning episodes were recorded, of which 51.4% were among males and 48.6% among females. The overall injury rate was 115 episodes per 1,000 population, with males experiencing higher rates (121 per 1,000 males) than females (108 per 1,000 females). Most injuries occurred in or around the home (47.5%), followed by injuries on streets, highways, sidewalks, and in parking lots (13.3%), and injuries at sport facilities, recreational areas, lakes, rivers, and pools (12.9%). Nationwide, injuries in public areas such as schools, hospitals, streets, recreational facilities, industrial and trade areas, and public buildings together accounted for 44.7% of the total injuries.

Among the 17.9 million injuries reported for males, the single most common place of injury occurrence was at home, with 18.5% occurring inside the home while injuries occurring outside contributed an additional 22.4%. More than half of the injuries among females occurred at home. Nearly twice as many injuries to females occurred inside the home than outside, consistent with 2009 National Health Interview Survey (NHIS) findings. Streets, parking lots, sidewalks, and highways, along with sport facilities and recreational areas, were the next most common locations for injuries among females, accounting for 14.1% and 10.4% of injuries, respectively. For males, sport facilities and recreational areas were the most common nonhome places for injuries to occur (15.3%), followed by streets, parking lots, sidewalks, and highways (12.4%).

The 2010 NHIS injury definitions are listed below for comparability with prior years and other injury figures published in *Injury Facts*.

Number and percent of injury episodes by place of occurrence and sex, United States, 2010

Place of occurrence of injury episode	Both sexes No. of episodes (000)	Percent	Male No. of episodes (000)	Percent	Female No. of episodes (000)	Percent
Total episodes[a]	34,895	100.0	17,943	100.0	16,952	100.0
Home (inside)	9,236	26.5	3,314	18.5	5,922	34.9
Home (outside)	7,325	21.0	4,016	22.4	3,309	19.5
School, child care center, or preschool	2,801	8.0	1,685	9.4	1,117	6.6
Hospital or residential institution	989	2.8	404	2.2	585[b]	3.4
Street, highway, sidewalk, or parking lot	4,628	13.3	2,233	12.4	2,395	14.1
Sport facility, recreational area, lake, river, or pool	4,496	12.9	2,738	15.3	1,759	10.4
Industrial, construction, or farm	1,083	3.1	893	5.0	189[b]	1.1
Trade or service area	662	2.9	246[b]	1.4	416[b]	2.4
Other public building	934	1.5	683	3.8	251[b]	1.5
Other (unspecified)	2,748	7.9	1,717	9.6	1,032	6.1

Source: Adams, P.F., Martinez, M.E., Vickerie, J.L., & Kirzinger, W.K. (2011, December). Summary health statistics for the U.S. population: National Health Interview Survey, 2010. National Center for Health Statistics. Vital and Health Statistics, Series 10 (No. 251).
[a]Numbers and percentages may not sum to respective totals due to rounding and unknowns.
[b]Estimate does not meet standard of reliability or precision and should be used with caution.

Injury definitions
National Health Interview Survey definitions. The 2010 National Health Interview Survey (NHIS) figures include medically consulted injury and poisoning *episodes* (e.g., call to a poison control center; use of an emergency vehicle or emergency room; visit to a doctor's office or other health clinic; or phone call to a doctor, nurse, or other health care professional) that reportedly occurred during the three months prior to the date of the interview and resulted in one or more *conditions*. Beginning in 2004, injury and poisoning estimates were calculated using only those episodes that occurred five weeks or less before the interview date. This reflects a change from 1997 to 2003, when NHIS data contained injury and poisoning episodes that were reported to occur within four months of the interview, and estimates were calculated using a three-month recall period. Also, an imputation procedure was performed for injury and poisoning episodes to assign a date of occurrence if it was not reported. Therefore, figures for 2004 and subsequent years are not comparable to estimates from prior years.

In the 2010 NHIS Injury and Poisoning file, an *injury episode* refers to the traumatic event in which the person was injured one or more times from an external cause (e.g., a fall or a motor vehicle traffic incident). An *injury condition* is the acute condition or the physical harm caused by the traumatic event. Likewise, a *poisoning episode* refers to the event resulting from ingestion of or contact with harmful substances, as well as overdoses or wrong use of any drug or medication, while a *poisoning condition* is the acute condition or the physical harm caused by the event. Each episode must have at least one injury condition or poisoning classified according to the nature-of-injury codes 800-909.2, 909.4, 909.9, 910-994.9, 995.5-995.59, and 995.80-995.85 in the Ninth Revision of the International Classification of Diseases (ICD-9-CM). Poisoning episodes exclude food poisoning, sun poisoning, or poison ivy rashes.

National Safety Council definition of injury. A medically consulted injury is defined as one that is serious enough that a medical professional was consulted or is a recordable work injury based on OSHA definitions (see Glossary). All injury totals labeled "medically consulted" in *Injury Facts* are based on this definition.

Of the 34.9 million medically consulted injuries in 2010, 39.2% were related to sports and leisure activities. Sports and leisure injuries accounted for 57.7% of all injury episodes among children younger than 12 and 74.4% of injury episodes among 12- to 17-year-olds.

The rate of injuries occurring during leisure activities was slightly higher for females (27 cases per 1,000 females) than for males (23 cases per 1,000 males). However, the rate of sports injuries among males (29 per 1,000 males) was substantially higher than among females (13 per 1,000 females). The charts on this page illustrate these gender differences in terms of percentages and rates.

Number of injury episodes by age and activity at time of injury, United States, 2010

	Total episodes[a] (000)	Activity at time of injury[b] (number in thousands)						
		Driving[c]	Working at paid job	Working around house or yard	Attending school	Sports	Leisure activities	Other[d]
All ages	**34,895**	**2,279**	**4,085**	**5,365**	**1,387**	**6,113**	**7,574**	**8,184**
Younger than 12	4,574	(e)	0	(e)	576[f]	841	1,796	1,124
12-17 years	4,341	(e)	(e)	0	452	2,420	808	513
18-44 years	11,686	1,204	2,555	1,681	279[f]	1,922	2,042	2,059
45-64 years	9,273	640	1,244	2,326	(e)	820	1,731	2,384
65-74 years	2,193	193[f]	(e)	443[f]	0	(e)	414[f]	881
75 and older	2,829	0	(e)	786	0	(e)	782	1,222

Percent and rates of injury episodes by sex and activity at time of injury, United States, 2010

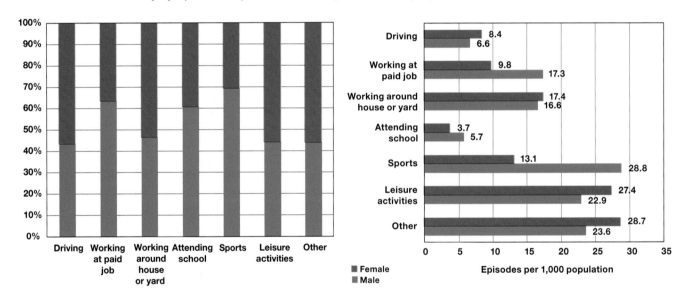

Source: Adams, P.F., Martinez, M.E., Vickerie, J.L., & Kirzinger, W.K. (2011, December). Summary health statistics for the U.S. population: National Health Interview Survey, 2010. National Center for Health Statistics. Vital and Health Statistics, Series 10 (No. 251).

[a]Numbers may not sum to respective totals due to rounding and unknowns.

[b]Activity at time of injury and poisoning episodes is based on the question, "What was [person] doing when the injury/poisoning happened?" Respondents could indicate up to two activities.

[c]Driving includes both drivers and passengers.

[d]"Other" includes unpaid work such as housework, shopping, volunteer work, sleeping, resting, eating, drinking, cooking, hands-on care from another person, and other unspecified activities.

[e]Estimate is not shown because it does not meet standard of reliability or precision.

[f]Estimate does not meet standard of reliability or precision and should be used with caution.

A wealth of research demonstrates the role of socioeconomic status in the etiology of medical conditions and disease. In general, people with the highest levels of income and education are healthier than those with median income and education, who, in turn, tend to be in better health than the poor and least educated.[a]

Lower socioeconomic status is known to contribute to increased rates of fatal injuries. Although research provides some evidence of links between socioeconomic status and non-fatal injuries, studies based on morbidity data provide results somewhat less consistent than those of mortality studies. Nonetheless, numerous studies show considerable differences between socioeconomic groups even for nonfatal injuries.[b] The National Health Interview Survey (NHIS) provides an opportunity to look at the occurrence of unintentional injuries in the U.S. population as a function of socioeconomic position using two socioeconomic status measures – family income and education.[c]

Although NHIS data indicate that all people are affected by injuries, families whose poverty status was poor (below the poverty threshold) and near poor (100% to less than 200% of the poverty threshold) had higher injury rates than families whose poverty status was not poor (200% of the poverty threshold and greater). In contrast, those with less than a high school education had the lowest medically consulted injury rate in 2010 (87 injuries per 1,000 population), while individuals with some college had the highest injury rate (123 per 1,000 population). The finding that individuals with some college education have the highest rate of medically consulted injuries does not seem to support the typical socioeconomic status pattern.

[a]Banks, J., Marmot, M., Oldfield, Z., & Smith, J.P. (2006). Disease and disadvantage in the United States and in England. Journal of American Medical Association, Issue 295, No. 17, pp. 2037-2045.
[b]Laflamme, L., Burrows, S., & Hasselberg, M. (2009). Socioeconomic differences in injury risks–A review of findings and a discussion of potential countermeasures. Denmark: World Health Organization–Europe.
[c]Education data are shown for people 25 and older.

Percentages and rates of medically consulted injuries by poverty status, United States, 2010

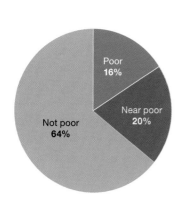
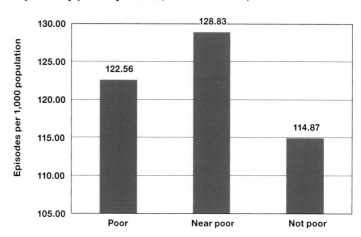

Percentages and rates of medically consulted injuries by level of education, United States, 2010

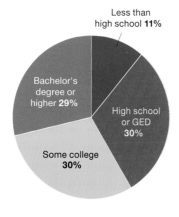
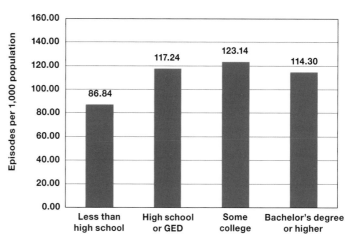

Source: Adams, P.F., Martinez, M.E., Vickerie, J.L., & Kirzinger, W.K. (2011, December). Summary health statistics for the U.S. population: National Health Interview Survey, 2010. National Center for Health Statistics. Vital and Health Statistics, Series 10 (No. 251).

Injury-Related Hospital Emergency Department Visits, 2009

◆ *More than 45.4 million visits to hospital emergency departments in 2009 were due to injuries.*

About 33% of all hospital emergency department visits in the United States were injury-related, according to information from the 2009 National Hospital Ambulatory Medical Care Survey conducted for the National Center for Health Statistics. Approximately 136.1 million visits were made to emergency departments in 2009, of which about 45.4 million were injury-related. This resulted in an annual rate of about 45.1 emergency department visits per 100 people, of which about 15.1 visits per 100 people were injury-related.

Males had a higher overall rate of injury-related visits than females. For males, about 16.2 visits per 100 people were recorded; for females, the rate was 13.9 per 100 people. Males also had higher rates of injury-related visits than females for those younger than 15 through age 64, while females had higher rates for age groups beginning at age 65. Those ages 15-24 had the highest rate of injury-related visits for males, while those 75 and older had the highest rate for females.

Falls and motor vehicle incidents were the leading causes of injury-related emergency department visits, accounting for 23% and 10% of the total, respectively. In total, about 10.2 million visits to emergency departments were made in 2009 due to unintentional falls, and about 4.5 million were made due to motor vehicle incidents. The next leading types were struck against or struck accidentally by objects or people, with more than 3.2 million visits (7% of the total), and incidents caused by overexertion and strenuous movements, which accounted for about 2.4 million visits (5% of the total).

The upper extremities were the most frequent body site of injuries treated in hospital emergency departments, followed by injuries to the lower extremities and those to the head and neck. These three body sites accounted for about 45% of injury-related visits. The most commonly mentioned specific body sites for injuries were wrist, hand, and fingers, followed by the vertebral column.

Number and percent distribution of emergency department visits by cause of injury, United States, 2009

Cause of injury and E-code[a]	No. of visits (000)	Percent
All injury-related visits	**45,420**	**100.0**
Unintentional injuries, E800-E848, E850-E869, E880-E929	**29,499**	**64.9**
Falls, E880.0-E886.9, E888	10,249	22.6
Total motor vehicle, E810-E819, E820-E825 (.0-.5, .7-.9)	4,475	9.8
Motor vehicle traffic, E810-E819	*3,916*	*8.6*
Motor vehicle, nontraffic, E820-E825(.0-.5, .7-.9)	*559*	*1.2*
Struck against or struck accidentally by objects or persons, E916-E917	3,221	7.1
Overexertion and strenuous movements, E927	2,363	5.2
Cutting or piercing instruments or objects, E920	2,189	4.8
Natural and environmental factors, E900-E909, E928.0-E928.2	2,152	4.7
Foreign body, E914-E915	812	1.8
Poisoning, E850-E869	711	1.6
Fire and flames, hot substances or object, caustic or corrosive material, and steam, E890-E899, E924	510	1.1
Caught accidentally in or between objects, E918	447	1.0
Pedalcycle, nontraffic, and other, E800-E807(.3), E820-E825(.6), E826.1, E826.9	435	1.0
Machinery, E919	248	0.5
Other transportation, E800-807(.0-.2, .8-.9), E826(.0, .2-.8), E827-E829, E831, E833-E845	(b)	(b)
Suffocation, E911-E913	(b)	(b)

Cause of injury and E-code[a]	No. of visits (000)	Percent
Other mechanism,[c] E830, E832, E846-E848, E910, E921-E923, E925-E926, E928.3, E928.8, E929.0-E929.5	1,419	3.1
Mechanism unspecified, E887, E928.9, E929.8, E929.9	(b)	(b)
Intentional injuries, E950-E959, E960-E969, E970-E978, E990-E999	**2,748**	**6.1**
Assault, E960-E969	2,065	4.5
Unarmed fight or brawl, striking by blunt or thrown object, E960.0, E968.2	*1,286*	*2.8*
Cutting or piercing instrument, E966	*194*	*0.4*
Other and unspecified mechanism,[d] E960.1, E961-E964, E965.0-E965.9, E967-E968.1, E968.3-E969	*585*	*1.3*
Self-inflicted injury, E950-E959	633	1.4
Poisoning by solid or liquid substances, gases, and vapors, E950-E952	*397*	*0.9*
Other and unspecified mechanism,[e] E954-E959	*236*	*0.5*
Other causes of violence, E970-E979, E990-E999	(b)	(b)
Injuries of undetermined intent, E980-E989	**540**	**1.2**
Adverse effects of medical treatment, E870-E879, E930-E949	**2,043**	**4.5**
Medical and surgical complications, E870-E879	1,220	2.7
Adverse drug effects, E930-E949	823	1.8
Alcohol and drug use[f]	**2,245**	**4.9**
Unknown[g]	**8,344**	**18.4**

Source: National Hospital Ambulatory Medical Care Survey: 2009 Emergency Department Summary Tables. Accessed Aug. 13, 2012 from www.cdc.gov/nchs/ahcd/web_tables.htm#2009.
Note: Sum of parts may not add to total due to rounding.
[a]Based on the International Classification of Diseases, 9th Revision, Clinical Modification (ICD-9-CM).
[b]Figure did not meet standard of reliability or precision.
[c]Includes drowning, firearms, and other or not elsewhere classified mechanism.

[d]Includes assault by firearms and explosives or other mechanism.
[e]Includes injury by cutting and piercing instrument and other or unspecified mechanism.
[f]Alcohol and drug abuse are not contained in the "Supplementary Classification of External Causes of Injury and Poisoning," but are frequently recorded as a cause of injury or poisoning.
[g]Includes illegible and blank E-codes.

Rate[a] of injury-related[b] visits to emergency departments by patient age and sex, 2009

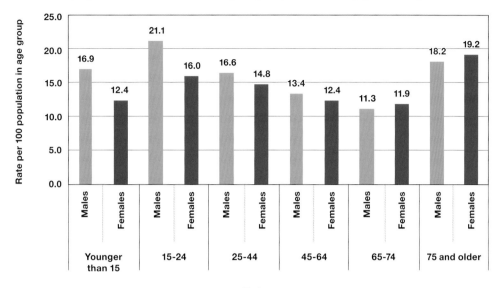

aNumber of visits per 100 population in each age group.
bInjury-related includes injuries, poisoning, and adverse effects.

Percent of injury-related[a] emergency department visits by body site of primary diagnosis, United States, 2009

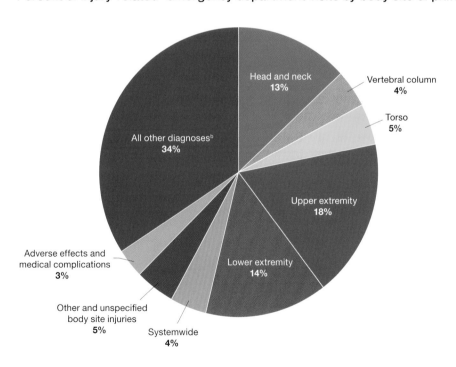

aInjury-related includes injuries, poisoning, and adverse effects.
b"All other diagnoses" includes musculoskeletal system, symptoms and ill-defined conditions, skin and subcutaneous tissue, mental disorders, nervous system and sense organs, other illnesses, supplementary classification, and unknown diagnoses.

Motor vehicle traffic fatalities are the leading cause of fatal unintentional injuries in the United States, according to the latest data from the National Center for Health Statistics. A total of 34,485 motor vehicle traffic fatalities occurred in 2009, accounting for about 29% of all unintentional-injury-related deaths. Motor vehicle traffic fatalities were the leading cause of unintentional-injury-related deaths in age groups from 5-9 through 15-24. Suffocation was the leading cause of unintentional-injury-related deaths for people younger than 1, while drowning was the leading cause for those 1-4 years old. The leading cause of unintentional-injury-related deaths among age groups from 25-34 through 55-64 was poisoning, and the leading cause for those age 65 and older was falls. Taken together, motor vehicle traffic, poisoning, and falls accounted for more than three-quarters of all unintentional-injury-related deaths. In addition to these three causes, drowning was a leading cause of unintentional-injury-related deaths for most age groups.

Leading causes of fatal unintentional injuries by age group, United States, 2009

Rank	All ages	Age group									
		Younger than 1	1-4	5-9	10-14	15-24	25-34	35-44	45-54	55-64	65 and older
1	Motor vehicle traffic 34,485	Suffocation 907	Drowning 450	Motor vehicle traffic 378	Motor vehicle traffic 491	Motor vehicle traffic 7,451	Poisoning 6,209	Poisoning 7,388	Poisoning 9,675	Poisoning 3,913	Falls 20,422
2	Poisoning 31,758	Motor vehicle traffic 91	Motor vehicle traffic 362	Drowning 119	Drowning 90	Poisoning 3,044	Motor vehicle traffic 5,651	Motor vehicle traffic 4,856	Motor vehicle traffic 5,448	Motor vehicle traffic 3,894	Motor vehicle traffic 5,854
3	Falls 24,792	Drowning 45	Fire/burn 169	Fire/burn 88	Other land transport 56	Drowning 548	Drowning 396	Falls 551	Falls 1,341	Falls 1,888	Unspecified 4,139
4	Suffocation 5,939	Fire/burn 25	Suffocation 125	Other land transport 31	Fire/burn 53	Other land transport 230	Falls 302	Drowning 392	Drowning 507	Suffocation 540	Suffocation 3,263
5	Unspecified 5,098	Poisoning 22	Pedestrian, other 112	Suffocation 26	Suffocation 41	Falls 192	Other land transport 220	Suffocation 257	Suffocation 497	Fire/burn 456	Poisoning 1,414
6	Drowning 3,517	Natural/ environment 20	Falls 46	Pedestrian, other 21	Poisoning 37	Fire/burn 142	Fire/burn 201	Other specified 239	Fire/burn 424	Drowning 418	Fire/burn 1,027
7	Fire/burn 2,823	Falls 19	Natural/ environment 37	Struck by/ against 19	Other transport 25	Firearms 132	Other specified 184	Fire/burn 238	Other specified 314	Unspecified 322	Drowning 545
8	Other land transport 1,398	Other specified 17	Poisoning 37	Poisoning 13	Pedestrian, other 21	Suffocation 131	Suffocation 152	Other land transport 183	Unspecified 280	Other specified 269	Other specified, n.e.c.[a] 514
9	Other specified 1,389	Unspecified 17	Struck by/ against 32	Falls 12	Firearms 20	Other specified 117	Other transport 147	Other transport 168	Natural/ environment 272	Natural/ environment 194	Natural/ environment 492
10	Natural/ environment 1,327	Struck by/ against 10	Other land transport 25	Firearms 12	Falls 16	Pedestrian, other 113	Pedestrian, other 133	Pedestrian, other 157	Other land transport 231	Other transport 191	Other land transport 273
All causes of fatal unintentional injury											
Number	118,021	1,181	1,466	773	916	12,458	14,062	15,102	19,974	12,933	39,156[b]
Per 100,000 population	37.2	27.7	8.6	3.7	4.6	28.9	33.8	36.4	44.8	37.2	98.9[b]

Source: Centers for Disease Control and Prevention, National Center for Injury Prevention and Control. Web-based Injury Statistics Query and Reporting System (WISQARS), data accessed June 26, 2012, at www.cdc.gov/injury/wisqars/index.html.
[a]"n.e.c." means not elsewhere classified.
[b]Includes 45 cases with age unknown.

Falls are the leading cause of nonfatal unintentional injuries that are treated in hospital emergency departments, according to data from the All Injury Program, a cooperative program involving the National Center for Injury Prevention and Control, the Centers for Disease Control and Prevention, and the Consumer Product Safety Commission. More than 9.1 million people were treated in an emergency department for fall-related injuries in 2010. Falls were the leading cause of nonfatal injuries for all age groups except for the 15- to 24-year-old age group, for which struck by or against an object or person was the leading cause. Struck by or against, overexertion, and motor vehicle crashes involving vehicle occupants also were leading causes for most age groups.

Leading causes of nonfatal unintentional injuries treated in hospital emergency departments by age group, United States, 2010

Rank	All ages	Age group									
		Younger than 1	1-4	5-9	10-14	15-24	25-34	35-44	45-54	55-64	65 and older
1	Falls 9,146,026	Falls 146,804	Falls 970,793	Falls 649,460	Falls 627,418	Struck by/against 1,039,307	Falls 834,102	Falls 794,258	Falls 988,097	Falls 860,611	Falls 2,350,009
2	Struck by/against 4,565,133	Struck by/against 32,933	Struck by/against 397,005	Struck by/against 421,482	Struck by/against 613,885	Falls 924,187	Overexertion 680,337	Overexertion 582,155	Overexertion 485,080	Stuck by/against 247,623	Stuck by/against 254,596
3	Overexertion 3,430,040	Other bite/sting[a] 11,937	Other bite/sting[a] 157,756	Cut/pierce 116,067	Overexertion 309,961	Overexertion 752,572	Struck by/against 647,509	Struck by/against 488,626	Struck by/against 421,944	Overexertion 241,380	Overexertion 196,972
4	Motor vehicle occupant 2,764,332	Foreign body 10,221	Foreign body 140,687	Other bite/sting[a] 101,982	Cut/pierce 137,375	Motor vehicle occupant 741,398	Motor vehicle occupant 587,529	Motor vehicle occupant 437,360	Motor vehicle occupant 386,741	Motor vehicle occupant 226,750	Motor vehicle occupant 194,850
5	Cut/pierce 2,143,400	Other specified[b] 9,594	Overexertion 95,002	Pedalcyclist 82,145	Pedalcyclist 110,602	Cut/pierce 448,110	Cut/pierce 413,117	Cut/pierce 319,336	Cut/pierce 292,052	Cut/pierce 182,614	Cut/pierce 140,823
6	Other specified[b] 1,278,313	Fire/burn 8,046	Cut/pierce 87,015	Overexertion 80,667	Unknown/unspecified 96,919	Other specified[b] 253,982	Other specified[b] 227,591	Other specified[b] 228,854	Other specified[b] 268,682	Other specified[b] 114,117	Poisoning 89,706
7	Other bite/sting[a] 1,145,713	Cut/pierce 6,891	Other specified[b] 73,524	Motor vehicle occupant 65,611	Motor vehicle occupant 82,439	Other bite/sting[a] 187,654	Other bite/sting[a] 178,893	Other bite/sting[a] 139,579	Poisoning 180,548	Poisoning 94,553	Other bite/sting[a] 75,349
8	Poisoning 831,295	Inhalation/suffocation 6,354	Fire/burn 52,367	Foreign body 61,816	Other bite/sting[a] 60,875	Unknown/unspecified 158,726	Poisoning 126,889	Poisoning 137,559	Other bite/sting[a] 139,798	Other bite/sting[a] 91,889	Other transport[c] 71,200
9	Unknown/unspecified 687,871	Overexertion 5,849	Poisoning 43,939	Dog bite 42,199	Other transport[c] 48,822	Poisoning 133,613	Unknown/unspecified 104,324	Unknown/unspecified 81,659	Other transport[c] 76,369	Other transport[c] 50,145	Other specified[b] 57,118
10	Other transport[c] 616,674	Motor vehicle occupant 5,555	Unknown/unspecified 42,080	Other transport[c] 41,378	Dog bite 36,062	Other transport[c] 119,760	Other transport[c] 97,810	Other transport[c] 81,255	Unknown/unspecified 73,956	Unknown/unspecified 42,181	Unknown/unspecified 50,813
All causes of unintentional injury											
Number	29,232,822	257,174	2,210,345	1,757,716	2,246,291	5,236,515	4,265,220	3,620,092	3,642,963	2,352,071	3,644,434[d]
Per 100,000 population	9,558.1	6,520.4	13,596.1	8,638.0	10,863.6	12,003.1	10,386.8	8,814.3	8,094.3	6,447.1	9,050.4[d]

Source: NEISS All Injury Program, Office of Statistics and Programming, National Center for Injury Prevention and Control, the Centers for Disease Control and Prevention, and the Consumer Product Safety Commission.
[a]Other than dog bite.
[b]Injury associated with any other specified cause that does not fit another category. Includes electric current, explosions, fireworks, radiation, animal scratch, etc. Excludes all causes listed in the table and bb/pellet gunshot, drowning and near drowning, firearm gunshot, suffocation, machinery, natural and environmental conditions, pedestrians, and motorcyclists.
[c]Includes occupant of any transport vehicle other than a motor vehicle or motorcycle (e.g., airplane, space vehicle, railcar, boat, all-terrain vehicle, animal and animal-drawn
conveyances, battery-powered carts, ski lifts, and other cable cars not on rails).
[d]Includes 2,050 cases with age unknown.

Disasters are front-page news, even though the lives lost in the United States are relatively few when compared to the day-to-day life losses from unintentional injuries (see "While You Speak!" on page 37). Listed below are the U.S. disasters, of which the National Safety Council is aware, that occurred in 2011 and took five or more lives.

There also were 14 motor vehicle traffic crashes in 2011 that resulted in five deaths each.

Disaster deaths, United States, 2011

Type and location	No. of deaths	Date of disaster
Major disasters (25 or more deaths)		
Tornadoes, Alabama	235	April 27
Tornado, Joplin, Missouri	158	May 22
Tornadoes, Tennessee	62	April 27
Hurricane Irene, Mid-Atlantic Coast states	45	August 20-29
Groundhog Day blizzard, Central, Eastern, and Northeastern states	36	January 29-February 3
Tornadoes, Mississippi	31	April 27
Tornadoes, North Carolina	26	April 16
Other disasters (5-24 deaths)		
Flooding, Pennsylvania	17	September 7
Excessive heat, Illinois	17	July 17
Motor vehicle traffic crash, New York	15	March 12
Tornadoes, Georgia	15	April 27
Tornadoes, Oklahoma	11	May 24
Excessive heat, Texas	9	July 1
Excessive heat, New York	8	July 22
Residential fire, Pennsylvania	7	March
Thunderstorm and high winds, Indiana	7	August 13
Tornadoes, Alabama	7	April 15
Motor vehicle traffic crash, Indiana	7	October 27
Motor vehicle traffic crash, Oklahoma	7	June 4
Motor vehicle traffic crash, Colorado	6	October 13
Flooding, Arkansas	6	May 1
Flash flood, Arkansas	6	April 25
Tornadoes, Massachusetts	6	June 1
Tornadoes, Virginia	6	April 28
Bed and breakfast fire, Minnesota	6	July
Grain elevator fire, Kansas	6	October
Residential fire, Texas	6	March
Residential fire, Washington	6	April
Residential fire, Illinois	6	May
Residential fire, Ohio	6	June
Residential fire, New York	6	July
Excessive heat, Pennsylvania	5	July 29
Thunderstorm and high winds, Arkansas	5	April 15
Tornadoes, Arkansas	5	May 24
Wildfire, Texas	5	September 4-6
Residential fire, Washington	5	January
Residential fire, Texas	5	January
Residential fire, Pennsylvania	5	February
Residential fire, Pennsylvania	5	March
Residential fire, Mississippi	5	August
Residential fire, Connecticut	5	December
Fireworks storage fire, Hawaii	5	April
Residential board-and-care facility, California	5	May

Source: The National Climatic Data Center, National Fire Protection Association, and National Highway Traffic Safety Administration.
Note: Some death totals are estimates and may differ among sources.

Provided below is a timeline of disasters[a] resulting in substantial loss of life from 1900 to the present. As can be seen, while some sources of disasters, such as steamships and coal mines, become less prevalent toward the end of the timeline, other disaster types, such as hurricanes, are represented throughout the timeline.

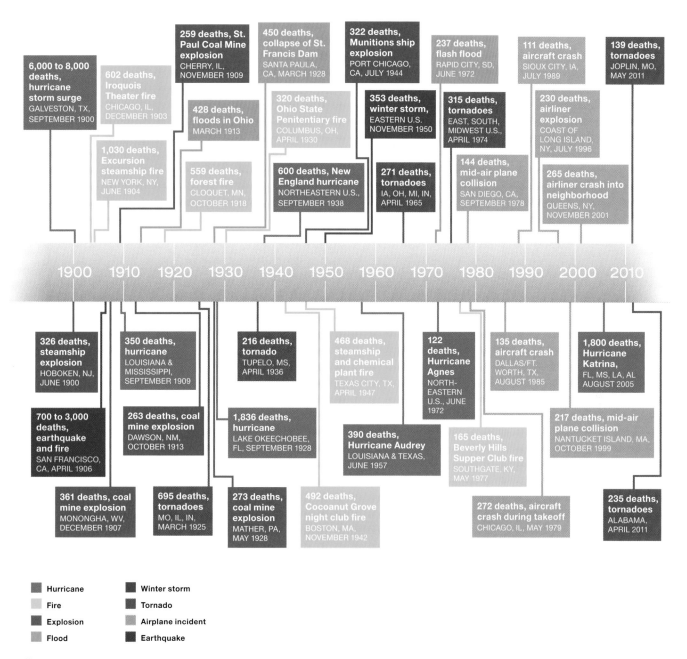

Hurricane
Fire
Explosion
Flood
Winter storm
Tornado
Airplane incident
Earthquake

[a]Timeline does not include epidemics or acts of terrorism. Because of space limitations, only a sample of disasters resulting in 100 or more fatalities are included.
Source: Info Please: www.infoplease.com, retrieved June 27, 2012; the National Centers for Environmental Prediction; U.S. Geological Survey; and the National Fire Protection Association.

Injuries may be divided into three broad groups – unintentional, intentional, and undetermined intent. Most of *Injury Facts* presents data on unintentional injuries. This page and the next two present data on intentional injuries.

Under the World Health Organization's Safe Communities initiative, for which the National Safety Council is the affiliate support center in the United States, injury prevention is not limited to unintentional injuries. Data on intentional injuries are presented here to support Safe Communities and to provide context to the unintentional-injury data provided in *Injury Facts*.

Intentional injuries may be divided into four subgroups – intentional self-harm (suicide), assault (homicide), legal intervention, and operations of war. The diagram below illustrates the injury groupings and shows the death totals for 2009.

Injury deaths by intent, United States, 2009

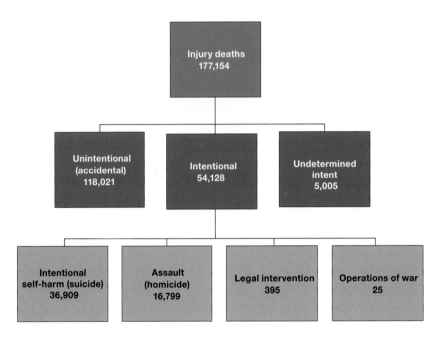

Intentional self-harm includes suicide and attempted suicide by purposely self-inflicted poisoning or injury. The most common methods of intentional self-harm that result in death are firearms; hanging, strangulation, and suffocation; and poisoning.

Assault includes homicide and injuries inflicted by another person with intent to injure or kill (excluding legal intervention and operations of war). The most common means of homicide are firearms; sharp objects; and hanging, strangulation, and suffocation.

Legal intervention includes legal execution. Operations of war include injuries to military personnel and civilians caused by war and civil insurrection. The death must have occurred in the United States. In the vital statistics system, war deaths (and other deaths) occurring outside the United States are counted by the country in which they occurred.

Each of the three broad groups of injuries was among the 15 leading causes of deaths in the United States in 2009. Unintentional (accidental) injuries ranked fifth, intentional self-harm (suicide) ranked 10th, and assault (homicide) ranked 13th.

Intentional self-harm ranked as high as second (after unintentional injuries) for people ages 14-16, 24, 25, and 27-34, and ranked third for those 12, 13, 17-23, and 26 years old. Suicide deaths were highest at age 50 (919) and ranked fourth at

this age after cancer, heart disease, and unintentional injuries. Assault ranked as high as second (after unintentional injuries) for people 17-23 and 26 years old. It ranked third among people 1, 2, 15, 16, 24, 25, and 27-30 years old. Homicide deaths were highest at age 21 (648). For people 15-30 years old, unintentional, homicide, and suicide are the three leading causes of death. The graph below shows the number of deaths due to injuries by single year of age from 0 to 100.

Injury deaths by age, United States, 2009

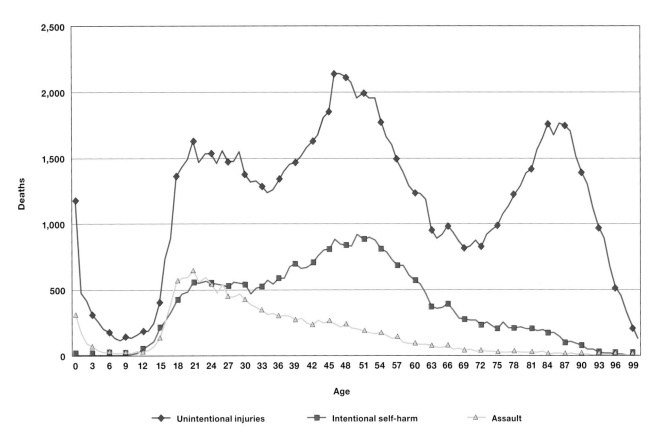

Source: National Safety Council analysis of National Center for Health Statistics–Mortality Data for 2009, as compiled from data provided by the 57 vital statistics jurisdictions through the Vital Statistics Cooperative Program.

Males have higher death rates than females for injuries of all intents. Males also have higher nonfatal injury rates than females for unintentional injuries and assault. Females, however, have a higher injury rate than males for intentional self-harm.

Death and nonfatal injury rates by intent and sex, United States, 2009

Sex	Deaths per 100,000 population			Nonfatal injuries per 100,000 population		
	Unintentional	Homicide	Suicide	Unintentional	Assault	Self-harm
Both sexes	38.4	5.5	12.0	9,001	503	122
Males	49.5	8.7	19.2	9,758	635	104
Females	27.6	2.4	5.0	8,261	375	139
Ratio of male to female	1.8	3.7	3.8	1.2	1.7	0.7

Source: National Safety Council analysis of National Center for Health Statistics (NCHS)–Mortality Data for 2009, as compiled from data provided by the 57 vital statistics jurisdictions through the Vital Statistics Cooperative Program. Rates are National Safety Council estimates based on data from NCHS and the U.S. Census Bureau.

The graph below shows the trends from 1992 to 2009 in injury deaths and death rates. Unintentional-injury-related deaths and death rates increased by 40.6% and 17.4%, respectively. Suicide deaths increased 21.1%, while the death rate increased only 1.2%. Homicide deaths and death rates decreased 33.2% and 44.2%, respectively, over the 1992-2009 period. Age-adjusted death rates, which remove the effects of the changing age distribution of the population, increased 11.9% for unintentional injuries, decreased 1.5% for suicide, and decreased 41.7% for homicide.

Injury deaths and death rates, United States, 1992-2009

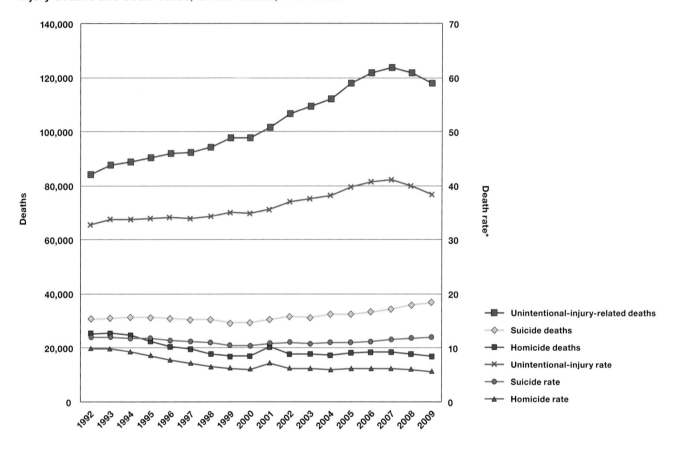

Deaths per 100,000 population.
Source: National Safety Council analysis of National Center for Health Statistics (NCHS)–Mortality Data for 2009, as compiled from data provided by the 57 vital statistics jurisdictions through the Vital Statistics Cooperative Program. Rates are National Safety Council estimates based on data from NCHS and the U.S. Census Bureau.

While you make a 10-minute safety speech, two people in the United States will be killed and about 704 will suffer an injury severe enough to require a consultation with a medical professional.[a] Costs will amount to $14,330,000. On average, 14 unintentional-injury-related deaths and about 4,220 medically consulted injuries occur every hour during the year.

Deaths and medically consulted injuries by class occurred in the nation at the following rates in 2011:

Deaths and medically consulted injuries by class, 2011

Class	Severity	One every ...	Number per ...			2010 total
			Hour	Day	Week	
All	Deaths	4 minutes	14	337	2,360	122,900
	Injuries[a]	1 second	4,220	101,400	711,500	37,000,000
Motor vehicle	Deaths	15 minutes	4	95	670	34,600
	Injuries	9 seconds	420	10,100	71,200	3,700,000
Work	Deaths	134 minutes	<1	11	80	3,909
	Injuries	6 seconds	570	13,700	96,200	5,000,000
Workers off the job	Deaths	10 minutes	6	142	1,000	52,000
	Injuries	2 seconds	1,500	35,900	257,900	13,100,000
Home	Deaths	9 minutes	7	166	1,170	60,600
	Injuries	2 seconds	2,150	51,500	361,500	18,800,000
Public non-motor vehicle	Deaths	21 minutes	3	70	490	25,500
	Injuries	3 seconds	1,110	26,600	186,500	9,700,000

Source: National Safety Council estimates.
[a]Starting with the 2011 edition of Injury Facts, the National Safety Council adopted the definition of "medically consulted injuries" to replace "disabling injuries." For a full description of medically consulted injuries, please see the Technical Appendix.

Deaths every hour...

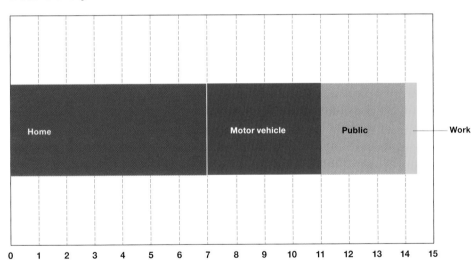

An unintentional-injury-related death occurs every four minutes.

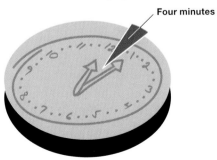

Four minutes

✦ *Motor vehicle crashes are the leading cause of injury-related deaths among children.*

Unintentional injuries are a major public health concern affecting children and adolescents in the United States. They are the underlying cause of death in nearly 4 out of 10 childhood mortality cases for people 1-19 years old, and 6 out of 10 deaths among 15- to 19-year-olds.

Fatal injuries in the first year of life numbered 1,181 in 2009, or approximately 28 deaths per 100,000 population. Mechanical suffocation constituted the majority (72%) of all injury-related mortality cases for infants. Motor vehicle crashes were the second leading cause of injury mortality. In addition, 317 infant deaths that year were attributed to homicide. (For more information on intentional injuries, see pages 34-36.)

In the second year of life, the risk of fatal injury is reduced by more than half. In 2009, 474 fatal injury cases, or about 11 deaths per 100,000 population, were recorded among 1-year-old children. Drowning was the leading cause of injury death in this age group, followed by motor vehicle crashes.

In the following three-year period (ages 2-4) the injury mortality rate dropped even lower, averaging about 8 deaths per 100,000 population in 2009. Drowning was the leading cause

for 2-year-olds, followed by motor vehicle crashes and fire, flames, or smoke. For 3- and 4-year-olds, motor vehicle crashes were the number one cause of injury mortality, followed by drowning and fire, flames, or smoke.

From the age of 5 to early adolescence (ages 12-14), the injury mortality rate shows a general U-shaped pattern, reaching its lowest level at around age 8. Motor vehicle crashes, unintentional drowning, and incidents related to fire, flames, or smoke were the leading causes of injury mortality for children 5-14 years old in 2009.

Teens (15-19 years) made up 27% of the U.S. population between the ages of 1 and 19 and 60% of all injury mortality cases in that age group. Most importantly, 70% of teen injury deaths are attributed to motor vehicle crashes. Of the 4,807 injury deaths among teens in 2009, 3,365 occurred in crashes. That same year, the injury mortality rate for 19-year-olds was 32 deaths per 100,000 population.

For all children and adolescents younger than 19, the injury mortality rate by age can be described as a J-shaped relationship, peaking during infancy and again in the late teen years.

Unintentional-injury-related deaths by event, ages 0-19, United States, 2009

Age	Population (000)	Unintentional-injury-related deaths										
		Total	Rates[a]	Motor vehicle	Falls	Poisoning	Drowning	Fire, flames, or smoke	Choking[b]	Mechanical suffocation	Firearms	All other
<1 year	4,261	1,181	27.7	95	19	22	45	24	54	853	1	68
1-19 years	**79,159**	**7,962**	**10.1**	**4,818**	**132**	**802**	**938**	**364**	**109**	**144**	**113**	**542**
1 year	4,298	474	11.0	136	15	14	167	34	31	31	2	44
2 years	4,336	414	9.5	127	16	8	147	36	20	14	5	41
3 years	4,224	317	7.5	102	9	11	91	47	9	11	6	31
4 years	4,181	261	6.2	114	6	4	45	50	4	5	2	31
5 years	4,186	200	4.8	111	4	2	36	19	4	2	7	15
6 years	4,139	178	4.3	92	0	4	32	25	1	3	2	19
7 years	4,108	134	3.3	71	2	2	26	18	1	3	0	11
8 years	4,167	116	2.8	65	2	3	14	8	2	2	1	19
9 years	4,010	145	3.6	84	4	2	11	18	1	7	2	16
10 years	3,946	136	3.4	74	4	4	13	16	2	2	2	19
11 years	3,941	155	3.9	104	3	2	10	13	1	7	4	11
12 years	3,957	189	4.8	109	1	7	19	14	3	9	6	21
13 years	4,033	185	4.6	115	4	7	18	7	1	6	3	24
14 years	4,096	251	6.1	149	4	17	30	3	1	9	5	33
15 years	4,134	395	9.6	250	10	35	38	6	5	6	10	35
16 years	4,225	738	17.5	509	9	86	65	9	8	7	12	33
17 years	4,307	888	20.6	631	8	114	53	18	2	6	13	43
18 years	4,389	1,355	30.9	993	17	203	62	7	11	6	13	43
19 years	4,484	1,431	31.9	982	14	277	61	16	2	8	18	53
0-4 years	**21,300**	**2,647**	**12.4**	**574**	**65**	**59**	**495**	**191**	**118**	**914**	**16**	**215**
5-9 years	**20,610**	**773**	**3.8**	**423**	**12**	**13**	**119**	**88**	**9**	**17**	**12**	**80**
10-14 years	**19,973**	**916**	**4.6**	**551**	**16**	**37**	**90**	**53**	**8**	**33**	**20**	**108**
15-19 years	**21,539**	**4,807**	**22.3**	**3,365**	**58**	**715**	**279**	**56**	**28**	**33**	**66**	**207**

Source: National Safety Council analysis of National Center for Health Statistics (NCHS)–Mortality Data for 2009, as compiled from data provided by the 57 vital statistics jurisdictions through the Vital Statistics Cooperative Program. Rates are National Safety Council estimates based on data from NCHS and the U.S. Census Bureau.
Note: Data do not include "age unknown" cases, which totaled 45 in 2009.
[a]Deaths per 100,000 population in each age group.
[b]Suffocation by inhalation or ingestion of food or other object.

Injury mortality and fall-related mortality rates increase with age.

Unintentional injuries cause significant mortality among adults in the United States. In 2009 alone, injuries were responsible for more than 108,000 deaths among Americans 20 and older.

The leading causes of injury mortality include motor vehicle crashes; poisoning; falls; choking; drowning; and fire, flames, and smoke. Motor vehicle crashes (29%), poisoning (28%), and falls (23%), the three leading causes of injury mortality, combined to account for nearly four-fifths of all fatal injuries sustained by adults older than 20 in 2009.

Age plays an important role in the occurrence of injuries. Motor vehicle crashes are the leading cause of injury mortality through the 20s. Starting with the early 30s, incidences of poisoning become the leading cause of death, with prevalence peaking in the 40s. Beginning in the early 60s, motor vehicle crashes once again take over as the leading cause of injury mortality until superseded by falls beginning in the early 70s.

The increase in the incidence of fatal falls appears to be the driving force behind a surge in the overall injury mortality rate in later life. The highest fall mortality rates occur among adults beginning at age 70 and older. As the table below illustrates, the number of injury-related deaths per 100,000 population in 2009 increased from 49 for 70- to 74-year-olds to 379 for 90- to 94-year-olds – a more than sevenfold increase.

A recent study examined risk factors for falls and fall-related injuries among 12,684 adults 85 and older using self-reported information for 2008 from the Behavioral Risk Factor Surveillance System.[a] In this most rapidly growing segment of the older adult population, 21.3% reported at least one fall in the past three months and 7.2% reported at least one fall-related injury requiring medical care or limited activity for a day or longer. Below-average general health, male sex, perceived insufficient sleep, health problems requiring assistive devices, alcohol consumption, increasing body mass index, and history of stroke were all independently associated with a greater risk of falls or fall-related injuries. Less-than-excellent general health status was strongly associated with the risk of a fall injury, with the risk progressively increasing over very good, good, fair, or poor health status. The authors indicated that some of the factors associated with increased risk, such as body mass index, alcohol consumption, and sleep problems are potentially modifiable and should be addressed accordingly, while factors that are not modifiable, such as age and sex, could serve to identify high-risk individuals who could be targeted for evidence-based prevention programs.

[a]Grundstrom, A.C., Guse, C.E., & Layde, P.M. (2012). Risk factors for falls and fall-related injuries in adults 85 years of age and older. Archives of Gerontology and Geriatrics, Issue 54, No. 3, pp. 421-428.

Unintentional-injury-related deaths by event, age 20 and older, United States, 2009

Age	Population (000)	Total	Rates[a]	Motor vehicle	Falls	Poisoning	Drowning	Fire, flames, or smoke	Choking[b]	Mechanical suffocation	Natural heat or cold	Firearms	All other
20-24	21,540	7,651	35.5	4,323	134	2,329	269	86	28	42	17	66	357
25-29	21,678	7,514	34.7	3,382	144	3,117	228	107	27	36	33	54	386
30-34	19,889	6,548	32.9	2,505	158	3,092	168	93	44	45	23	45	375
35-39	20,538	6,903	33.6	2,439	200	3,310	182	98	60	57	46	35	476
40-44	20,992	8,199	39.1	2,627	351	4,078	210	135	83	57	48	41	569
45-49	22,831	10,328	45.2	2,943	553	5,272	271	192	153	67	86	30	761
50-54	21,761	9,646	44.3	2,752	788	4,403	236	225	208	69	115	31	819
55-59	18,975	7,425	39.1	2,222	889	2,740	240	225	190	54	75	41	749
60-64	15,812	5,508	34.8	1,860	999	1,173	178	219	257	39	64	19	700
65-69	11,784	4,535	38.5	1,458	1,220	505	138	202	297	25	55	25	610
70-74	9,008	4,405	48.9	1,235	1,630	259	109	184	338	13	43	21	573
75-79	7,326	5,711	78.0	1,183	2,760	221	106	205	449	19	70	10	688
80-84	5,822	7,771	133.5	1,242	4,226	194	97	188	642	20	68	11	1,083
85-89	3,662	8,401	229.4	783	5,233	155	64	121	693	17	86	8	1,241
90-94	1,502	5,690	378.8	286	3,680	53	24	67	478	9	49	3	1,041
95-99	402	2,207	549.0	53	1,420	23	7	19	220	2	12	0	451
100 and older	64	391	610.9	1	253	4	0	2	40	1	6	0	84
20 and older	223,586	108,833	48.7	31,294	24,638	30,928	2,527	2,368	4,207	572	896	440	10,963
25 and older	202,046	101,182	50.1	26,971	24,504	28,599	2,258	2,282	4,179	530	879	374	10,606
35 and older	160,479	87,120	54.3	21,084	24,202	22,390	1,862	2,082	4,108	449	823	275	9,845
45 and older	118,949	72,018	60.5	16,018	23,651	15,002	1,470	1,849	3,965	335	729	199	8,800
55 and older	74,357	52,044	70.0	10,323	22,310	5,327	963	1,432	3,604	199	528	138	7,220
65 and older	39,570	39,111	98.8	6,241	20,422	1,414	545	988	3,157	106	389	78	5,771
75 and older	18,778	30,171	160.7	3,548	17,572	650	298	602	2,522	68	291	32	4,588

Source: National Safety Council analysis of National Center for Health Statistics (NCHS)–Mortality Data for 2009, as compiled from data provided by the 57 vital statistics jurisdictions through the Vital Statistics Cooperative Program. Rates are National Safety Council estimates based on data from NCHS and the U.S. Census Bureau.
Note: Data do not include "age unknown" cases, which totaled 45 in 2009.
[a]Deaths per 100,000 population in each age group.
[b]Suffocation by inhalation or ingestion of food or other object.

The table on the following pages was prepared in response to frequent questions such as, "What are the odds of being killed by lightning?" or "What are the chances of dying in a plane crash?"

The odds given in the table are statistical averages over the whole U.S. population and do not necessarily reflect the chances of death for a particular person from a particular external cause. Any individual's odds of dying from various external causes are affected by the activities in which they participate, where they live and drive, what kind of work they do, and other factors.

The table has four columns. The first column gives the manner of injury, such as motor vehicle crash, fall, fire, etc. The second column gives the total number of deaths nationwide due to the manner of injury in 2009 (the latest year for which data are available). The third column gives the odds of dying in one year due to the manner of injury. The fourth column gives the lifetime odds of dying from the manner of injury. Statements about the odds or chances of dying from a given cause of death may be made as follows:

- The odds of dying from (manner of injury) in 2009 were 1 in (value given in the "One-year odds" column).
- The lifetime odds of dying from (manner of injury) for a person born in 2009 were 1 in (value given in the "Lifetime odds" column).

For example, referring to the first line of the table:
- The odds of dying from an injury in 2009 were 1 in 1,708.

- The lifetime odds of dying from an injury for a person born in 2009 were 1 in 22.

The one-year odds are approximated by dividing the 2009 population (307,006,550) by the number of deaths. The lifetime odds are approximated by dividing the one-year odds by the life expectancy of a person born in 2009 (78.5 years). Please note that odds based on less than 20 deaths are likely to be unstable from year to year and are therefore not included in the table and figure on the following pages.

The figure on page 43 represents the lifetime odds of death for selected causes from the odds table. The total lifetime odds of death from any cause are 1 in 1, or 100%, and thus the largest rectangle representing the total odds actually extends off the page in all directions to infinity. The rectangles for selected causes are sized according to their relative lifetime probabilities, with the least probable event – death from fireworks discharge – depicted using the smallest box.

Source: National Safety Council estimates based on data from National Center for Health Statistics–Mortality Data for 2009, as compiled from data provided by the 57 vital statistics jurisdictions through the Vital Statistics Cooperative Program. Population and life expectancy data are from the U.S. Census Bureau. Deaths are classified on the basis of the 10th revision of the World Health Organization's International Classification of Diseases (ICD-10). Numbers following titles refer to External Cause of Morbidity and Mortality classifications in ICD-10.

Odds of death due to injury, United States, 2009[a]

Type of accident or manner of injury	Deaths	One-year odds	Lifetime odds
All external causes of mortality, V01-Y89, *U01, *U03[b]	179,770	1,708	22
Deaths due to unintentional (accidental) injuries, V01-X59, Y85-Y86	118,021	2,601	33
Transport accidents, V01-V99, Y85	39,031	7,866	100
Motor vehicle accidents, V02-V04, V09.0, V09.2, V12-V14, V19.0-V19.2, V19.4-V19.6, V20-V79, V80.3-V80.5, V81.0-V81.1, V82.0-V82.1, V83-V86, V87.0-V87.8, V88.0-V88.8, V89.0, V89.2	36,216	8,477	108
Pedestrian, V01-V09	5,219	58,825	749
Pedalcyclist, V10-V19	785	391,091	4,982
Motorcycle rider, V20-V29	4,310	71,231	907
Occupant of three-wheeled motor vehicle, V30-V39	12	(c)	(c)
Car occupant, V40-V49	9,415	32,608	415
Occupant of pick-up truck or van, V50-V59	2,449	125,360	1,597
Occupant of heavy transport vehicle, V60-V69	246	1,247,994	15,898
Bus occupant, V70-V79	22	13,954,843	177,769
Animal rider or occupant of animal-drawn vehicle, V80	118	2,601,750	33,143
Occupant of railway train or railway vehicle, V81	22	13,954,843	177,769
Occupant of streetcar, V82	2	(c)	(c)
Other and unspecified land transport accidents, V83-V89	14,649	20,958	267
Occupant of special industrial vehicle, V83	14	(c)	(c)
Occupant of special agricultural vehicle, V84	87	3,528,811	44,953
Occupant of special construction vehicle, V85	21	14,619,360	186,234
Occupant of all-terrain or other off-road motor vehicle, V86	1,004	305,783	3,895
Other and unspecified person, V87-V89	13,523	22,703	289
Water transport accidents, V90-V94	462	664,516	8,465
Drowning, V90, V92	329	933,151	11,887
Other and unspecified injuries, V91, V93-V94	133	2,308,320	29,405
Air and space transport accidents, V95-V97	541	567,480	7,229
Other and unspecified transport accidents and sequelae, V98-V99, Y85	779	394,103	5,020
Other specified transport accidents, V98	1	(c)	(c)
Unspecified transport accident, V99	2	(c)	(c)
Nontransport unintentional (accidental) injuries, W00-X59, Y86	78,990	3,887	50
Falls, W00-W19	24,792	12,383	158
Fall on same level from slipping, tripping, and stumbling, W01	788	389,602	4,963
Other fall on same level, W00, W02-W03, W18	7,439	41,270	526
Fall involving bed, chair, other furniture, W06-W08	1,090	281,657	3,588
Fall on and from stairs and steps, W10	1,960	156,636	1,995
Fall on and from ladder or scaffolding, W11-W12	448	685,282	8,730
Fall from out of or through building or structure, W13	476	644,972	8,216
Other fall from one level to another, W09, W14-W17	635	483,475	6,159
Other and unspecified fall, W04-W05, W19	11,956	25,678	327
Exposure to inanimate mechanical forces, W20-W49	2,353	130,475	1,662
Struck by or striking against object, W20-W22	755	406,631	5,180
Caught between objects, W23	140	2,192,904	27,935
Contact with machinery, W24, W30-W31	608	504,945	6,432
Contact with sharp objects, W25-W29	121	2,537,244	32,322
Firearms discharge, W32-W34	554	554,163	7,059
Explosion and rupture of pressurized devices, W35-W38	29	10,586,433	134,859
Fireworks discharge, W39	4	(c)	(c)
Explosion of other materials, W40	78	3,935,981	50,140
Foreign body entering through skin or natural orifice, W44-W45	29	10,586,433	134,859
Other and unspecified inanimate mechanical forces, W41-W43, W49	35	8,771,616	111,740
Exposure to animate mechanical forces, W50-W64	146	2,102,785	26,787
Struck by or against another person, W50-W52	21	14,619,360	186,234
Bitten or struck by dog, W54	32	9,593,955	122,216
Bitten or struck by other mammals, W53, W55	68	4,514,802	57,513
Bitten or stung by nonvenomous insect and other arthropods, W57	10	(c)	(c)
Bitten or crushed by other reptiles, W59	0	0	0
Other and unspecified animate mechanical forces, W56, W58, W60, W64	15	(c)	(c)
Accidental drowning and submersion, W65-W74	3,517	87,292	1,112
Drowning and submersion while in or falling into bathtub, W65-W66	438	700,928	8,929
Drowning and submersion while in or falling into swimming pool, W67-W68	705	435,470	5,547
Drowning and submersion while in or falling into natural water, W69-W70	1,656	185,390	2,362
Other and unspecified drowning or submersion, W73-W74	718	427,586	5,447
Other accidental threats to breathing, W75-W84	5,939	51,693	659
Accidental suffocation and strangulation in bed, W75	717	428,182	5,455
Other accidental hanging and strangulation, W76	259	1,185,353	15,100
Threat to breathing due to cave-in, falling earth and other substances, W77	34	9,029,604	115,027
Inhalation of gastric contents, W78	264	1,162,904	14,814
Inhalation and ingestion of food causing obstruction of respiratory tract, W79	1,018	301,578	3,842
Inhalation and ingestion of other objects causing obstruction of respiratory tract, W80	3,088	99,419	1,266
Confined to and trapped in a low-oxygen environment, W81	6	(c)	(c)
Other and unspecified threats to breathing, W83-W84	553	555,166	7,072

See source and footnotes on page 42.

Odds of death due to injury, United States, 2009[a] (cont.)

Type of accident or manner of injury	Deaths	One-year odds	Lifetime odds
Exposure to electric current, radiation, temperature, and pressure, W85-W99	322	953,436	12,146
Electric transmission lines, W85	71	4,324,036	55,083
Other and unspecified electric current, W86-W87	232	1,323,304	16,857
Radiation, W88-W91	0	0	0
Excessive heat or cold of man-made origin, W92-W93	8	(c)	(c)
High and low air pressure and changes in air pressure, W94	11	(c)	(c)
Other and unspecified man-made environmental factors, W99	0	0	0
Exposure to smoke, fire, and flames, X00-X09	2,756	111,396	1,419
Uncontrolled fire in building or structure, X00	2,219	138,354	1,762
Uncontrolled fire not in building or structure, X01	52	5,903,972	75,210
Controlled fire in building or structure, X02	23	13,348,111	170,040
Controlled fire not in building or structure, X03	27	11,370,613	144,849
Ignition of highly flammable material, X04	39	7,871,963	100,280
Ignition or melting of nightwear, X05	5	(c)	(c)
Ignition or melting of other clothing and apparel, X06	97	3,165,016	40,319
Other and unspecified smoke, fire, and flames, X08-X09	294	1,044,240	13,302
Contact with heat and hot substances, X10-X19	67	4,582,187	58,372
Contact with hot tap water, X11	23	13,348,111	170,040
Other and unspecified heat and hot substances, X10, X12-X19	44	6,977,422	88,884
Contact with venomous animals and plants, X20-X29	80	3,837,582	48,886
Contact with venomous snakes and lizards, X20	5	(c)	(c)
Contact with venomous spiders, X21	6	(c)	(c)
Contact with hornets, wasps, and bees, X23	55	5,581,937	71,107
Contact with other and unspecified venomous animal or plant, X22, X24-X29	14	(c)	(c)
Exposure to forces of nature, X30-X39	1,084	283,216	3,608
Exposure to excessive natural heat, X30	352	872,178	11,111
Exposure to excessive natural cold, X31	616	498,387	6,349
Lightning, X33	31	9,903,437	126,158
Earthquake and other earth movements, X34-X36	19	(c)	(c)
Cataclysmic storm, X37	31	9,903,437	126,158
Flood, X38	15	(c)	(c)
Exposure to other and unspecified forces of nature, X32, X39	20	15,350,328	195,546
Accidental poisoning by or exposure to noxious substances, X40-X49	31,758	9,667	123
Nonopioid analgesics, antipyretics, and antirheumatics, X40	252	1,218,280	15,519
Antiepileptic, sedative-hypnotic, antiparkinsonism, and psychotropic drugs n.e.c., X41	1,681	182,633	2,327
Narcotics and psychodysleptics [hallucinogens] n.e.c., X42	12,458	24,643	314
Other and unspecified drugs, medicaments, and biologicals, X43-X44	14,363	21,375	272
Alcohol, X45	2,014	152,436	1,942
Gases and vapors, X46-X47	784	391,590	4,988
Other and unspecified chemicals and noxious substances, X48-X49	206	1,490,323	18,985
Overexertion, travel, and privation, X50-X57	28	10,964,520	139,675
Accidental exposure to other and unspecified factors and sequelae, X58-X59, Y86	6,148	49,936	636
Intentional self-harm, X60-X84, Y87.0, *U03	**36,909**	**8,318**	**106**
Intentional self-poisoning, X60-X69	6,398	47,985	611
Intentional self-harm by hanging, strangulation, and suffocation, X70	9,000	34,112	435
Intentional self-harm by firearm, X72-X74	18,735	16,387	209
Other and unspecified means and sequelae, X71, X75-X84, Y87.0	2,776	110,593	1,409
Terrorism, *U03	0	0	0
Assault, X85-Y09, Y87.1, *U01	**16,799**	**18,275**	**233**
Assault by firearm, X93-X95	11,493	26,712	340
Assault by sharp object, X99	1,874	163,824	2,087
Other and unspecified means and sequelae, X85-X92, X96-X98, Y00-Y09, Y87.1	3,432	89,454	1,140
Terrorism, *U01	0	0	0
Event of undetermined intent, Y10-Y34, Y87.2, Y89.9	**5,005**	**61,340**	**781**
Poisoning, Y10-Y19	3,349	91,671	1,168
Hanging, strangulation, and suffocation, Y20	163	1,883,476	23,993
Drowning and submersion, Y21	264	1,162,904	14,814
Firearm discharge, Y22-Y24	232	1,323,304	16,857
Exposure to smoke, fire, and flames, Y26	117	2,623,988	33,427
Falling, jumping, and pushed from a high place, Y30	67	4,582,187	58,372
Other and unspecified means and sequelae, Y25, Y27-Y29, Y31-Y34,Y87.2, Y89.9	813	377,622	4,810
Legal intervention, Y35, Y89.0	**395**	**777,232**	**9,901**
Legal intervention involving firearm discharge, Y35.0	333	921,942	11,744
Legal execution, Y35.5	49	6,265,440	79,815
Other and unspecified means and sequelae, Y35.1-Y35.4, Y35.6-Y35.7, Y89.0	13	(c)	(c)
Operations of war and sequelae, Y36, Y89.1	**25**	**12,280,262**	**156,436**
Complications of medical and surgical care and sequelae, Y40-Y84, Y88.0-Y88.3	**2,616**	**117,357**	**1,495**

Source: National Center for Health Statistics–Mortality Data for 2009, as compiled from data provided by the 57 vital statistics jurisdictions through the Vital Statistics Cooperative Program. Deaths are classified on the basis of the 10th revision of the International Classification of Diseases (ICD-10), which became effective in 1999.

Note: "n.e.c." means not elsewhere classified.

[a]Latest official figures.

[b]Numbers following titles refer to external cause of injury and poisoning classifications in ICD-10.

[c]Odds based on less than 20 deaths are likely to be unstable from year to year and are therefore not included.

Lifetime odds of death for selected causes, United States, 2009[a]

Total, any cause
1 in 1

Heart disease **1 in 7**

Cancer **1 in 7**

Chronic lower respiratory
disease **1 in 28**

Intentional self-harm **1 in 106**

Motor vehicle incidents **1 in 108**

Unintentional poisoning by and exposure to noxious substances **1 in 123**

Falls **1 in 158**

Assault by firearm **1 in 340**

Car occupant **1 in 415**

Pedestrian **1 in 749**

Motorcycle rider **1 in 907**

Accidental drowning and submersion **1 in 1,112**

Exposure to fire, flames, or smoke **1 in 1,419**

Choking from inhalation and ingestion of food **1 in 3,842**

Pedalcyclist **1 in 4,982**

Firearms discharge **1 in 7,059**

Air and space transport accidents **1 in 7,229**

Exposure to excessive natural heat **1 in 11,111**

Exposure to electric current, radiation, temperature, and pressure **1 in 12,146**

Contact with sharp objects **1 in 32,322**

Contact with heat and hot substances **1 in 58,372**

Contact with hornets, wasps, and bees **1 in 71,107**

Legal execution **1 in 79,815**

Bitten or struck by dog **1 in 122,216**

Cataclysmic storm **1 in 126,158**

Lightning **1 in 126,158**

Source: National Safety Council estimates based on data from National Center for Health Statistics–Mortality Data for 2009, as compiled from data provided by the 57 vital statistics jurisdictions through the Vital Statistics Cooperative Program. Population and life expectancy data are from the U.S. Census Bureau. For mortality figures, estimated one-year and lifetime odds, and external cause classification codes based on the 10th revision of the World Health Organization's International Classification of Diseases *for the causes illustrated, see table on pages 41-42.*
[a]*See explanation of odds of dying on page 40.*

Age-adjusted rates, which eliminate the effect of shifts in the age distribution of the population, decreased 62% from 1912 to 2011 – from 100.4 to 38.2 deaths per 100,000 population. The adjusted rates, which are shown in the graphs on the opposite page, are standardized to the year 2000 standard U.S. population. The break in the lines at 1948 shows the estimated effect of changes in the International Classification of Diseases (ICD). The break in the lines at 1992 resulted from the adoption of the Bureau of Labor Statistics Census of Fatal Occupational Injuries for work-related deaths. Another change in the ICD in 1999 also affects the trends. See the Technical Appendix for comparability.

The table below shows the change in the age distribution of the population since 1910. The age-adjusted death rate for all unintentional injuries increased and decreased significantly several times during the period from 1910 to 1940 (top chart on next page). Since 1940, there were some setbacks, such as in the early 1960s, but the overall trend through the early 1990s was positive. The age-adjusted death rates for unintentional-injury-

related deaths in the work and home classes declined fairly steadily since they became available in the late 1920s, and the home class rates have increased since the early 1990s. The rates in the public class declined for three decades, rose in the 1960s and then continued declining until leveling out in the 1990s to present. The age-adjusted motor vehicle death rate rose steadily from 1910 to the late 1930s as the automobile became more widely used. A sharp drop in use occurred during World War II and a sharp rise in rates occurred in the 1960s, with death rates reflecting economic cycles and a long-term downward trend since then.

Looking at individual leading causes (bottom chart on next page), at the turn of the last century falls were the leading cause of unintentional-injury-related death, while motor vehicle and poisoning deaths were only minor concerns. Today, although falls continue to be a major concern, poisonings and motor vehicle incidents have become the two leading causes of unintentional-injury-related deaths.

United States population, selected years

Year	All ages	Younger than 15	15-24	25-44	45-64	65 and older
Number (in thousands)						
1910	91,973[a]	29,499	18,121	26,810	13,424	3,950
2000[b]	274,634	58,964	38,077	81,892	60,991	34,710
2011	311,591	61,201	43,798	82,418	82,780	41,394
Percent						
1910	100.0%	32.1%	19.7%	29.2%	14.6%	4.3%
2000[b]	100.0%	21.5%	13.9%	29.8%	22.2%	12.6%
2011	100.0%	19.6%	14.1%	26.4%	26.6%	13.3%

Source: For 1910: U.S. Census Bureau. (1960). Historical Statistics of the United States, Colonial Times to 1957. Series A 71-85. Washington, DC: U.S. Government Printing Office. For 2000: Anderson, R.N., & Rosenberg, H.M. (1998). Age standardization of death rates: Implementation of the year 2000 standard. National Vital Statistics Reports, Issue 47, No. 3 p. 13. For 2010: U.S. Census Bureau, Table 1. Monthly Population Estimates for the United States: April 1, 2000 to December 1, 2010. Revised December 2009.
[a]Includes 169,000 people with age unknown.
[b]This is the population used for standardization (age adjustment) and differs slightly from the actual 2000 population, which totaled 275,306,000.

Age-adjusted death rates by class of injury, United States, 1910-2011

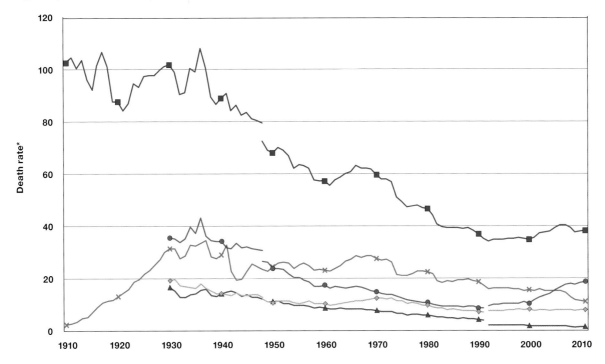

Deaths per 100,000 population adjusted to the year 2000 standard population. The break at 1948 shows the estimated effect of classification changes. The break at 1992 is due to the adoption of the Bureau of Labor Statistics Census of Fatal Occupational Injuries for work-related deaths.

- ■ All
- ✕ Motor vehicle
- ● Home
- ▲ Work
- ◆ Public

Age-adjusted death rates by leading cause of unintentional injury, United States, 1910-2011

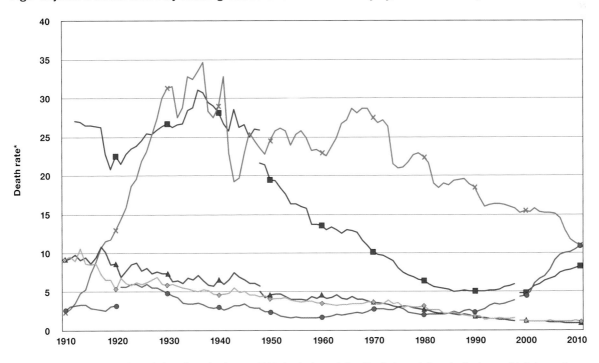

Deaths per 100,000 population adjusted to the year 2000 standard population. Breaks in graph lines signify changes fatal injury coding.

- ■ Falls
- ✕ Motor vehicle
- ● Poisoning
- ▲ Fire, flames, or smoke
- ◆ Drowning

Principal Classes of Unintentional-Injury-Related Deaths

Principal classes of unintentional-injury-related deaths, United States, 1903-2011

Year	Total[a] Deaths	Rate[b]	Motor vehicle Deaths	Rate[b]	Work Deaths	Rate[b]	Home Deaths	Rate[b]	Public non-motor vehicle Deaths	Rate[b]
1903	70,600	87.2	(c)	–	(c)	–	(c)	–	(c)	–
1904	71,500	86.6	(c)	–	(c)	–	(c)	–	(c)	–
1905	70,900	84.2	(c)	–	(c)	–	(c)	–	(c)	–
1906	80,000	93.2	400	0.5	(c)	–	(c)	–	(c)	–
1907	81,900	93.6	700	0.8	(c)	–	(c)	–	(c)	–
1908	72,300	81.2	800	0.9	(c)	–	(c)	–	(c)	–
1909	72,700	80.1	1,300	1.4	(c)	–	(c)	–	(c)	–
1910	77,900	84.4	1,900	2.0	(c)	–	(c)	–	(c)	–
1911	79,300	84.7	2,300	2.5	(c)	–	(c)	–	(c)	–
1912	78,400	82.5	3,100	3.3	(c)	–	(c)	–	(c)	–
1913	82,500	85.5	4,200	4.4	(c)	–	(c)	–	(c)	–
1914	77,000	78.6	4,700	4.8	(c)	–	(c)	–	(c)	–
1915	76,200	76.7	6,600	6.6	(c)	–	(c)	–	(c)	–
1916	84,800	84.1	8,200	8.1	(c)	–	(c)	–	(c)	–
1917	90,100	88.2	10,200	10.0	(c)	–	(c)	–	(c)	–
1918	85,100	82.1	10,700	10.3	(c)	–	(c)	–	(c)	–
1919	75,500	71.9	11,200	10.7	(c)	–	(c)	–	(c)	–
1920	75,900	71.2	12,500	11.7	(c)	–	(c)	–	(c)	–
1921	74,000	68.4	13,900	12.9	(c)	–	(c)	–	(c)	–
1922	76,300	69.4	15,300	13.9	(c)	–	(c)	–	(c)	–
1923	84,400	75.7	18,400	16.5	(c)	–	(c)	–	(c)	–
1924	85,600	75.6	19,400	17.1	(c)	–	(c)	–	(c)	–
1925	90,000	78.4	21,900	19.1	(c)	–	(c)	–	(c)	–
1926	91,700	78.7	23,400	20.1	(c)	–	(c)	–	(c)	–
1927	92,700	78.4	25,800	21.8	(c)	–	(c)	–	(c)	–
1928	95,000	79.3	28,000	23.4	19,000	15.8	30,000	24.9	21,000	17.4
1929	98,200	80.8	31,200	25.7	20,000	16.4	30,000	24.6	20,000	16.4
1930	99,100	80.5	32,900	26.7	19,000	15.4	30,000	24.4	20,000	16.3
1931	97,300	78.5	33,700	27.2	17,500	14.1	29,000	23.4	20,000	16.1
1932	89,000	71.3	29,500	23.6	15,000	12.0	29,000	23.2	18,000	14.4
1933	90,932	72.4	31,363	25.0	14,500	11.6	29,500	23.6	18,500	14.7
1934	100,977	79.9	36,101	28.6	16,000	12.7	34,000	26.9	18,000	14.2
1935	99,773	78.4	36,369	28.6	16,500	13.0	32,000	25.2	18,000	14.2
1936	110,052	85.9	38,089	29.7	18,500	14.5	37,000	28.9	19,500	15.2
1937	105,205	81.7	39,643	30.8	19,000	14.8	32,000	24.8	18,000	14.0
1938	93,805	72.3	32,582	25.1	16,000	12.3	31,000	23.9	17,000	13.1
1939	92,623	70.8	32,386	24.7	15,500	11.8	31,000	23.7	16,000	12.2
1940	96,885	73.4	34,501	26.1	17,000	12.9	31,500	23.9	16,500	12.5
1941	101,513	76.3	39,969	30.0	18,000	13.5	30,000	22.5	16,500	12.4
1942	95,889	71.6	28,309	21.1	18,000	13.4	30,500	22.8	16,000	12.0
1943	99,038	73.8	23,823	17.8	17,500	13.0	33,500	25.0	17,000	12.7
1944	95,237	71.7	24,282	18.3	16,000	12.0	32,500	24.5	16,000	12.0
1945	95,918	72.4	28,076	21.2	16,500	12.5	33,500	25.3	16,000	12.1
1946	98,033	70.0	33,411	23.9	16,500	11.8	33,000	23.6	17,500	12.5
1947	99,579	69.4	32,697	22.8	17,000	11.9	34,500	24.1	18,000	12.6
1948 (5th Rev.)[d]	98,001	67.1	32,259	22.1	16,000	11.0	35,000	24.0	17,000	11.6
1948 (6th Rev.)[d]	93,000	63.7	32,259	22.1	16,000	11.0	31,000	21.2	16,000	11.0
1949	90,106	60.6	31,701	21.3	15,000	10.1	31,000	20.9	15,000	10.1
1950	91,249	60.3	34,763	23.0	15,500	10.2	29,000	19.2	15,000	9.9
1951	95,871	62.5	36,996	24.1	16,000	10.4	30,000	19.6	16,000	10.4
1952	96,172	61.8	37,794	24.3	15,000	9.6	30,500	19.6	16,000	10.3
1953	95,032	60.1	37,955	24.0	15,000	9.5	29,000	18.3	16,500	10.4
1954	90,032	55.9	35,586	22.1	14,000	8.7	28,000	17.4	15,500	9.6
1955	93,443	56.9	38,426	23.4	14,200	8.6	28,500	17.3	15,500	9.4
1956	94,780	56.6	39,628	23.7	14,300	8.5	28,000	16.7	16,000	9.6
1957	95,307	55.9	38,702	22.7	14,200	8.3	28,000	16.4	17,500	10.3
1958	90,604	52.3	36,981	21.3	13,300	7.7	26,500	15.3	16,500	9.5
1959	92,080	52.2	37,910	21.5	13,800	7.8	27,000	15.3	16,500	9.3
1960	93,806	52.1	38,137	21.2	13,800	7.7	28,000	15.6	17,000	9.4
1961	92,249	50.4	38,091	20.8	13,500	7.4	27,000	14.8	16,500	9.0
1962	97,139	52.3	40,804	22.0	13,700	7.4	28,500	15.3	17,000	9.2
1963	100,669	53.4	43,564	23.1	14,200	7.5	28,500	15.1	17,500	9.3
1964	105,000	54.9	47,700	25.0	14,200	7.4	28,000	14.6	18,500	9.7
1965	108,004	55.8	49,163	25.4	14,100	7.3	28,500	14.7	19,500	10.1
1966	113,563	58.1	53,041	27.1	14,500	7.4	29,500	15.1	20,000	10.2
1967	113,169	57.3	52,924	26.8	14,200	7.2	29,000	14.7	20,500	10.4
1968	114,864	57.6	54,862	27.5	14,300	7.2	28,000	14.0	21,500	10.8
1969	116,385	57.8	55,791	27.7	14,300	7.1	27,500	13.7	22,500	11.2
1970	114,638	56.2	54,633	26.8	13,800	6.8	27,000	13.2	23,500	11.5
1971	113,439	54.8	54,381	26.3	13,700	6.6	26,500	12.8	23,500	11.4
1972	115,448	55.2	56,278	26.9	14,000	6.7	26,500	12.7	23,500	11.2
1973	115,821	54.8	55,511	26.3	14,300	6.8	26,500	12.5	24,500	11.6

See source and footnotes on page 47.

Principal classes of unintentional-injury-related deaths, United States, 1903-2011 (cont.)

Year	Total[a] Deaths	Total[a] Rate[b]	Motor vehicle Deaths	Motor vehicle Rate[b]	Work Deaths	Work Rate[b]	Home Deaths	Home Rate[b]	Public non-motor vehicle Deaths	Public non-motor vehicle Rate[b]
1974	104,622	49.0	46,402	21.8	13,500	6.3	26,000	12.2	23,000	10.8
1975	103,030	47.8	45,853	21.3	13,000	6.0	25,000	11.6	23,000	10.6
1976	100,761	46.3	47,038	21.6	12,500	5.7	24,000	11.0	21,500	10.0
1977	103,202	47.0	49,510	22.5	12,900	5.9	23,200	10.6	22,200	10.1
1978	105,561	47.5	52,411	23.6	13,100	5.9	22,800	10.3	22,000	9.9
1979	105,312	46.9	53,524	23.8	13,000	5.8	22,500	10.0	21,000	9.4
1980	105,718	46.5	53,172	23.4	13,200	5.8	22,800	10.0	21,300	9.4
1981	100,704	43.9	51,385	22.4	12,500	5.4	21,700	9.5	19,800	8.6
1982	94,082	40.6	45,779	19.8	11,900	5.1	21,200	9.2	19,500	8.4
1983	92,488	39.6	44,452	19.0	11,700	5.0	21,200	9.1	19,400	8.3
1984	92,911	39.4	46,263	19.6	11,500	4.9	21,200	9.0	18,300	7.8
1985	93,457	39.3	45,901	19.3	11,500	4.8	21,600	9.1	18,800	7.9
1986	95,277	39.7	47,865	19.9	11,100	4.6	21,700	9.0	18,700	7.8
1987	95,020	39.2	48,290	19.9	11,300	4.7	21,400	8.8	18,400	7.6
1988	97,100	39.7	49,078	20.1	11,000	4.5	22,700	9.3	18,400	7.5
1989	95,028	38.5	47,575	19.3	10,900	4.4	22,500	9.1	18,200	7.4
1990	91,983	36.9	46,814	18.8	10,100	4.0	21,500	8.6	17,400	7.0
1991	89,347	35.4	43,536	17.3	9,800	3.9	22,100	8.8	17,600	7.0
1992	86,777	34.0	40,982	16.1	4,968[e]	1.9[e]	24,000[e]	9.4[e]	19,000[e]	7.4[e]
1993	90,523	35.1	41,893	16.3	5,035	2.0	26,100	10.1	19,700	7.6
1994	91,437	35.1	42,524	16.3	5,338	2.1	26,300	10.1	19,600	7.5
1995	93,320	35.5	43,363	16.5	5,018	1.9	27,200	10.3	20,100	7.6
1996	94,948	35.8	43,649	16.5	5,058	1.9	27,500	10.4	21,000	7.9
1997	95,644	35.7	43,458	16.2	5,162	1.9	27,700	10.3	21,700	8.1
1998	97,835	36.2	43,501	16.1	5,120	1.9	29,000	10.7	22,600	8.4
1999[f]	97,860	35.9	42,401	15.5	5,185	1.9	30,500	11.2	22,200	8.1
2000	97,900	35.6	43,354	15.7	5,022	1.8	29,200	10.6	22,700	8.2
2001	101,537	35.6	43,788	15.4	5,042	1.8	33,200	11.6	21,800	7.6
2002	106,742	37.1	45,380	15.8	4,726	1.6	36,400	12.6	22,500	7.8
2003	109,277	37.6	44,757	15.4	4,725	1.6	38,800	13.3	23,200	8.0
2004	112,012	38.1	44,933	15.3	5,000	1.7	41,700	14.2	22,700	7.7
2005	117,809	39.7	45,343	15.3	4,987	1.7	46,400	15.6	23,400	7.9
2006	121,599	40.8	45,316	15.2	5,092	1.7	49,600	16.6	23,900	8.0
2007	123,706	41.1	43,945	14.6	4,833	1.6	53,500	17.8	23,700	7.9
2008	121,902	40.0	39,790	13.1	4,425	1.5	55,200	18.1	24,500	8.0
2009[g]	118,046	38.5	36,216	11.8	3,744	1.2	55,800	18.2	24,000	7.8
2010[g]	120,834	39.0	35,332	11.4	3,902	1.3	58,100	18.8	25,300	8.2
2011[h]	122,900	39.4	34,600	11.1	3,909	1.3	60,600	19.4	25,500	8.2
Changes										
2001 to 2011	+21%	+11%	-21%	-28%	-22%	-28%	+82%	+67%	+17%	+8%
2010 to 2011	+2%	+1%	-2%	-3%	+<1%	0%	+4%	+3%	+1%	0%

Source: Total and motor vehicle deaths, 1903-1932 based on National Center for Health Statistics (NCHS) death registration states; 1933-1948 (5th Rev.), 1949-1963, 1965-2010 are NCHS totals for the United States. Work deaths for 1992-2011 are from the Bureau of Labor Statistics Census of Fatal Occupational Injuries. All other figures are National Safety Council estimates.

[a]Duplications between motor vehicle, work, and home are eliminated in the total column.
[b]Rates are deaths per 100,000 population.
[c]Data insufficient to estimate yearly totals.
[d]In 1948, a revision was made in the International Classification of Diseases. The first figures for 1948 are comparable with those for earlier years, the second with those for later years.
[e]Adoption of the Census of Fatal Occupational Injuries figure for the work class necessitated adjustments to the home and public classes. See the Technical Appendix for details.
[f]In 1999, a revision was made in the International Classification of Diseases. See the Technical Appendix for comparability with earlier years.
[g]Revised.
[h]Preliminary.

Unintentional-injury-related deaths by age, United States, 1903-2011

Year	All ages	Younger than 5 years	5-14 years	15-24 years	25-44 years	45-64 years	65-74 years	75 years and older[a]
1903	70,600	9,400	8,200	10,300	20,100	12,600	10,000	
1904	71,500	9,700	9,000	10,500	19,900	12,500	9,900	
1905	70,900	9,800	8,400	10,600	19,600	12,600	9,900	
1906	80,000	10,000	8,400	13,000	24,000	13,600	11,000	
1907	81,900	10,500	8,300	13,400	24,900	14,700	10,100	
1908	72,300	10,100	7,600	11,300	20,500	13,100	9,700	
1909	72,700	9,900	7,400	10,700	21,000	13,300	10,400	
1910	77,900	9,900	7,400	11,900	23,600	14,100	11,000	
1911	79,300	11,000	7,500	11,400	22,400	15,100	11,900	
1912	78,400	10,600	7,900	11,500	22,200	14,700	11,500	
1913	82,500	9,800	7,400	12,200	24,500	16,500	12,100	
1914	77,000	10,600	7,900	11,000	21,400	14,300	11,800	
1915	76,200	10,300	8,200	10,800	20,500	14,300	12,100	
1916	84,800	11,600	9,100	7,700	24,900	17,800	13,700	
1917	90,100	11,600	9,700	11,700	24,400	18,500	14,200	
1918	85,100	10,600	10,100	10,600	21,900	17,700	14,200	
1919	75,500	10,100	10,000	10,200	18,600	13,800	12,800	
1920	75,900	10,200	9,900	10,400	18,100	13,900	13,400	
1921	74,000	9,600	9,500	9,800	18,000	13,900	13,200	
1922	76,300	9,700	9,500	10,000	18,700	14,500	13,900	
1923	84,400	9,900	9,800	11,000	21,500	16,900	15,300	
1924	85,600	10,200	9,900	11,900	20,900	16,800	15,900	
1925	90,000	9,700	10,000	12,400	22,200	18,700	17,000	
1926	91,700	9,500	9,900	12,600	22,700	19,200	17,800	
1927	92,700	9,200	9,900	12,900	22,900	19,700	18,100	
1928	95,000	8,900	9,800	13,100	23,300	20,600	19,300	
1929	98,200	8,600	9,800	14,000	24,300	21,500	20,000	
1930	99,100	8,200	9,100	14,000	24,300	22,200	21,300	
1931	97,300	7,800	8,700	13,500	23,100	22,500	21,700	
1932	89,000	7,100	8,100	12,000	20,500	20,100	21,200	
1933	90,932	6,948	8,195	12,225	21,005	20,819	21,740	
1934	100,977	7,034	8,272	13,274	23,288	24,197	24,912	
1935	99,773	6,971	7,808	13,168	23,411	23,457	24,958	
1936	110,052	7,471	7,866	13,701	24,990	26,535	29,489	
1937	105,205	6,969	7,704	14,302	23,955	24,743	27,532	
1938	93,805	6,646	6,593	12,129	20,464	21,689	26,284	
1939	92,628	6,668	6,378	12,066	20,164	20,842	26,505	
1940	96,885	6,851	6,466	12,763	21,166	21,840	27,799	
1941	101,513	7,052	6,702	14,346	22,983	22,509	27,921	
1942	95,889	7,220	6,340	13,732	21,141	20,764	26,692	
1943	99,038	8,039	6,636	15,278	20,212	20,109	28,764	
1944	95,237	7,912	6,704	14,750	19,115	19,097	27,659	
1945	95,918	7,741	6,836	12,446	19,393	20,097	29,405	
1946	98,033	7,949	6,545	13,366	20,705	20,249	29,219	
1947	99,579	8,219	6,069	13,166	21,155	20,513	30,457	
1948 (5th Rev.)[b]	98,001	8,387	5,859	12,595	20,274	19,809	31,077	
1948 (6th Rev.)[b]	93,000	8,350	5,850	12,600	20,300	19,300	9,800	16,800
1949	90,106	8,469	5,539	11,522	19,432	18,302	9,924	16,918
1950	91,249	8,389	5,519	12,119	20,663	18,665	9,750	16,144
1951	95,871	8,769	5,892	12,366	22,363	19,610	10,218	16,653
1952	96,172	8,871	5,980	12,787	21,950	19,892	10,026	16,667
1953	95,032	8,678	6,136	12,837	21,422	19,479	9,927	16,553
1954	90,032	8,380	5,939	11,801	20,023	18,299	9,652	15,938
1955	93,443	8,099	6,099	12,742	29,911	19,199	9,929	16,464
1956	94,780	8,173	6,319	13,545	20,986	19,207	10,160	16,393
1957	95,307	8,423	6,454	12,973	20,949	19,495	10,076	16,937
1958	90,604	8,789	6,514	12,744	19,658	18,095	9,431	15,373
1959	92,080	8,748	6,511	13,269	19,666	18,937	9,475	15,474
1960	93,806	8,950	6,836	13,457	19,600	19,385	9,689	15,829
1961	92,249	8,622	6,717	13,431	19,273	19,134	9,452	15,620
1962	97,139	8,705	6,751	14,557	19,955	20,335	10,149	16,687
1963	100,669	8,688	6,962	15,889	20,529	21,262	10,194	17,145
1964	100,500	8,670	7,400	17,420	22,080	22,100	10,400	16,930
1965	108,004	8,586	7,391	18,688	22,228	22,900	10,430	17,781
1966	113,563	8,507	7,958	21,030	23,134	24,022	10,706	18,206
1967	113,169	7,825	7,874	21,645	23,255	23,826	10,645	18,099
1968	114,864	7,263	8,369	23,012	23,684	23,896	10,961	17,679
1969	116,385	6,973	8,186	24,668	24,410	24,192	10,643	17,313
1970	114,638	6,594	8,203	24,336	23,979	24,164	10,644	16,718
1971	113,439	6,496	8,143	24,733	23,535	23,240	10,494	16,798
1972	115,448	6,142	8,242	25,762	23,852	23,658	10,446	17,346
1973	115,821	6,037	8,102	26,550	24,750	23,059	10,243	17,080

See source and footnotes on page 49.

Unintentional-injury-related deaths by age, United States, 1903-2011 (cont.)

Year	All ages	Younger than 5	5-14 years	15-24 years	25-44 years	45-64 years	65-74 years	75 and older[a]
1974	104,622	5,335	7,037	24,200	22,547	20,334	9,323	15,846
1975	103,030	4,948	6,818	24,121	22,877	19,643	9,220	15,403
1976	100,761	4,692	6,308	24,316	22,399	19,000	8,823	15,223
1977	103,202	4,470	6,305	25,619	23,460	19,167	9,006	15,175
1978	105,561	4,766	6,118	26,622	25,024	18,774	9,072	15,185
1979	105,312	4,429	5,689	26,574	26,097	18,346	9,013	15,164
1980	105,718	4,479	5,224	26,206	26,722	18,140	8,997	15,950
1981	100,704	4,130	4,866	23,582	26,928	17,339	8,639	15,220
1982	94,082	4,108	4,504	21,306	25,135	15,907	8,224	14,898
1983	92,488	3,999	4,321	19,756	24,996	15,444	8,336	15,636
1984	92,911	3,652	4,198	19,801	25,498	15,273	8,424	16,065
1985	93,457	3,746	4,252	19,161	25,940	15,251	8,583	16,524
1986	95,277	3,843	4,226	19,975	27,201	14,733	8,499	16,800
1987	95,020	3,871	4,198	18,695	27,484	14,807	8,686	17,279
1988	97,100	3,794	4,215	18,507	28,279	15,177	8,971	18,157
1989	95,028	3,770	4,090	16,738	28,429	15,046	8,812	18,143
1990	91,983	3,496	3,650	16,241	27,663	14,607	8,405	17,921
1991	89,347	3,626	3,660	15,278	26,526	13,693	8,137	18,427
1992	86,777	3,286	3,388	13,662	25,808	13,882	8,165	18,586
1993	90,523	3,488	3,466	13,966	27,277	14,434	8,125	19,767
1994	91,437	3,406	3,508	13,898	27,012	15,200	8,279	20,134
1995	93,320	3,067	3,544	13,842	27,660	16,004	8,400	20,803
1996	94,948	2,951	3,433	13,809	27,092	16,717	8,780	22,166
1997	95,644	2,770	3,371	13,367	27,129	17,521	8,578	22,908
1998	97,835	2,689	3,254	13,349	27,172	18,286	8,892	24,193
1999[c]	97,860	2,743	3,091	13,656	27,121	18,924	8,208	24,117
2000	97,900	2,707	2,979	14,113	27,182	19,783	7,698	23,438
2001	101,537	2,690	2,836	14,411	27,784	21,002	7,835	24,979
2002	106,742	2,587	2,718	15,412	29,279	23,020	8,086	25,640
2003	109,277	2,662	2,618	15,272	29,307	25,007	8,081	26,330
2004	112,012	2,693	2,666	15,449	29,503	26,593	8,116	26,992
2005	117,809	2,747	2,415	15,753	30,916	29,192	8,632	28,154
2006	121,599	2,757	2,258	16,229	32,488	31,121	8,420	28,326
2007	123,706	2,873	2,194	15,897	31,908	32,508	8,753	29,573
2008	121,902	2,784	1,859	14,089	30,653	33,136	8,994	30,387
2009[d]	118,046	2,674	1,680	12,454	29,159	32,945	8,976	30,158
2010[d]	120,834	2,528	1,594	12,306	29,412	33,662	9,458	31,874
2011[e]	122,900	2,600	1,500	11,900	29,600	35,100	10,000	32,200
Changes								
2001 to 2011	+21%	-3%	-47%	-17%	+7%	+67%	+28%	+29%
2010 to 2011	+2%	+3%	-6%	-3%	+1%	+4%	+6%	+1%

Source: 1903-1932 based on National Center for Health Statistics (NCHS) data for registration states; 1933-1948 (5th Rev.), 1949-1963, 1965-2010 are NCHS totals. All other figures are National Safety Council estimates. See Technical Appendix for comparability.

[a]Includes age unknown. In 2009, these deaths numbered 45; in 2010, they numbered 16.

[b]In 1948, a revision was made in the International Classification of Diseases. The first figures for 1948 are comparable with those for earlier years, the second with those for later years.

[c]In 1999, a revision was made in the International Classification of Diseases. See the Technical Appendix for comparability with earlier years.

[d]Revised.

[e]Preliminary.

Unintentional-injury-related death rates[a] by age, United States, 1903-2011

Year	Standardized rate[b]	All ages	Younger than 5 years	5-14 years	15-24 years	25-44 years	45-64 years	65-74 years	75 years and older[c]
1903	99.4	87.2	98.7	46.8	65.0	87.4	111.7	299.8	
1904	103.4	86.6	99.1	50.9	64.9	84.6	108.1	290.0	
1905	98.4	84.2	98.6	47.0	64.1	81.4	106.2	282.5	
1906	114.2	93.2	99.1	46.5	77.1	97.3	111.7	306.0	
1907	112.4	93.6	102.7	45.5	78.0	98.8	117.8	274.2	
1908	99.7	81.2	97.5	41.2	64.4	79.5	102.2	256.7	
1909	97.4	80.1	94.2	39.6	59.9	79.6	101.0	268.2	
1910	103.0	84.4	92.8	39.1	65.3	87.3	104.0	276.0	
1911	104.7	84.7	101.9	39.3	62.1	81.4	108.7	292.1	
1912	100.4	82.5	97.1	40.5	62.3	79.2	103.2	275.8	
1913	103.5	85.5	88.4	37.4	65.2	85.6	112.5	281.7	
1914	95.9	78.6	94.3	38.9	58.5	73.2	94.6	268.1	
1915	92.1	76.7	90.8	39.7	57.3	69.0	92.1	268.8	
1916	101.4	84.1	101.4	43.3	40.8	82.5	112.1	297.6	
1917	106.7	88.2	108.4	45.3	62.1	79.8	113.8	301.2	
1918	101.2	82.1	91.0	46.5	58.7	72.2	106.3	294.2	
1919	87.7	71.9	87.2	45.9	55.3	60.1	81.8	262.0	
1920	87.8	71.2	87.4	44.9	55.5	56.9	85.6	289.5	
1921	84.3	68.4	80.8	42.4	51.4	55.5	79.4	259.8	
1922	86.9	69.4	80.6	41.5	51.4	57.1	81.4	265.1	
1923	94.5	75.7	82.0	42.4	55.6	64.5	92.6	282.8	
1924	93.3	75.6	82.9	42.4	58.6	61.7	90.2	283.5	
1925	97.2	78.4	78.6	42.3	59.7	64.7	97.8	293.9	
1926	97.7	78.7	77.9	41.4	59.9	65.4	98.2	298.7	
1927	97.5	78.4	75.9	41.0	60.2	65.2	98.0	295.4	
1928	99.6	79.3	74.4	40.4	59.9	65.6	99.9	306.2	
1929	101.2	80.8	73.3	40.0	63.1	67.7	102.1	308.9	
1930	101.8	80.5	71.8	36.9	62.3	67.0	102.9	317.9	
1931	99.2	78.5	69.9	35.2	59.7	63.0	102.1	313.3	
1932	90.5	71.3	65.1	32.8	52.7	55.6	89.3	296.9	
1933	91.1	72.4	65.5	33.4	53.6	56.3	90.8	295.3	
1934	100.5	79.9	68.1	33.9	57.8	61.8	103.3	328.5	
1935	97.9	78.4	68.5	32.2	56.9	61.6	98.0	319.8	
1936	108.1	85.9	74.4	32.9	58.8	65.3	108.6	367.4	
1937	100.7	81.7	69.6	32.7	60.9	62.1	99.3	333.4	
1938	89.4	72.3	65.3	28.5	51.3	52.5	85.4	308.9	
1939	86.7	70.8	62.9	28.2	50.7	51.2	81.0	300.0	
1940	89.1	73.4	64.8	28.8	53.5	53.2	83.4	305.7	
1941	90.7	76.3	65.0	29.7	60.9	57.2	84.8	297.4	
1942	84.3	71.6	63.9	27.9	59.8	52.4	77.1	275.5	
1943	86.3	73.8	66.9	29.0	69.7	50.3	73.6	287.8	
1944	82.5	71.7	63.2	29.1	72.9	48.9	68.9	268.6	
1945	83.4	72.4	59.8	29.5	64.5	50.5	71.6	277.6	
1946	81.0	70.0	60.2	28.1	61.7	48.8	70.9	267.9	
1947	80.5	69.4	57.4	25.8	59.6	49.0	70.6	270.7	
1948 (5th Rev.)[d]	79.5	67.1	56.3	24.6	56.8	46.2	66.8	267.4	
1948 (6th Rev.)[d]	72.5	63.7	56.0	24.5	56.8	46.2	65.1	122.4	464.3
1949	69.0	60.6	54.4	23.0	52.2	43.5	60.6	120.4	450.7
1950	68.1	60.3	51.4	22.6	55.0	45.6	60.5	115.8	414.7
1951	70.1	62.5	50.8	23.6	57.7	49.0	62.7	117.1	413.6
1952	69.0	61.8	51.5	22.5	60.9	47.7	62.7	111.1	399.8
1953	67.0	60.1	49.5	22.1	61.4	46.4	60.5	106.7	383.6
1954	62.2	55.9	46.7	20.5	56.4	43.0	55.9	100.7	354.4
1955	63.4	56.9	43.9	20.7	60.1	44.7	57.7	100.8	350.2
1956	63.0	56.6	43.3	20.2	63.3	44.7	56.7	100.6	335.6
1957	62.2	55.9	43.5	19.9	59.5	44.6	56.6	97.5	333.3
1958	57.5	52.3	44.5	19.6	56.2	42.0	51.7	89.3	292.6
1959	57.4	52.2	43.6	18.9	56.5	42.1	53.2	87.7	284.7
1960	57.3	52.1	44.0	19.1	55.6	42.0	53.6	87.6	281.4
1961	55.4	50.4	42.0	18.1	54.0	41.2	52.1	83.8	267.9
1962	57.5	52.3	42.6	18.0	55.0	42.7	54.6	88.5	277.7
1963	58.6	53.4	42.8	18.2	57.2	44.0	56.3	87.9	277.0
1964	60.0	54.9	43.1	19.1	59.9	47.3	57.6	88.9	263.9
1965	61.9	55.8	43.4	18.7	61.6	47.7	58.8	88.5	268.7
1966	63.0	58.1	44.4	19.9	66.9	49.6	60.7	89.8	267.4
1967	62.1	57.3	42.2	19.4	66.9	49.7	59.2	88.5	257.4
1968	62.0	57.6	40.6	20.5	69.2	50.1	58.5	90.2	244.0
1969	61.8	57.8	40.2	20.0	71.8	51.2	58.4	86.6	232.0
1970	59.8	56.2	38.4	20.1	68.0	49.8	57.6	85.2	219.6
1971	58.1	54.8	37.7	20.1	66.1	48.4	54.7	82.7	213.2
1972	58.0	55.2	35.9	20.6	67.6	47.5	55.2	80.8	214.2
1973	57.1	54.8	35.8	20.6	68.2	48.0	53.3	77.3	206.3

See source and footnotes on page 51.

Unintentional-injury-related death rates[a] by age, United States, 1903-2011 (cont.)

Year	Standardized rate[b]	All ages	Younger than 5 years	5-14 years	15-24 years	25-44 years	45-64 years	65-74 years	75 years and older[c]
1974	50.9	49.0	32.4	18.2	60.9	42.7	46.7	68.7	186.7
1975	49.3	47.8	30.7	17.8	59.5	42.3	44.9	66.2	175.5
1976	47.3	46.3	30.0	16.7	58.9	40.3	43.2	62.0	168.4
1977	47.6	47.0	28.7	17.0	61.3	40.9	43.4	61.5	164.0
1978	47.8	47.5	30.3	16.9	63.1	42.3	42.4	60.5	159.7
1979	47.0	46.9	27.6	16.1	62.6	42.7	41.3	58.8	154.8
1980	46.5	46.5	27.2	15.0	61.7	42.3	40.8	57.5	158.6
1981	44.0	43.9	24.4	14.2	55.9	41.2	39.0	54.4	147.4
1982	40.6	40.6	23.8	13.2	51.2	37.3	35.8	50.9	140.0
1983	39.6	39.6	22.8	12.7	48.2	36.0	34.7	50.8	142.8
1984	39.4	39.4	20.6	12.4	48.9	35.7	34.3	50.7	142.8
1985	39.2	39.3	21.0	12.6	47.9	35.3	34.2	50.9	143.0
1986	39.4	39.7	21.4	12.6	50.5	36.1	33.0	49.6	141.5
1987	39.0	39.2	21.4	12.4	48.1	35.7	33.0	49.8	141.6
1988	39.5	39.7	20.9	12.3	48.5	36.1	33.4	50.9	145.3
1989	38.4	38.5	20.4	11.8	44.8	35.7	32.8	49.3	141.5
1990	36.8	36.9	18.5	10.4	44.0	34.2	31.6	46.4	136.5
1991	35.3	35.4	18.9	10.2	42.0	32.3	29.3	44.5	136.7
1992	34.0	34.0	16.8	9.3	37.8	31.3	28.7	44.2	134.5
1993	35.0	35.1	17.7	9.4	38.8	33.0	29.1	43.6	139.9
1994	35.0	35.1	17.3	9.4	38.4	32.5	29.9	44.3	139.2
1995	35.0	35.5	15.7	9.3	38.2	33.2	30.6	44.8	140.6
1996	35.3	35.8	15.3	8.9	38.1	32.3	31.1	47.0	145.9
1997	35.1	35.7	14.5	8.7	36.5	32.5	31.6	46.3	146.2
1998	35.5	36.2	14.2	8.3	35.9	32.6	31.9	48.3	151.1
1999[e]	35.2	35.9	14.5	7.8	36.1	32.7	32.0	45.0	147.7
2000	34.8	35.6	14.3	7.5	36.7	33.0	32.3	42.3	140.8
2001	35.7	35.6	13.9	6.9	36.1	32.7	32.6	42.8	146.8
2002	37.1	37.1	13.2	6.6	37.9	34.7	34.6	44.2	148.2
2003	37.6	37.6	13.5	6.4	37.0	34.8	36.4	44.0	149.6
2004	38.1	38.1	13.4	6.5	37.1	35.1	37.6	43.9	151.4
2005	39.5	39.7	13.5	6.0	37.4	36.8	40.1	46.3	155.2
2006	40.4	40.8	13.5	5.6	38.5	38.9	41.6	44.5	154.4
2007	40.5	41.1	13.9	5.5	37.5	38.2	42.4	45.2	159.2
2008	39.4	40.0	13.2	4.6	32.8	36.8	42.6	44.7	162.8
2009[f]	37.7	38.5	12.6	4.1	28.9	35.1	41.5	43.2	160.6
2010[f]	38.1	39.0	11.8	3.9	28.6	35.4	41.7	45.5	168.0
2011[g]	38.2	39.4	12.9	3.7	27.2	35.9	42.4	44.5	170.3
Changes									
2001 to 2011		+11%	-7%	-46%	-25%	+10%	+30%	+4%	+16%
2010 to 2011		+1%	+9%	-5%	-5%	+1%	+2%	-2%	+1%
2011 population (thousands)									
Total[h]		311,591	20,162	41,039	43,798	82,418	82,780	22,482	18,912
Male		153,291	10,300	20,971	22,432	41,268	40,377	10,476	7,467
Female		158,301	9,863	20,068	21,366	41,151	42,403	12,005	11,445

Source: All figures are National Safety Council estimates. See Technical Appendix for comparability.
[a]*Rates are deaths per 100,000 resident population in each age group.*
[b]*Adjusted to the year 2000 standard population to remove the influence of changes in age distribution between 1903 and 2011.*
[c]*Includes age unknown.*
[d]*In 1948, a revision was made in the International Classification of Diseases. The first figures for 1948 are comparable with those for earlier years, the second with those for later years.*
[e]*In 1999, a revision was made in the International Classification of Diseases. See the Technical Appendix for comparability.*
[f]*Revised.*
[g]*Preliminary.*
[h]*Sum of parts may not equal total due to rounding.*

Principal Types of Unintentional-Injury-Related Deaths

Principal types of unintentional-injury-related deaths, United States, 1903-1998

Year	Total	Motor vehicle	Falls	Drowning[a]	Fire, flames, or smoke[b]	Choking[b]	Firearms	Poison (solid or liquid)	Poison (gas or vapor)	All other
1903	70,600	(c)	(c)	9,200	(c)	(c)	2,500	(c)	(c)	58,900
1904	71,500	(c)	(c)	9,300	(c)	(c)	2,800	(c)	(c)	59,400
1905	70,900	(c)	(c)	9,300	(c)	(c)	2,000	(c)	(c)	59,600
1906	80,000	400	(c)	9,400	(c)	(c)	2,100	(c)	(c)	68,100
1907	81,900	700	(c)	9,000	(c)	(c)	1,700	(c)	(c)	70,500
1908	72,300	800	(c)	9,300	(c)	(c)	1,900	(c)	(c)	60,300
1909	72,700	1,300	(c)	8,500	(c)	(c)	1,600	(c)	(c)	61,300
1910	77,900	1,900	(c)	8,700	(c)	(c)	1,900	(c)	(c)	65,400
1911	79,300	2,300	(c)	9,000	(c)	(c)	2,100	(c)	(c)	65,900
1912	78,400	3,100	(c)	8,600	(c)	(c)	2,100	(c)	(c)	64,600
1913	82,500	4,200	15,100	10,300	8,900	(c)	2,400	3,200	(c)	38,400
1914	77,000	4,700	15,000	8,700	9,100	(c)	2,300	3,300	(c)	33,900
1915	76,200	6,600	15,000	8,600	8,400	(c)	2,100	2,800	(c)	32,700
1916	84,800	8,200	15,200	8,900	9,500	(c)	2,200	2,900	(c)	37,900
1917	90,100	10,200	15,200	7,600	10,800	(c)	2,300	2,800	(c)	41,200
1918	85,100	10,700	13,200	7,000	10,200	(c)	2,500	2,700	(c)	38,800
1919	75,500	11,200	11,900	9,100	9,100	(c)	2,800	3,100	(c)	28,300
1920	75,900	12,500	12,600	6,100	9,300	(c)	2,700	3,300	(c)	29,400
1921	74,000	13,900	12,300	7,800	7,500	(c)	2,800	2,900	(c)	26,800
1922	76,300	15,300	13,200	7,000	8,300	(c)	2,900	2,800	(c)	26,800
1923	84,400	18,400	14,100	6,800	9,100	(c)	2,900	2,800	2,700	27,600
1924	85,600	19,400	14,700	7,400	7,400	(c)	2,900	2,700	2,900	28,200
1925	90,000	21,900	15,500	7,300	8,600	(c)	2,800	2,700	2,800	28,400
1926	91,700	23,400	16,300	7,500	8,800	(c)	2,800	2,600	3,200	27,100
1927	92,700	25,800	16,500	8,100	8,200	(c)	3,000	2,600	2,700	25,800
1928	95,000	28,000	17,000	8,600	8,400	(c)	2,900	2,800	2,800	24,500
1929	98,200	31,200	17,700	7,600	8,200	(c)	3,200	2,600	2,800	24,900
1930	99,100	32,900	18,100	7,500	8,100	(c)	3,200	2,600	2,500	24,200
1931	97,300	33,700	18,100	7,600	7,100	(c)	3,100	2,600	2,100	23,000
1932	89,000	29,500	18,600	7,500	7,100	(c)	3,000	2,200	2,100	19,000
1933	90,932	31,363	18,962	7,158	6,781	(c)	3,014	2,135	1,633	19,886
1934	100,977	36,101	20,725	7,077	7,456	(c)	3,033	2,148	1,643	22,794
1935	99,773	36,369	21,378	6,744	7,253	(c)	2,799	2,163	1,654	21,413
1936	110,052	38,089	23,562	6,659	7,939	(c)	2,817	2,177	1,665	27,144
1937	105,205	39,643	22,544	7,085	7,214	(c)	2,576	2,190	1,675	22,278
1938	93,805	32,582	23,239	6,881	6,491	(c)	2,726	2,077	1,428	18,381
1939	92,623	32,386	23,427	6,413	6,675	(c)	2,618	1,963	1,440	17,701
1940	96,885	34,501	23,356	6,202	7,521	(c)	2,375	1,847	1,583	19,500
1941	101,513	39,969	22,764	6,389	6,922	(c)	2,396	1,731	1,464	19,878
1942	95,889	28,309	22,632	6,696	7,901	(c)	2,678	1,607	1,741	24,325
1943	99,038	23,823	24,701	7,115	8,726	921	2,282	1,745	2,014	27,711
1944	95,237	24,282	22,989	6,511	8,372	896	2,392	1,993	1,860	25,942
1945	95,918	28,076	23,847	6,624	7,949	897	2,385	1,987	2,120	22,033
1946	98,033	33,411	23,109	6,442	7,843	1,076	2,801	1,961	1,821	19,569
1947	99,579	32,697	24,529	6,885	8,033	1,206	2,439	1,865	1,865	14,060
1948 (5th Rev.)[d]	98,001	32,259	24,836	6,428	7,743	1,315	2,191	1,753	2,045	19,611
1948 (6th Rev.)[d]	93,000	32,259	22,000	6,500	6,800	1,299	2,330	1,600	2,020	17,192
1949	90,106	31,701	22,308	6,684	5,982	1,341	2,326	1,634	1,617	16,513
1950	91,249	34,763	20,783	6,131	6,405	1,350	2,174	1,584	1,769	16,290
1951	95,871	36,996	21,376	6,489	6,788	1,456	2,247	1,497	1,627	17,395
1952	96,172	37,794	20,945	6,601	6,922	1,434	2,210	1,440	1,397	17,429
1953	95,032	37,955	20,631	6,770	6,579	1,603	2,277	1,391	1,223	16,603
1954	90,032	35,586	19,771	6,334	6,083	1,627	2,271	1,339	1,223	15,798
1955	93,443	38,426	20,192	6,344	6,352	1,608	2,120	1,431	1,163	15,807
1956	94,780	39,628	20,282	6,263	6,405	1,760	2,202	1,422	1,213	15,605
1957	95,307	38,702	20,545	6,613	6,269	2,043	2,369	1,390	1,143	16,233
1958	90,604	36,981	18,248	6,582[e]	7,291[e]	2,191[e]	2,172	1,429	1,187	14,523
1959	92,080	37,910	18,774	6,434	6,898	2,189	2,258	1,661	1,141	14,815
1960	93,806	38,137	19,023	6,529	7,645	2,397	2,334	1,679	1,253	14,809
1961	92,249	38,091	18,691	6,525	7,102	2,499	2,204	1,804	1,192	14,141
1962	97,139	40,804	19,589	6,439	7,534	1,813	2,092	1,833	1,376	15,659
1963	100,669	43,564	19,335	6,347	8,172	1,949	2,263	2,061	1,489	15,489
1964	105,000	47,700	18,941	6,709	7,379	1,865	2,275	2,100	1,360	16,571
1965	108,004	49,163	19,984	6,799	7,347	1,836	2,344	2,110	1,526	16,895
1966	113,563	53,041	20,066	7,084	8,084	1,831	2,558	2,283	1,648	16,968
1967	113,169	52,924	20,120	7,076	7,423	1,980	2,896	2,506	1,574	16,670
1968	114,864	54,862	18,651	7,372[e]	7,335	3,100[e]	2,394[e]	2,583	1,526	17,041
1969	116,385	55,791	17,827	7,699	7,163	3,712	2,309	2,967	1,549	16,368
1970	114,638	54,633	16,926	7,860	6,718	2,753	2,406	3,679	1,620	18,043
1971	113,439	54,381	16,755	7,396	6,776	2,877	2,360	3,710	1,646	17,538
1972	115,448	56,278	16,744	7,586	6,714	2,830	2,442	3,728	1,690	17,436
1973	115,821	55,511	16,506	8,725	6,503	3,013	2,618	3,683	1,652	17,610

See source and footnotes on page 53.

Principal types of unintentional-injury-related deaths, United States, 1903-1998 (cont.)

Year	Total	Motor vehicle	Falls	Drowning[a]	Fire, flames, or smoke[b]	Choking[b]	Firearms	Poison (solid or liquid)	Poison (gas or vapor)	All other
1974	104,622	46,402	16,339	7,876	6,236	2,991	2,513	4,016	1,518	16,731
1975	103,030	45,853	14,896	8,000	6,071	3,106	2,380	4,694	1,577	16,453
1976	100,761	47,038	14,136	6,827	6,338	3,033	2,059	4,161	1,569	15,600
1977	103,202	49,510	13,773	7,126	6,357	3,037	1,982	3,374	1,596	16,447
1978	105,561	52,411	13,690	7,026	6,163	3,063	1,806	3,035	1,737	16,630
1979	105,312	53,524	13,216	6,872	5,991	3,243	2,004	3,165	1,472	15,825
1980	105,718	53,172	13,294	7,257	5,822	3,249	1,955	3,089	1,242	16,638
1981	100,704	51,385	12,628	6,277	5,697	3,331	1,871	3,243	1,280	14,992
1982	94,082	45,779	12,077	6,351	5,210	3,254	1,756	3,474	1,259	14,922
1983	92,488	44,452	12,024	6,353	5,028	3,387	1,695	3,382	1,251	14,916
1984	92,911	46,263	11,937	5,388	5,010	3,541	1,668	3,808	1,103	14,193
1985	93,457	45,901	12,001	5,316	4,938	3,551	1,649	4,091	1,079	14,931
1986	95,277	47,865	11,444	5,700	4,835	3,692	1,452	4,731	1,009	14,549
1987	95,020	48,290	11,733	5,100	4,710	3,688	1,440	4,415	900	14,744
1988	97,100	49,078	12,096	4,966	4,965	3,805	1,501	5,353	873	14,463
1989	95,028	47,575	12,151	4,015	4,716	3,578	1,489	5,603	921	14,980
1990	91,983	46,814	12,313	4,685	4,175	3,303	1,416	5,055	748	13,474
1991	89,347	43,536	12,662	4,818	4,120	3,240	1,441	5,698	736	13,096
1992	86,777	40,982	12,646	3,542	3,958	3,182	1,409	6,449	633	13,976
1993	90,523	41,893	13,141	3,807	3,900	3,160	1,521	7,877	660	14,564
1994	91,437	42,524	13,450	3,942	3,986	3,065	1,356	8,309	685	14,120
1995	93,320	43,363	13,986	4,350	3,761	3,185	1,225	8,461	611	14,378
1996	94,948	43,649	14,986	3,959	3,741	3,206	1,134	8,872	638	14,763
1997	95,644	43,458	15,447	4,051	3,490	3,275	981	9,587	576	14,779
1998	97,835	43,501	16,274	4,406	3,255	3,515	866	10,255	546	15,217

Principal types of unintentional-injury-related deaths, United States, 1999-2011

Year	Total	Motor vehicle	Falls	Poisoning	Choking[b]	Drowning[f]	Fire, flames, or smoke[b]	Mechanical suffocation	Firearms	All other
1999[g]	97,860	42,401	13,162	12,186	3,885	3,529	3,348	1,618	824	16,907
2000	97,900	43,354	13,322	12,757	4,313	3,482	3,377	1,335	776	15,184
2001	101,537	43,788	15,019	14,078	4,185	3,281	3,309	1,370	802	15,705
2002	106,742	45,380	16,257	17,550	4,128	3,447	3,159	1,389	762	13,670
2003	109,277	44,757	17,229	19,457	4,272	3,306	3,369	1,309	730	14,850
2004	112,012	44,933	18,807	20,950	4,470	3,308	3,229	1,421	649	14,245
2005	117,809	45,343	19,656	23,617	4,386	3,582	3,197	1,514	789	15,725
2006	121,599	45,316	20,823	27,531	4,332	3,579	3,109	1,580	642	14,687
2007	123,706	43,945	22,631	29,846	4,344	3,443	3,286	1,653	613	14,558
2008	121,902	39,790	24,013	31,116	4,366	3,548	2,912	1,759	592	14,398
2009[h]	118,046	36,216	24,792	31,758	4,370	3,517	2,756	1,569	554	13,068
2010[h]	120,834	35,332	26,009	33,041	4,570	3,782	2,782	1,595	606	13,117
2011[i]	122,900	34,600	27,500	34,900	4,600	3,600	2,800	1,600	600	12,700
Changes										
2001 to 2011	+21%	-21%	+83%	+148%	+10%	+10%	-15%	+17%	-25%	-19%
2010 to 2011	+2%	-2%	+6%	+6%	+1%	-5%	+1%	+<1%	-<1%	-3%

Source: National Center for Health Statistics and National Safety Council. See Technical Appendix for comparability.

[a]*Includes drowning in water transport incidents.*

[b]*Fire, flames, or smoke includes burns by fire and deaths resulting from conflagration regardless of nature of injury. Choking is the inhalation of food or other object obstructing breathing.*

[c]*Comparable data not available.*

[d]*In 1948, a revision was made in the International Classification of Diseases. The first figures for 1948 are comparable with those for earlier years, the second with those for later years.*

[e]*Data are not comparable to previous years shown due to classification changes in 1958 and 1968.*

[f]*Excludes water transport drownings.*

[g]*In 1999, a revision was made in the International Classification of Diseases. See the Technical Appendix for comparability.*

[h]*Revised.*

[i]*Preliminary.*

Unintentional-Injury-Related Death Rates for Principal Types

Unintentional-injury-related death rates[a] for principal types, United States, 1903-1998

Year	Total	Motor vehicle	Falls	Drowning[b]	Fire, flames, or smoke[c]	Choking[c]	Firearms	Poison (solid or liquid)	Poison (gas or vapor)	All other
1903	87.2	(d)	(d)	11.4	(d)	(d)	3.1	(d)	(d)	72.7
1904	86.6	(d)	(d)	11.3	(d)	(d)	3.4	(d)	(d)	71.9
1905	84.2	(d)	(d)	11.1	(d)	(d)	2.4	(d)	(d)	70.7
1906	93.2	0.5	(d)	11.0	(d)	(d)	2.4	(d)	(d)	79.3
1907	93.6	0.8	(d)	10.4	(d)	(d)	2.0	(d)	(d)	80.4
1908	81.2	0.9	(d)	10.5	(d)	(d)	2.1	(d)	(d)	67.7
1909	80.1	1.4	(d)	9.4	(d)	(d)	1.8	(d)	(d)	67.5
1910	84.4	2.0	(d)	9.4	(d)	(d)	2.1	(d)	(d)	70.9
1911	84.7	2.5	(d)	9.6	(d)	(d)	2.2	(d)	(d)	70.4
1912	82.5	3.3	(d)	9.0	(d)	(d)	2.2	(d)	(d)	68.0
1913	85.5	4.4	15.5	10.6	9.1	(d)	2.5	3.3	(d)	40.1
1914	78.6	4.8	15.1	8.8	9.1	(d)	2.3	3.3	(d)	35.2
1915	76.7	6.6	14.9	8.6	8.4	(d)	2.1	2.8	(d)	33.3
1916	84.1	8.1	14.9	8.7	9.3	(d)	2.2	2.8	(d)	38.1
1917	88.2	10.0	14.7	7.4	10.5	(d)	2.2	2.7	(d)	40.7
1918	82.1	10.3	12.8	6.8	9.9	(d)	2.4	2.6	(d)	37.3
1919	71.9	10.7	11.4	6.9	8.7	(d)	2.7	3.0	(d)	28.5
1920	71.2	11.7	11.8	5.7	8.7	(d)	2.5	3.1	(d)	27.7
1921	68.4	12.9	11.3	7.2	6.9	(d)	2.6	2.7	(d)	24.8
1922	69.4	13.9	12.0	6.4	7.5	(d)	2.6	2.5	(d)	24.5
1923	75.7	16.5	12.6	6.1	8.1	(d)	2.6	2.5	2.4	24.9
1924	75.6	17.1	12.9	6.5	8.4	(d)	2.5	2.4	2.5	23.3
1925	78.4	19.1	13.4	6.3	7.4	(d)	2.4	2.3	2.4	25.1
1926	78.7	20.1	13.9	6.4	7.5	(d)	2.4	2.2	2.7	23.5
1927	78.4	21.8	13.9	6.8	6.9	(d)	2.5	2.2	2.3	22.0
1928	79.3	23.4	14.1	7.1	7.0	(d)	2.4	2.3	2.3	20.7
1929	80.8	25.7	14.5	6.2	6.7	(d)	2.6	2.1	2.3	20.7
1930	80.5	26.7	14.7	6.1	6.6	(d)	2.6	2.1	2.0	19.7
1931	78.5	27.2	14.6	6.1	5.7	(d)	2.5	2.1	1.7	18.6
1932	71.3	23.6	14.9	6.0	5.7	(d)	2.4	1.8	1.7	15.2
1933	72.4	25.0	15.1	5.7	5.4	(d)	2.4	1.7	1.3	15.8
1934	79.9	28.6	16.4	5.6	5.9	(d)	2.4	1.7	1.3	18.0
1935	78.4	28.6	16.8	5.3	5.7	(d)	2.2	1.7	1.3	16.8
1936	85.9	29.7	18.4	5.2	6.2	(d)	2.2	1.7	1.3	21.2
1937	81.7	30.8	17.5	5.5	5.6	(d)	2.0	1.7	1.3	17.3
1938	72.3	25.1	17.9	5.3	5.0	(d)	2.1	1.6	1.1	14.2
1939	70.8	24.7	17.9	4.9	5.1	(d)	2.0	1.5	1.1	13.6
1940	73.4	26.1	17.7	4.7	5.7	(d)	1.8	1.4	1.2	14.8
1941	76.3	30.0	17.1	4.8	5.2	(d)	1.8	1.3	1.1	15.0
1942	71.6	21.1	16.9	5.0	5.9	(d)	2.0	1.2	1.3	18.2
1943	73.8	17.8	18.4	5.3	6.5	0.7	1.7	1.3	1.5	20.6
1944	71.7	18.3	17.3	4.9	6.3	0.7	1.8	1.5	1.4	19.5
1945	72.4	21.2	18.0	5.0	6.0	0.7	1.8	1.5	1.6	16.6
1946	70.0	23.9	16.5	4.6	5.6	0.8	2.0	1.4	1.3	13.9
1947	69.4	22.8	17.1	4.8	5.6	0.8	1.7	1.3	1.3	14.0
1948 (5th Rev.)[e]	67.1	22.1	17.0	4.4	5.3	0.9	1.5	1.2	1.4	13.3
1948 (6th Rev.)[e]	63.7	22.1	15.1	4.5	4.7	0.9	1.6	1.1	1.4	12.3
1949	60.6	21.3	15.0	4.5	4.0	0.9	1.6	1.1	1.1	11.1
1950	60.3	23.0	13.7	4.1	4.2	0.9	1.4	1.1	1.2	10.7
1951	62.5	24.1	13.9	4.2	4.4	1.0	1.5	1.0	1.1	11.3
1952	61.8	24.3	13.5	4.2	4.5	0.9	1.4	0.9	Poison	11.2
1953	60.1	24.0	13.0	4.3	4.2	1.0	1.4	0.9	0.8	10.2
1954	55.9	22.1	12.3	3.9	3.8	1.0	1.4	0.8	0.8	9.8
1955	56.9	23.4	12.3	3.9	3.9	1.0	1.3	0.9	0.7	9.5
1956	56.6	23.7	12.1	3.7	3.8	1.1	1.3	0.8	0.7	9.4
1957	55.9	22.7	12.1	3.9	3.7	1.2	1.4	0.8	0.7	9.4
1958	52.3	21.3	10.5	3.8[f]	4.2[f]	1.3[f]	1.3	0.8	0.7	8.4
1959	52.2	21.5	10.6	3.7	3.9	1.2	1.3	0.9	0.7	8.4
1960	52.1	21.2	10.6	3.6	4.3	1.3	1.3	0.9	0.7	8.2
1961	50.4	20.8	10.2	3.6	3.9	1.4	1.2	1.0	0.7	7.6
1962	52.3	22.0	10.5	3.5	4.1	1.0	1.1	1.0	0.7	8.4
1963	53.4	23.1	10.3	3.4	4.3	1.0	1.2	1.1	0.8	8.2
1964	54.9	25.0	9.9	3.5	3.9	1.0	1.2	1.1	0.7	8.4
1965	55.8	25.4	10.3	3.5	3.8	1.0	1.2	1.1	0.8	8.7
1966	58.1	27.1	10.3	3.6	4.8	0.9	1.3	1.2	0.8	8.1
1967	57.3	26.8	10.2	3.6	3.8	1.0	1.5	1.3	0.8	8.3
1968	57.6	27.5	9.4	3.7[f]	3.7[f]	1.6[f]	1.2[f]	1.3	0.8	8.4
1969	57.8	27.7	8.9	3.8	3.6	1.8	1.2	1.5	0.8	8.5
1970	56.2	26.8	8.3	3.9	3.3	1.4	1.2	1.8	0.8	8.7
1971	54.8	26.3	8.1	3.6	3.3	1.4	1.1	1.8	0.8	8.4
1972	55.2	26.9	8.0	3.6	3.2	1.4	1.2	1.8	0.8	8.3
1973	54.8	26.3	7.8	4.1	3.1	1.4	1.2	1.7	0.8	8.4

See source and footnotes on page 55.

Unintentional-injury-related death rates[a] for principal types, United States, 1903-1998 (cont.)

Year	Total	Motor vehicle	Falls	Drowning[b]	Fire, flames, or smoke[c]	Choking[c]	Firearms	Poison (solid or liquid)	Poison (gas or vapor)	All other
1974	49.0	21.8	7.7	3.7	2.9	1.4	1.2	1.8	0.7	7.8
1975	47.8	21.3	6.9	3.7	2.8	1.4	1.1	2.2	0.7	7.7
1976	46.3	21.6	6.5	3.1	2.9	1.4	0.9	1.9	0.7	7.3
1977	47.0	22.5	6.3	3.2	2.9	1.4	0.9	1.5	0.7	7.6
1978	47.5	23.6	6.2	3.2	2.8	1.4	0.8	1.4	0.8	7.3
1979	46.9	23.8	5.9	3.1	2.7	1.4	0.9	1.4	0.7	7.0
1980	46.5	23.4	5.9	3.2	2.6	1.4	0.9	1.4	0.5	7.2
1981	43.9	22.4	5.5	2.7	2.5	1.5	0.8	1.4	0.6	6.5
1982	40.6	19.8	5.2	2.7	2.2	1.4	0.8	1.5	0.5	6.5
1983	39.6	19.0	5.1	2.7	2.2	1.4	0.7	1.4	0.5	6.6
1984	39.4	19.6	5.1	2.3	2.1	1.5	0.7	1.6	0.5	6.0
1985	39.3	19.3	5.0	2.2	2.1	1.5	0.7	1.7	0.5	6.3
1986	39.7	19.9	4.8	2.4	2.0	1.5	0.6	2.0	0.4	6.1
1987	39.2	19.9	4.8	2.1	1.9	1.5	0.6	1.8	0.4	6.2
1988	39.7	20.1	4.9	2.0	2.0	1.6	0.6	2.2	0.4	5.9
1989	38.5	19.3	4.9	1.9	1.9	1.4	0.6	2.3	0.4	5.8
1990	36.9	18.8	4.9	1.9	1.7	1.3	0.6	2.0	0.3	5.4
1991	35.4	17.3	5.0	1.8	1.6	1.3	0.6	2.3	0.3	5.2
1992	34.0	16.1	5.0	1.4	1.6	1.2	0.6	2.5	0.2	5.4
1993	35.1	16.3	5.1	1.5	1.5	1.2	0.6	3.1	0.3	5.5
1994	35.1	16.3	5.2	1.5	1.5	1.2	0.5	3.2	0.3	5.4
1995	35.5	16.5	5.3	1.7	1.4	1.2	0.5	3.2	0.2	5.5
1996	35.8	16.5	5.6	1.5	1.4	1.2	0.4	3.3	0.2	5.7
1997	35.7	16.2	5.8	1.5	1.3	1.2	0.4	3.6	0.2	5.5
1998	36.2	16.1	6.0	1.6	1.2	1.3	0.3	3.8	0.2	5.7

Unintentional-injury-related death rates[a] for principal types, United States, 1999-2011

Year	Total	Motor vehicle	Falls	Poisoning	Choking[c]	Drowning[g]	Fire, flames, or smoke[c]	Mechanical suffocation	Firearms	All other
1999[h]	35.9	15.5	4.8	4.5	1.4	1.3	1.2	0.6	0.3	6.3
2000	35.6	15.7	4.8	4.6	1.6	1.3	1.2	0.5	0.3	5.5
2001	35.6	15.4	5.3	4.9	1.5	1.2	1.2	0.5	0.3	5.5
2002	37.1	15.8	5.6	6.4	1.4	1.2	1.1	0.5	0.3	4.7
2003	37.6	15.4	5.9	6.7	1.5	1.1	1.2	0.4	0.3	5.1
2004	38.1	15.3	6.4	7.1	1.5	1.1	1.1	0.5	0.2	4.9
2005	39.7	15.3	6.6	8.0	1.5	1.2	1.1	0.5	0.3	5.3
2006	40.8	15.2	7.0	9.2	1.5	1.2	1.0	0.5	0.2	4.9
2007	41.1	14.6	7.5	9.9	1.4	1.1	1.1	0.5	0.2	4.8
2008	40.0	13.1	7.9	10.2	1.4	1.2	1.0	0.6	0.2	4.7
2009[i]	38.5	11.8	8.1	10.3	1.4	1.1	0.9	0.5	0.2	4.1
2010[i]	39.0	11.4	8.4	10.7	1.5	1.2	0.9	0.5	0.2	4.3
2011[j]	39.4	11.1	8.8	11.2	1.5	1.2	0.9	0.5	0.2	4.1
Changes										
2001 to 2011	+11%	-28%	+66%	+129%	0%	0%	-25%	0%	-33%	-25%
2010 to 2011	+1%	-3%	+5%	+5%	0%	0%	0%	0%	0%	-5%

Source: National Safety Council estimates. See Technical Appendix for comparability.

[a]Deaths per 100,000 population.

[b]Includes drowning in water transport incidents.

[c]Fire, flames, or smoke includes burns by fire and deaths resulting from conflagration regardless of nature of injury. Choking is the inhalation of food or other object obstructing breathing.

[d]Comparable data not available.

[e]In 1948, a revision was made in the International Classification of Diseases. The first figures for 1948 are comparable with those for earlier years, the second with those for later years.

[f]Data are not comparable to previous years shown due to classification changes in 1958 and 1968.

[g]Excludes water transport drownings.

[h]In 1999, a revision was made in the International Classification of Diseases. See the Technical Appendix for comparability.

[i]Revised.

[j]Preliminary.

Occupational

The 2011 fatality data presented in this section are preliminary. All Census of Fatal Occupational Injuries fatal injury rates published by the Bureau of Labor Statistics (BLS) for the years 1992-2007 were employment-based, and measured the risk of fatal injury for those employed during a given period of time, regardless of hours worked.

Starting in 2008, BLS moved to hours-based rates to measure fatal injury risk per standardized length of exposure, which are generally considered more accurate than employment-based rates. Caution should be used when comparing fatality rates prior to 2008.

In addition to unintentional fatal work injuries, 700 homicides and suicides occurred in the workplace in 2011. These intentional injuries are not included in the unintentional-injury data shown here.

The State Data section, which begins on page 171, shows fatal occupational injuries and nonfatal injury and illness incidence rates by state.

Unintentional-injury-related deaths..**3,905**
Unintentional-injury-related deaths per 100,000 full-time equivalent workers[a] **3.0**
Medically consulted injuries **5,000,000**
Workers...**141,087,000**
Costs..**$188.9 billion**

Unintentional injuries at work by industry (preliminary), United States, 2011

Industry division	Hours worked[a] (millions)	Deaths[a]		Deaths per 100,000 full-time equivalent workers[a]		Medically consulted injuries[c]
		2011	Change from 2010	2011	Change from 2010	
All industries	**258,293**	**3,905**	**<0.5%**	**3.0**	**0%**	**5,000,000**
Agriculture[b]	4,410	543	-10%	24.6	-12%	120,000
Mining[b]	1,945	149	-12%	15.3	-22%	20,000
Construction	16,048	699	-6%	8.7	-7%	310,000
Manufacturing	29,079	292	3%	2.0	0%	640,000
Wholesale trade	7,700	176	12%	4.6	12%	120,000
Retail trade	27,602	132	-11%	1.0	-9%	540,000
Transportation and warehousing	9,764	681	14%	13.9	12%	240,000
Utilities	1,847	34	31%	3.7	32%	30,000
Information	5,822	49	53%	1.7	55%	50,000
Financial activities	17,804	51	-22%	0.6	-14%	120,000
Professional and business services	29,149	370	17%	2.5	9%	250,000
Educational and health services	38,114	110	-17%	0.6	-14%	900,000
Leisure and hospitality	20,003	140	-1%	1.4	0%	400,000
Other services[b]	11,603	118	-10%	2.0	-9%	150,000
Government	37,255	361	3%	1.9	6%	1,060,000

Source: Deaths are preliminary data from the Bureau of Labor Statistics (BLS) Census of Fatal Occupational Injuries. All other figures are National Safety Council estimates based on data from BLS.
[a]*Deaths include persons of all ages. Workers and death rates include persons 16 years and older. The rate is calculated as: (number of fatal work injuries x 200,000,000/total hours worked). The base for 100,000 full-time equivalent workers is 200,000,000 hours. Prior to 2008, rates were based on estimated employment – not hours worked.*
[b]*Agriculture includes forestry, fishing, and hunting. Mining includes oil and gas extraction. "Other services" excludes public administration.*
[c]*See Technical Appendix for the definition of medically consulted injury.*

Occupational unintentional-injury-related deaths and death rates by industry, United States, 2011

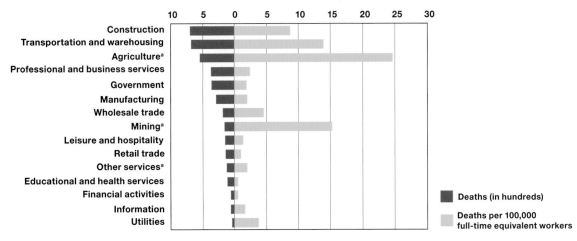

[a]*Agriculture includes forestry, fishing, and hunting. Mining includes oil and gas extraction. "Other services" excludes public administration.*

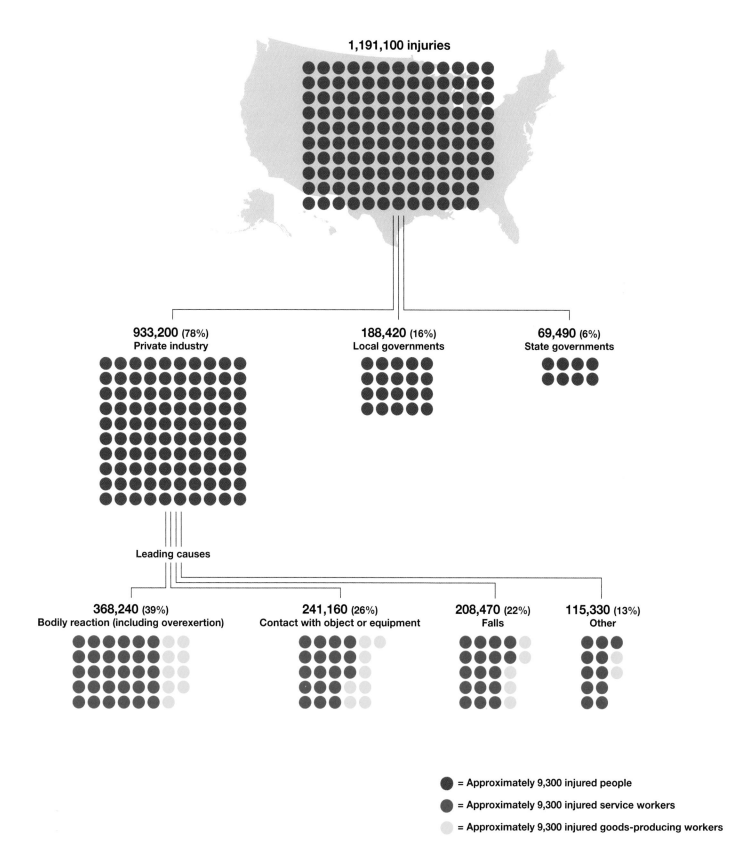

1,191,100 injuries

933,200 (78%)
Private industry

188,420 (16%)
Local governments

69,490 (6%)
State governments

Leading causes

368,240 (39%)
Bodily reaction (including overexertion)

241,160 (26%)
Contact with object or equipment

208,470 (22%)
Falls

115,330 (13%)
Other

● = Approximately 9,300 injured people

● = Approximately 9,300 injured service workers

○ = Approximately 9,300 injured goods-producing workers

Unintentional-work-related-injury deaths and death rates, United States, 1992-2011

Year	Deaths	Workers (in thousands)	Hours worked[a] (in millions)	Deaths per 100,000 workers[a]
1992	4,965	119,168		4.2
1993	5,034	120,778		4.2
1994	5,338	124,470		4.3
1995	5,015	126,248		4.0
1996	5,069	127,997		4.0
1997	5,160	130,810		3.9
1998	5,117	132,772		3.9
1999	5,184	134,688		3.8
2000	5,022	136,402		3.7
2001	5,042	136,246		3.7
2002	4,726	137,731		3.4
2003	4,725	138,988		3.4
2004	4,995	140,504		3.6
2005	4,984	142,946		3.5
2006	5,088	145,607		3.5
2007	4,829	147,203		3.3
2008[a]	4,423	146,535	271,958	3.3[a]
2009	3,744	141,102	254,771	2.9
2010[b]	3,896	140,298	255,948	3.0
2011[c]	3,905	141,087	258,293	3.0

Source: Deaths are from the Bureau of Labor Statistics (BLS) Census of Fatal Occupational Injuries (CFOI). Employment is from BLS and is based on the Current Population Survey. All other data are National Safety Council estimates.

Note: Deaths include persons of all ages. Workers and death rates include persons 16 years and older. Workers are persons 16 years and older who are gainfully employed, including owners, managers, other paid employees, the self-employed, unpaid family workers, and active-duty resident military personnel. Because of adoption of CFOI, deaths and rates from 1992 to present are not comparable to prior years. See the Technical Appendix for additional information.

[a]Starting in 2008, BLS moved from employment-based rates to hours-based rates to measure fatal injury risk per standardized length of exposure, which are generally considered more accurate than employment-based rates. Caution should be used when comparing with rates prior to 2008.

[b]Revised.

[c]Preliminary. BLS urges caution when using preliminary estimates.

Workers, unintentional-work-related-injury deaths, and death rates, United States, 1992-2011

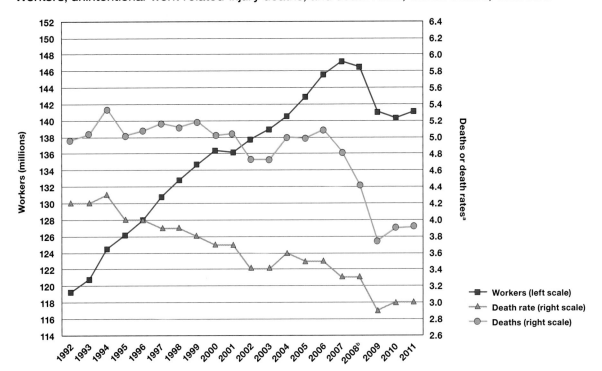

[a]Deaths in thousands; rate per 100,000 workers.

[b]Starting in 2008, the Bureau of Labor Statistics changed from an employment-based rate to an hours-based rate.

Occupational injury-related deaths and death rates, United States, 1992-2002

Year	Total	Homicide and suicide	Unintentional All industries[a]	Agriculture[b]	Mining, quarrying[c]	Construction	Manufacturing	Transportation and public utilities	Trade[d]	Services[e]	Government
Deaths											
1992	6,217	1,252	4,965	779	175	889	707	767	415	601	586
1993	6,331	1,297	5,034	842	169	895	698	753	450	631	527
1994	6,632	1,294	5,338	814	177	1,000	734	819	492	676	534
1995	6,275	1,260	5,015	769	155	1,021	640	784	461	608	528
1996	6,202	1,133	5,069	762	151	1,025	660	883	451	615	321
1997	6,238	1,078	5,160	799	156	1,075	678	882	451	593	504
1998	6,055	938	5,117	808	143	1,136	631	830	443	634	465
1999	6,054	870	5,184	776	122	1,168	671	918	425	623	451
2000	5,920	898	5,022	693	153	1,114	624	872	447	643	460
2001	5,915	873[f]	5,042	714	169	1,183	546	844	431	636	507
2002	5,534	808	4,726	758	120	1,092	523	843	381	569	437
Deaths per 100,000 workers											
1992	5.2	1.0	4.2	23.1	26.4	13.7	3.6	11.5	1.7	1.6	3.0
1993	5.2	1.0	4.2	26.0	25.3	13.3	3.6	11.0	1.8	1.6	2.6
1994	5.3	1.0	4.3	22.8	26.5	14.4	3.7	11.6	1.9	1.7	2.7
1995	4.9	1.0	4.0	21.4	24.8	14.3	3.1	11.0	1.8	1.5	2.7
1996	4.8	0.9	4.0	21.2	26.6	13.7	3.2	12.2	1.7	1.4	1.6
1997	4.8	0.8	3.9	22.5	24.7	13.7	3.3	11.6	1.7	1.3	2.6
1998	4.5	0.7	3.9	22.7	23.1	14.1	3.1	10.8	1.6	1.4	2.4
1999	4.5	0.6	3.8	22.6	21.7	13.8	3.4	11.5	1.5	1.3	2.2
2000	4.3	0.7	3.7	20.1	29.4	12.4	3.1	10.8	1.6	1.4	2.3
2001	4.3	0.6[f]	3.7	22.0	29.9	13.0	2.9	10.4	1.6	1.3	2.5
2002	4.0	0.6	3.4	21.8	23.3	11.9	2.9	10.5	1.4	1.1	2.1

Source: Deaths are from the Bureau of Labor Statistics (BLS) Census of Fatal Occupational Injuries. Rates are National Safety Council estimates based on BLS employment data. Deaths include persons of all ages. Death rates include persons 16 years and older. Industry divisions are based on the Standard Industrial Classification Manual.
[a]Includes deaths with industry unknown.
[b]Agriculture includes forestry, fishing, and agricultural services.
[c]Mining includes oil and gas extraction.
[d]Trade includes wholesale and retail trade.
[e]Services includes finance, insurance, and real estate.
[f]Excludes 2,886 homicides of workers on Sept. 11, 2001.

Occupational injury-related deaths and death rates, United States, 2003-2011

Year	Total	Homicide and suicide	All industries[a]	Agriculture, forestry, fishing, and hunting	Mining	Construction	Manufacturing	Wholesale trade	Retail trade	Transportation and warehousing	Utilities	Information	Financial activities	Professional and business services	Educational and health services	Leisure and hospitality	Other services	Government
Deaths																		
2003	5,575	850	4,725	676	141	1,094	379	169	148	735	29	57	82	396	116	142	123	434
2004	5,764	769	4,995	651	151	1,203	421	187	189	779	49	49	68	401	123	144	144	432
2005	5,734	750	4,984	697	154	1,161	357	197	198	831	28	56	66	442	122	114	149	404
2006	5,840	752	5,088	635	190	1,199	423	210	190	803	52	61	82	407	142	136	142	409
2007	5,657	828	4,829	564	180	1,163	364	193	160	819	33	70	69	415	121	138	116	421
2008	5,214	791	4,423	640	173	937	364	157	158	724	37	36	65	351	110	118	130	414
2009	4,551	807	3,744	545	96	793	290	168	137	576	13	28	58	363	101	119	110	347
2010[b]	4,690	794	3,896	603	170	744	284	157	148	595	26	32	65	316	133	142	131	350
2011[c]	4,605	700	3,905	543	149	699	292	176	132	681	34	49	51	370	110	140	118	361
Deaths per 100,000 workers[d]																		
2003	4.0	0.6	3.4	30.0	26.9	11.4	2.3	3.8	0.9	16.0	3.3	1.6	0.9	2.9	0.6	1.3	1.8	2.1
2004	4.1	0.5	3.6	29.7	28.1	11.7	2.6	4.1	1.2	16.7	5.9	1.5	0.7	2.9	0.7	1.3	2.1	2.0
2005	4.0	0.5	3.5	31.7	24.8	10.8	2.2	4.3	1.2	16.7	3.4	1.7	0.7	3.2	0.6	1.0	2.1	1.9
2006	4.0	0.5	3.5	29.1	27.8	10.6	2.6	4.6	1.1	15.7	6.2	1.8	0.8	2.8	0.7	1.2	2.0	1.9
2007	3.8	0.5	3.3	26.9	24.7	10.2	2.2	4.4	1.0	15.6	3.9	2.1	0.7	2.7	0.6	1.2	1.7	1.9
2008[d]	3.8	0.6	3.3	29.4	17.8	9.4	2.3	3.8	1.1	13.6	4.0	1.1	0.7	2.4	0.6	1.1	2.1	2.1
2009	3.6	0.6	2.9	26.3	12.2	9.5	2.1	4.4	1.0	12.1	1.4	1.0	0.6	2.7	0.5	1.2	1.8	1.8
2010[b]	3.7	0.6	3.0	27.9	19.6	9.4	2.0	4.1	1.1	12.4	2.8	1.1	0.7	2.3	0.7	1.4	2.2	1.8
2011[c]	3.6	0.5	3.0	24.6	15.3	8.7	2.0	4.6	1.0	13.9	3.7	1.7	0.6	2.5	0.6	1.4	2.0	1.9

Source: Deaths are from the Bureau of Labor Statistics (BLS) Census of Fatal Occupational Injuries. Rates are National Safety Council estimates based on BLS employment data. Deaths include persons of all ages. Death rates include persons 16 years and older. Industry sectors are based on the North American Industry Classification System.
[a]Includes deaths with industry unknown.
[b]Revised.
[c]Preliminary. BLS urges caution when using preliminary estimates.
[d]Starting in 2008, BLS moved from employment-based rates to hours-based rates to measure fatal injury risk per standardized length of exposure. Caution should be used when comparing with rates prior to 2008.

The true cost to the nation, employers, and individuals of work-related deaths and injuries is much greater than the cost of workers' compensation insurance alone. The figures presented below show National Safety Council estimates of the total economic costs of occupational deaths and injuries. Cost-estimating procedures were revised for the 1993 edition of *Accident Facts* and additional revisions were made for the 2005-2006 edition. For this reason, costs should not be compared to prior years.

TOTAL COST IN 2011 ....$188.9 BILLION

Includes wage and productivity losses of $86.7 billion, medical costs of $52.3 billion, and administrative expenses of $34.2 billion. Includes employers' uninsured costs of $10.5 billion, such as the money value of time lost by workers other than those with disabling injuries; who are directly or indirectly involved in injuries; and the cost of time required to investigate injuries, write up injury reports, etc. Also includes damage to motor vehicles in work-related injuries of $2.4 billion and fire losses of $2.8 billion.

COST PER WORKER **$1,340**

Includes the value of goods or services each worker must produce to offset the cost of work injuries. It is *not* the average cost of a work-related injury.

COST PER DEATH...$1,390,000

COST PER MEDICALLY CONSULTED INJURY $37,000

Includes estimates of wage losses, medical expenses, administrative expenses, and employer costs; excludes property damage costs except to motor vehicles.

Time Lost Due to Work-Related Injuries

	Days lost
TOTAL TIME LOST IN 2011	95,000,000
Due to injuries in 2011	60,000,000

Includes primarily the actual time lost during the year from disabling injuries, except it does not include time lost on the day of the injury or time required for further medical treatment or check-up following the injured person's return to work.

Fatalities are included at an average loss of 150 days per case, and permanent impairments are included at actual days lost plus an allowance for lost efficiency resulting from the impairment.

Not included is time lost by people with nondisabling injuries or other people directly or indirectly involved in the incidents.

	Days lost
Due to injuries in prior years...	35,000,000

Represents productive time lost in 2011 due to permanently disabling injuries that occurred in prior years.

	Days lost
TIME LOST IN FUTURE YEARS FROM 2011 INJURIES	50,000,000

Includes time lost in future years due to on-the-job deaths and permanently disabling injuries that occurred in 2011.

Nine out of 10 deaths and about 70% of the medically consulted injuries[a] suffered by workers in 2011 occurred off the job. While more than 13 times the number of deaths occur off the job compared to on the job (13.3 to 1), more than twice as many medically consulted injuries occur off the job (2.6 to 1).

Production time lost due to off-the-job injuries totaled about 235,000,000 days in 2011, compared with 60,000,000 days lost by workers injured on the job.

Production time lost in future years due to off-the-job injuries in 2011 will total an estimated 510,000,000 days, more than 10 times the 50,000,000 days lost in future years from 2011's on-the-job injuries.

Off-the-job injuries to workers cost the nation at least $262.2 billion in 2011 compared with $188.9 billion for on-the-job injuries.

Workers' on- and off-the-job injuries, United States, 2011

Place	Deaths		Medically consulted injuries[a]	
	Number	Rate[b]	Number	Rate[b]
On and off the job	55,909	0.013	18,100,000	4.4
On the job	3,909	0.003	5,000,000	3.3
Off the job	52,000	0.019	13,100,000	4.8
Motor vehicle	*17,800*	*0.063*	*1,900,000*	*6.7*
Public non-motor vehicle	*8,700*	*0.020*	*3,300,000*	*7.5*
Home	*25,500*	*0.013*	*7,900,000*	*4.0*

Source: National Safety Council estimates. Procedures for allocating time spent on and off the job were revised for the 1990 edition. Rate basis changed to 200,000 hours for the 1998 edition. Death and injury rates are not comparable to rate estimates prior to the 1998 edition.
[a]Medically consulted injuries are not comparable to estimates provided in earlier editions that used the definition of disabling injury. Please see the Technical Appendix for more information on medically consulted injuries.
[b]Per 200,000 hours exposure by place.

Workers' on- and off-the-job injuries, United States, 2011

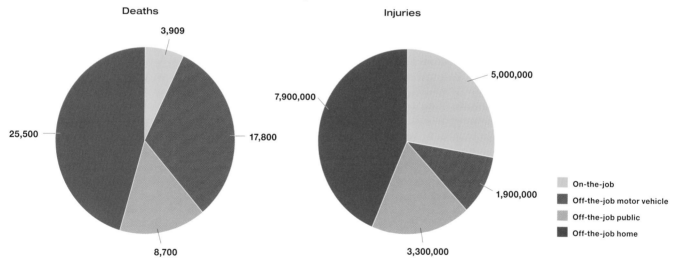

Workers' off-the-job fatalities by event, 2011

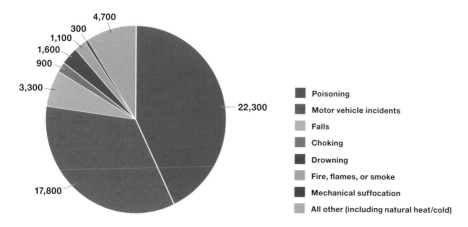

According to the National Academy of Social Insurance, an estimated $57.5 billion, including benefits under deductible provisions, was paid out under workers' compensation in 2010 (the latest year for which data were available) – a decrease of 0.7% from 2009. Of this total, $29.5 billion was for income benefits and $28.1 billion was for medical and hospitalization costs. Private carriers paid about $30.5 billion of the total

workers' compensation benefits in 2010. In 2010, approximately 124.5 million workers were covered by workers' compensation – a decrease of 0.3% from the 124.9 million in 2009.

The table below shows the trend in the number of compensated or reported cases in each reporting state. Due to the differences in population, industries, and coverage of compensation laws, comparisons among states should not be made.

Workers' compensation cases, 2009-2011

State	Deaths[a]			Cases[a]			2010 compensation paid ($000)
	2011	2010	2009	2011	2010	2009	
Arizona	–	77	76	96,480	96,704	98,718	698,459
California	400	487	553	526,970	554,789	565,740	9,396,443
District of Columbia	5	7	4	10,187	10,045	10,034	105,636
Florida[b]	114	118	118	52,193	56,519	56,958	2,526,580
Hawaii	23	27	20	20,515	20,654	21,520	242,400
Idaho	31	34	25	30,822	31,578	32,370	245,622
Indiana	81	83	85	54,796	63,204	53,492	603,193
Kansas	54	52	41	57,181	59,064	59,045	407,776
Kentucky[c]	–	30	33	–	31,162	29,178	650,701
Maine	19	31	24	36,633	37,570	37,487	253,872
Maryland[d]	52	64	74	23,366	23,003	22,622	953,533
Minnesota[e]	–	36	45	–	98,000	96,400	1,038,272
Mississippi[f]	84	75	48	11,845	11,365	11,138	337,633
Missouri	120	108	119	110,269	113,418	110,093	811,427
Nebraska	41	47	61	43,659	43,911	45,761	313,066
Nevada[f]	–	197	105	–	49,223	54,666	429,686
New Hampshire	20	16	14	39,663	39,471	42,189	237,168
New Mexico[f]	34	33	34	21,699	23,452	22,094	276,697
North Carolina	94	132	120	62,409	61,145	62,462	1,316,291
North Dakota	24	15	16	21,693	19,388	20,543	114,985
Oklahoma	77	106	94	13,960	14,779	15,838	845,726
Oregon[f]	28	17	31	18,691	18,012	18,949	633,054
Pennsylvania[c]	–	111	100	–	85,671	89,073	2,909,341
South Carolina[f]	72	108	147	67,354	58,753	71,973	891,283
South Dakota	9	13	6	23,169	21,705	22,015	100,348
Utah	36	49	45	49,864	49,181	51,842	257,522
Vermont	5	8	12	16,992	16,082	17,186	138,170
West Virginia	13	52	25	40,058	40,954	43,123	362,375
Wisconsin[c]	–	91[g]	94	–	33,049	33,237	1,070,534

Source: Deaths and Cases–State workers' compensation authorities for calendar or fiscal year. States not listed did not respond to the survey. Compensation paid–Sengupta, I., Reno, V., Burton, J.F., Jr., & Baldwin, M. (2012 August). Workers' compensation: benefits, coverage, and costs, 2010. Washington, DC: National Academy of Social Insurance.
Note: Dash (–) indicates data not available.

Definitions
Reported case: A reported case may or may not be work-related and may not receive compensation.
Compensated case: A case determined to be work-related and for which compensation was paid.
[a]Reported cases involving medical and indemnity benefits, unless otherwise noted.
[b]Closed or compensated cases involving indemnity benefits only.
[c]Reported cases involving indemnity benefits only.
[d]Data are for claims filed.
[e]Number of paid cases by year of injury, projected to full maturity.
[f]Closed or compensated cases only.
[g]Preliminary.

The most disabling workplace injuries and illnesses in 2009 amounted to $50.1 billion in direct workers' compensation costs, according to the 2011 Liberty Mutual Workplace Safety Index (WSI). WSI combines information from Liberty Mutual, the Bureau of Labor Statistics, and the National Academy of Social Insurance to identify the top causes of serious workplace injuries.[a]

The top 10 causes of serious workplace injuries produced about 89% of the direct workers' compensation costs of disabling workplace injuries in 2009 – a slight increase from 2008. Overexertion injuries remained the largest contributor to the overall burden, accounting for $12.75 billion, or more than 25%, of the total cost. "Fall on the same level" ($7.94 billion) and "fall to lower level" ($5.35 billion) were the next most costly injury causes. The cost of the combined fall categories slightly exceeded that for the "overexertion" category, indicating that total falls were comparable to "overexertion" in terms of impact on the overall cost burden.

The 2011 WSI showed a 6.5% decrease in the real (inflation adjusted) cost of the most disabling workplace injuries – from $37.8 billion in 2008 to $35.4 billion in 2009. Over the 12-year period from 1998 to 2009, these costs declined from $37.1 billion to $35.4 billion – a decrease of 4.6%. Based on these real growth figures, the "fall on same level," "fall to lower level," and "bodily reaction" categories exhibited the largest increases over the 12-year period, while the "repetitive motion" and "highway incident" categories showed the largest decreases.

Workers' compensation costs for the top 10 causes of disabling workplace injuries, United States, 2009

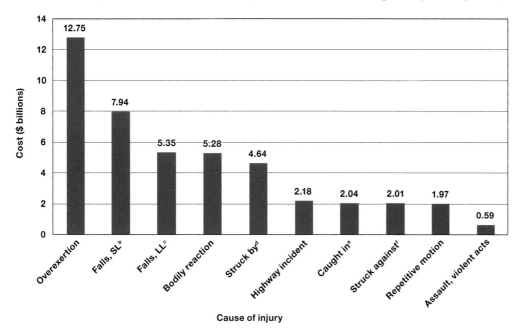

Percent change in inflation-adjusted workers' compensation costs for the top 10 causes of disabling workplace injuries, United States, 1998-2009

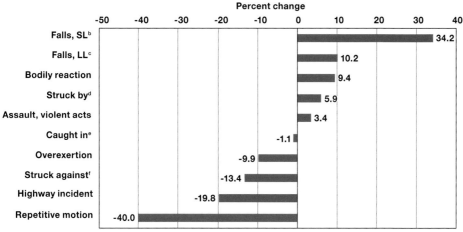

Source: 2011 Liberty Mutual Workplace Safety Index, retrieved July 11, 2012 from www.libertymutualgroup. com/researchinstitute.
[a]Injury events that cause an employee to miss six or more days of work.
[b]Falls on same level.
[c]Falls to lower level.
[d]Struck by object.
[e]Caught in or compressed by object or equipment.
[f]Struck against object.

⬧ *Head injuries are the most costly workers' compensation claims.*

The data in the graphs on this and the next page are from the National Council on Compensation Insurance's (NCCI) Workers Compensation Statistical Plan (WCSP) database.[a] WCSP reflects claims experience on workers' compensation insurance policies issued in states in which NCCI collects such data. The aggregate unit statistical data were valued 30 months after the inception date of the policy (as of the second report). The average cost for all claims combined in 2009-2010 was $36,551.

NCCI data that appeared in *Injury Facts* prior to the 2011 edition were sourced to NCCI's Detailed Claim Information file, which was a stratified random sample of lost-time claims in 42 states. Workers' compensation estimates provided in this edition are not comparable to estimates provided in editions prior to 2011.

Cause of injury. The most costly lost-time workers' compensation claims by cause of injury, according to NCCI data, are for those resulting from motor vehicle crashes. These

injuries averaged $69,206 per workers' compensation claim filed in 2009 and 2010. The only other causes with above-average costs were falls or slips ($41,393) and burns ($40,995).

Nature of injury. The most costly lost-time workers' compensation claims by the nature of the injury are for those resulting from amputation. These injuries averaged $72,774 per workers' compensation claim filed in 2009 and 2010. The next highest costs were for injuries resulting in fracture, crush, or dislocation ($50,126); other trauma ($43,568); and burns ($41,300).

Part of body. The most costly lost-time workers' compensation claims are for those involving the head or central nervous system. These injuries averaged $82,382 per claim filed in 2009 and 2010. The next highest costs were for injuries involving the neck ($55,994) and multiple body parts ($54,327). Injuries to the arm or shoulder; hip, thigh, and pelvis; leg; and lower back also had above-average costs.

Average total incurred costs per claim by cause of injury, 2009-2010

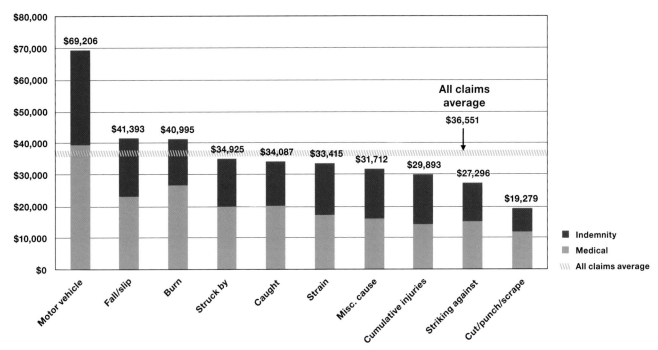

[a]National Council on Compensation Insurance makes no representations or warranties of any kind nor assumes any responsibility for the accuracy of the underlying data or any third-party use of the data on this and the following page.

Average total incurred costs per claim by nature of injury, 2009-2010

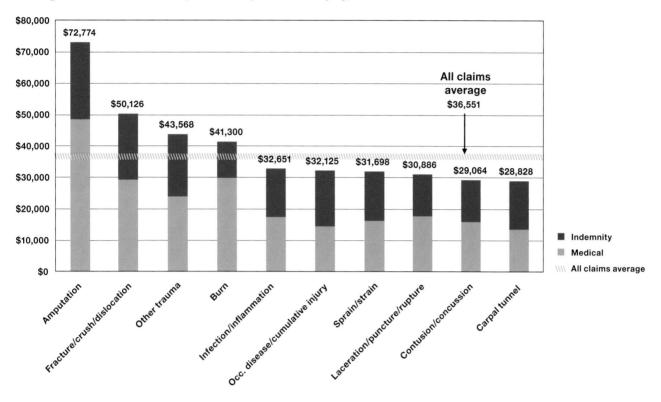

Average total incurred costs per claim by part of body, 2009-2010

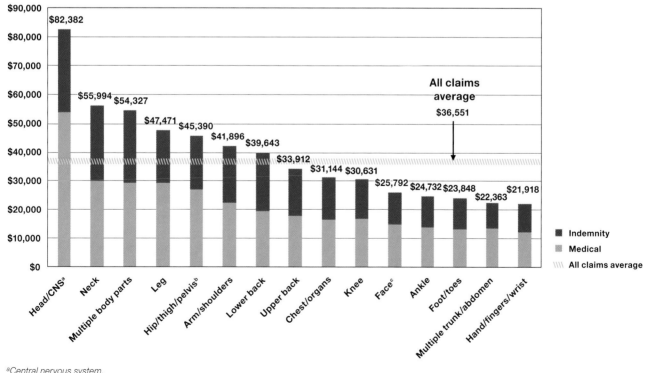

aCentral nervous system.
bIncludes sacrum and coccyx.
cIncludes teeth, mouth, and eyes.

Fatal occupational injuries with a forklift as the primary source of injury numbered 78 in 2007 and then decreased each year over the three-year period from 2008 to 2010 to 68, 58, and 54 fatal injuries, respectively. Similarly, fatal occupational injuries with a forklift as the secondary source of injury numbered 43, 41, 33, and 31 over the same four-year period. The table below shows the percent distribution of fatalities with a forklift as the primary and secondary source of injury by industry division for the period of 2007-2010. Forklift fatalities are most prevalent in the trade, transportation, and utilities; manufacturing; and construction industries.

The rate of nonfatal forklift injuries involving days away from work averaged 1.2 per 10,000 full-time workers and exhibited a consistent downward trend over the seven-year period from 2004 to 2010. Trade, transportation, and utilities had the highest rate of nonfatal forklift injuries, followed by manufacturing.

Percent distribution of fatal occupational injuries with a forklift as the source of injury, private industry, United States, 2007-2010

Industry division	Year							
	2007		2008		2009		2010	
	Forklift as primary[a] source	Forklift as secondary[b] source	Forklift as primary[a] source	Forklift as secondary[b] source	Forklift as primary[a] source	Forklift as secondary[b] source	Forklift as primary[a] source	Forklift as secondary[b] source
All industries	100%	100%	100%	100%	100%	100%	100%	100%
Natural resources and mining[c]	6.4	7.0	17.6	12.2	10.3	–	9.2	–
Construction	24.3	30.2	25.0	29.3	19.0	24.2	14.8	12.9
Manufacturing	29.5	25.6	25.0	17.1	25.9	21.2	16.7	35.5
Trade, transportation, and utilities	33.3	30.2	23.5	29.3	37.9	39.4	38.9	41.9
Information	–	–	–	–	–	–	–	–
Financial activities	–	–	–	–	–	–	–	–
Professional and business services	–	–	–	7.3	–	–	13.0	–
Education and health services	–	–	–	–	–	–	–	–
Leisure and hospitality	–	–	–	–	–	–	–	–
Other services[c]	–	–	–	–	–	–	5.6	–

Source: Bureau of Labor Statistics Census of Fatal Occupational Injuries and Illnesses, accessed July 11, 2012 from www.bls.gov/iif/oshcfoi1.htm. Percent distributions are from the National Safety Council. Percentages may not add to totals because of rounding or exclusion of data that do not meet publication guidelines. Dashes (–) indicate no data reported or data that do not meet publication guidelines.
[a]The primary source of injury identifies the object, substance, or exposure that directly produced or inflicted the injury. For transportation incidents, the source identifies the vehicle in which the deceased was an occupant.
[b]The secondary source of injury, if any, identifies the object, substance, or person who generated the source of injury or contributed to the event or exposure. For vehicle collisions, the deceased's vehicle is the primary source and the other object (truck, road, divider, etc.) is the secondary source. For most homicides, the "bullet" is the primary source and the "assailant" is the secondary source.
[c]"Natural resources" includes agriculture, forestry, fishing, and hunting and excludes farms with fewer than 11 employees. "Mining" includes oil and gas extraction. "Other services" excludes public administration.

Incidence rates[a] of nonfatal occupational injuries and illnesses involving days away from work[b] with a forklift as the source of injury or illness, private industry, United States, 2004-2010

Industry division	All sources rate[a]	Forklift injury rate[a]						
	2010	2004	2005	2006	2007	2008	2009	2010
All industries	107.7	1.5	1.4	1.3	1.2	1.1	0.9	0.8
Natural resources and mining[c]	137.7	1.4	1.5	1.9	1.5	1.2	0.6	1.1
Construction	149.6	1.4	1.2	1.5	0.8	0.9	0.8	0.7
Manufacturing	111.7	2.6	2.5	2.4	2.3	2.0	1.5	1.9
Trade, transportation, and utilities	137.0	3.6	3.0	2.9	2.7	2.6	2.3	2.0
Information	77.1	0.2	0.3	0.4	0.3	0.5	0.2	0.2
Financial activities	40.2	0.1	0.0[d]	0.1	0.0[d]	0.0[d]	0.2	0.0[d]
Professional and business services	58.0	0.6	0.7	0.5	0.4	0.3	0.4	0.3
Education and health services	130.6	0.1	0.1	0.1	0.0[d]	0.1	0.1	0.0[d]
Leisure and hospitality	106.6	–	–	0.1	0.1	0.1	0	0.0[d]
Other services[c]	94.2	0.5	0.4	0.3	0.1	0.2	0.1	0.3

Source: Bureau of Labor Statistics Occupational Injuries and Illnesses and Fatal Injuries Profiles, accessed July 11, 2012. Available at http://data.bls.gov/gqt/InitialPage.
Dashes (–) indicate no data reported or data that do not meet publication guidelines.
[a]Incidence rates represent the number of injuries and illnesses per 10,000 full-time workers and were calculated as: (N/EH) x 20,000,000, where N = number of injuries and illnesses, EH = total hours worked by all employees during the calendar year, and 20,000,000 = base for 10,000 full-time equivalent workers (working 40 hours per week 50 weeks per year).
[b]Days away from work include those that result in days away from work with or without restricted work activity.
[c]"Natural resources" includes agriculture, forestry, fishing, and hunting and excludes farms with fewer than 11 employees. "Mining" includes oil and gas extraction. "Other services" excludes public administration.
[d]Rounded to zero.

Following highway crashes, falls to a lower level is the second leading unintentional fatal workplace event and the sixth leading event resulting in cases with days away from work. In 2010, 522 workers died while an additional 59,440 were injured. The 2010 fatality count represents about a 3% decrease from 2009, while the nonfatal injuries represent a 6% decrease. From 2003, fall-to-a-lower-level fatalities have decreased more than 13%, while nonfatal cases with days away from work have decreased by 28%.

Fatal falls to a lower level typically involve injuries to the head or multiple body parts while nonfatal injuries most often involve the lower extremities, trunk, or multiple body parts. The most common nonfatal injuries include sprains and strains, followed by fractures. Falls to a lower level result in dramatically more days away from work than typical injury events. Fall-to-a-lower-level cases result in a median of 16 days away from work compared with eight days across all injury events. In fact, more than 38% of the fall-to-a-lower-level cases involving days away from work result in 31 or more lost workdays. Falls to a lower level resulting in days away from work most often occur on stairs or steps (28%), followed by ladders (25%). New employees are disproportionably represented, with 26% of nonfatal injuries involving workers with less than one year of service.

By far, construction is the industry most at risk from falls to

a lower level. In 2010, 255 workers in the construction industry died as a result of falls to a lower level, representing 49% of all fall-to-a-lower-level fatalities. The fall-to-a-lower-level fatality rate in the construction industry is 3.2 per 100,000 workers, 8 times the general industry rate of 0.4. Falls to a lower level also represent the single most dangerous injury event within the construction industry, representing 33% of all construction fatalities. The construction industry also experiences the most nonfatal cases involving days away from work, representing 17% of all nonfatal fall-to-a-lower-level cases with 10,050. Forty-one percent of these nonfatal cases resulted from falls from ladders (4,160 cases).

Compared to falls to a lower level, falls on the same level tend to result in less severe but more frequent injuries. In 2010, there were 139,660 fall-on-the-same-level cases involving days away from work and 100 fatalities. The rate for cases involving days away from work was 15.6 per 10,000 workers compared with 7.0 for falls to a lower level. Education and health services has the highest fall-on-the-same-level rate with 26.7 per 10,000 workers, followed by leisure and hospitality (20.3) and trade, transportation, and utilities (17.3).

The following two pages provide injury profiles for both falls to a lower level and falls on the same level.

Workplace falls to a lower level, United States, 2003-2010

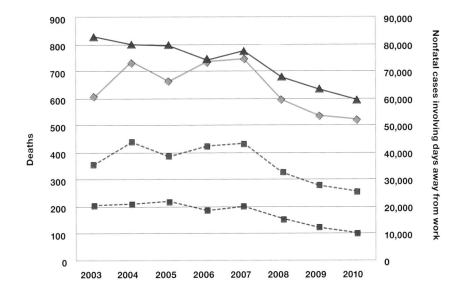

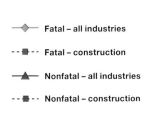

Source: National Safety Council analysis of Bureau of Labor Statistics data.

Fall to Lower Level

"Fall to lower level" applies to instances in which the injury was produced by impact between the injured person and the source of injury – the motion producing the contact being that of the person – under the following circumstances:

- The motion of the person and the force of impact were generated by gravity.

- The point of contact with the source of injury was lower than the surface supporting the person at the inception of the fall.

Fall to lower level ranks second behind highway crashes in number of workplace fatalities, and is the sixth leading event resulting in cases involving days away from work.

Fall-to-lower-level nonfatal occupational injuries and illnesses involving days away from work[a] and fatal occupational injuries by selected worker and case characteristics, United States, 2010

Characteristic	Private industry[b,c] nonfatal cases	All industries fatalities
Total	**59,440**	**522**
Sex		
Men	39,980	499
Women	18,930	23
Age		
Younger than 16	–	–
16 to 19	1,000	–
20 to 24	4,040	21
25 to 34	9,810	65
35 to 44	12,590	82
45 to 54	17,740	158
55 to 64	10,480	122
65 and older	3,110	69
Occupation		
Management, business, and financial	3,050	42
Professional and related	3,560	5
Service	10,280	73
Sales and related	4,050	14
Office and administrative support	5,220	–
Farming, fishing, and forestry	1,080	15
Construction and extractive	7,970	248
Installation, maintenance, and repair	7,640	52
Production	3,900	20
Transportation and material moving	12,630	48
Military occupations	–	–
Race or ethnic origin[d]		
White, non-Hispanic	27,730	364
Black, non-Hispanic	3,250	24
Hispanic	8,460	116
Other, multiple, and not reported	20,000	18
Nature of injury or illness		
Sprains or strains	17,120	–
Fractures	12,510	14
Cuts, lacerations, or punctures	1,280	–
Bruises or contusions	6,480	–
Heat burns	–	–
Chemical burns	–	–
Amputations	–	–
Carpal tunnel syndrome	–	–
Tendonitis	–	–
Multiple injuries	7,500	203
Soreness or pain	5,400	–
Back pain	1,440	–
All other	9,140	301

Characteristic	Private industry[b,c] nonfatal cases	All industries fatalities
Part of body affected		
Head	2,020	232
Eye	20	–
Neck	350	18
Trunk	15,300	52
Back	7,300	10
Shoulder	3,740	–
Upper extremities	6,820	–
Finger	250	–
Hand, except finger	500	–
Wrist	2,840	–
Lower extremities	19,050	11
Knee	5,880	–
Foot or toe	3,050	–
Body systems	30	–
Multiple	15,460	205
All other	420	–
Industry		
Agriculture, Forestry, Fishing, and Hunting	1,160	28
Mining	390	9
Construction	10,050	255
Manufacturing	5,720	32
Wholesale Trade	3,160	12
Retail Trade	6,720	21
Transportation and Warehousing	6,640	29
Utilities	360	–
Information	1,600	–
Financial Activities	3,210	18
Professional and Business Services	6,290	54
Education and Health Services	7,480	14
Leisure and Hospitality	4,140	13
Other Services	2,520	17
Government	N/A	15

Source: National Safety Council tabulations of Bureau of Labor Statistics (BLS) data.
Note: Because of rounding and data exclusion of nonclassifiable responses, data may not sum to the totals. Dashes (–) indicate data that do not meet publication guidelines. "N/A" means not applicable.
[a]Days away from work include those that result in days away from work with or without restricted work activity or job transfer.
[b]Excludes farms with fewer than 11 employees.
[c]Data for mining operators in coal, metal, and nonmetal mining and for employees in railroad transportation are provided to BLS by the Mine Safety and Health Administration (MSHA), U.S. Department of Labor; and the Federal Railroad Administration (FRA), U.S. Department of Transportation. Independent mining contractors are excluded from the coal, metal, and nonmetal mining industries. MSHA and FRA data do not reflect the changes in OSHA recordkeeping requirements in 2002.
[d]In the fatalities column, non-Hispanic categories include cases with Hispanic origin not reported.

"Fall on same level" applies to instances in which the injury was produced between the injured person and the source of injury – the motion producing the contact being that of the person – under the following circumstances:

• The motion of the person was generated by gravity following the employee's loss of equilibrium (the person was unable to maintain an upright position).

• The point of contact with the source of injury was at the same level or above the surface supporting the person at the inception of the fall.

Fall on same level ranks second behind overexertion in the number of nonfatal injuries involving days away from work, but generally is not one of the top 10 events resulting in fatalities.

Fall-on-same-level nonfatal occupational injuries and illnesses involving days away from work[a] and fatal occupational injuries by selected worker and case characteristics, United States, 2010

Characteristic	Private industry[b,c] nonfatal cases	All industries fatalities
Total	139,660	100
Sex		
Men	59,840	76
Women	79,710	24
Age		
Younger than 16	–	–
16 to 19	3,140	–
20 to 24	8,390	–
25 to 34	21,020	7
35 to 44	25,010	5
45 to 54	40,520	18
55 to 64	30,370	41
65 and older	9,710	28
Occupation		
Management, business, and financial	5,900	9
Professional and related	16,880	5
Service	43,290	24
Sales and related	11,100	12
Office and administrative support	14,510	7
Farming, fishing, and forestry	1,250	–
Construction and extractive	6,700	5
Installation, maintenance, and repair	7,010	6
Production	11,710	10
Transportation and material moving	21,190	21
Military occupations	–	–
Race or ethnic origin[d]		
White, non-Hispanic	61,300	78
Black, non-Hispanic	11,130	8
Hispanic	17,160	11
Other, multiple, and not reported	50,070	–
Nature of injury or illness		
Sprains or strains	42,420	–
Fractures	24,380	16
Cuts, lacerations, or punctures	3,450	–
Bruises or contusions	21,490	–
Heat burns	–	–
Chemical burns	–	–
Amputations	20	–
Carpal tunnel syndrome	–	–
Tendonitis	30	–
Multiple injuries	13,860	5
Soreness or pain	16,050	–
Back pain	3,870	–
All other	17,970	74

Characteristic	Private industry[b,c] nonfatal cases	All industries fatalities
Part of body affected		
Head	7,470	63
Eye	130	–
Neck	700	–
Trunk	33,570	12
Back	15,060	–
Shoulder	9,810	–
Upper extremities	21,740	–
Finger	1,730	–
Hand, except finger	1,680	–
Wrist	8,440	–
Lower extremities	44,350	17
Knee	22,670	–
Foot or toe	3,150	–
Body systems	220	–
Multiple	30,960	5
All other	650	–
Industry		
Agriculture, Forestry, Fishing, and Hunting	1,720	–
Mining	780	–
Construction	7,170	7
Manufacturing	13,140	10
Wholesale Trade	7,150	–
Retail Trade	18,600	17
Transportation and Warehousing	11,040	10
Utilities	770	–
Information	3,660	–
Financial Activities	5,110	–
Professional and Business Services	12,740	6
Education and Health Services	35,970	12
Leisure and Hospitality	17,610	11
Other Services	4,200	–
Government	N/A	16

Source: National Safety Council tabulations of Bureau of Labor Statistics (BLS) data.
Note: Because of rounding and data exclusion of nonclassifiable responses, data may not sum to the totals. Dashes (–) indicate data that do not meet publication guidelines. "N/A" means not applicable.
[a]Days away from work include those that result in days away from work with or without restricted work activity or job transfer.
[b]Excludes farms with fewer than 11 employees.
[c]Data for mining operators in coal, metal, and nonmetal mining and for

employees in railroad transportation are provided to BLS by the Mine Safety and Health Administration (MSHA), U.S. Department of Labor; and the Federal Railroad Administration (FRA), U.S. Department of Transportation. Independent mining contractors are excluded from the coal, metal, and nonmetal mining industries. MSHA and FRA data do not reflect the changes in OSHA recordkeeping requirements in 2002.
[d]In the fatalities column, non-Hispanic categories include cases with Hispanic origin not reported.

Incidents involving motor vehicles are the leading cause of work-related deaths, followed by assaults and violent acts and contact with objects or equipment. For nonfatal cases with days away from work, events involving bodily reaction and exertion are the leading cause, followed by contact with objects or equipment and falls.

Work-related deaths and injuries by event or exposure, United States, 2010

Event or exposure	Deaths[a]
Total, all events or exposures	**4,690**
Contact with object or equipment	738
Struck against object	*13*
Struck by object	*404*
Caught in object or equipment	*228*
Caught in collapsing materials	*91*
Fall	646
Fall to lower level	*522*
Fall on same level	*100*
Bodily reaction or exertion	9
Exposure to harmful substance	414
Contact with electric current	*164*
Contact with temperature extremes	*48*
Exposure to caustic or noxious substances	*140*
Oxygen deficiency	*61*
Drowning	45
Choking on object or substance	6
Transportation incidents	1,857
Motor vehicle incidents	*1,600*
Highway incident	1,044
Nonhighway incident, except rail, air, and water	276
Pedestrian struck by vehicle or mobile equipment	280
Railway incident	*45*
Water vehicle incident	*60*
Aircraft incident	*152*
Fires or explosions	191
Fires	*110*
Explosions	*80*
Assaults or violent acts	832
By person	*518*
Self-inflicted	*270*
By animals	*38*
Other and nonclassifiable	3

Event or exposure	Cases with days away from work[b]
Total, all events or exposures	**933,200**
Contact with object or equipment	241,160
Struck against object	*67,170*
Struck by object	*119,130*
Caught in object or equipment	*40,770*
Caught in collapsing material	*270*
Fall	208,470
Fall to lower level	*59,440*
Fall on same level	*139,660*
Bodily reaction or exertion	368,240
Bodily reaction	*103,810*
Bending, climbing, crawling, reaching, or twisting	44,310
Slips, trips, loss of balance – without fall	29,140
Overexertion	*223,970*
Overexertion in lifting	112,170
Repetitive motion	*30,080*
Exposure to harmful substance	42,780
Contact with electric current	*1,890*
Contact with temperature extremes	*17,690*
Exposure to caustic or noxious substances	*19,840*
Transportation incidents	38,330
Highway incident	*24,060*
Nonhighway incident, except rail, air, and water	*4,920*
Pedestrian struck by vehicle or mobile equipment	*6,510*
Railway incident	*250*
Water vehicle incident	*220*
Aircraft incident	*340*
Fires or explosions	1,510
Fires	*910*
Explosions	*520*
Assaults or violent acts	23,410
By person	*16,910*
By animals	*6,130*
Other and nonclassifiable	9,300

Source: Bureau of Labor Statistics.
[a]Includes deaths among all workers.
[b]Includes cases with days away from work among private-sector wage and salary workers. Excludes government employees, the self-employed, and unpaid family workers.

Deaths[a] by event or exposure, United States, 2010

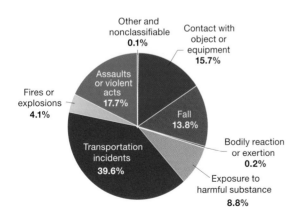

Cases with days away from work[b] by event or exposure, United States, 2010

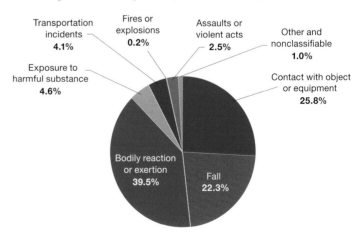

Source: Bureau of Labor Statistics.
[a]Includes deaths among all workers.
[b]Includes cases with days away from work among private-sector wage and salary workers. Excludes government employees, the self-employed, and unpaid family workers.

Under the Occupational Safety and Health Act of 1970, the role of the Occupational Safety and Health Administration (OSHA) is to ensure safe and healthful conditions for working men and women in the United States. OSHA fulfills this role through a variety of methods, including consultation, education and enforcement. Over the past several years, OSHA has enhanced its enforcement activities by conducting more inspections and identifying more violations. As shown in the graphs below, from 2006 to 2010, OSHA increased its total number of inspections by 8%, while the number of total citations issued increased 15%.

However, the degree to which OSHA inspections are effective in improving health and safety has often been questioned. Two reports from the U.S. Government Accountability Office (2002, 2009) identified shortcomings in how OSHA conducts inspections, such as weak overall program management and lack of employee interviews during the process. Past research investigating the relationship between OSHA inspections and subsequent safety performance has had mixed results, with some concluding that safety benefits from inspections and others finding no benefit or even negative outcomes. However, two recent studies (Levine et al., 2012; Haviland et al., 2012) found evidence that inspections provide substantial safety benefit without negatively impacting business.

The Levine study compared single-establishment firms in California that were inspected by California OSHA from 1996 to 2006 with similar firms that were eligible but not selected for inspection. The unique aspect of this study was that the firms were randomly selected for inspection by Cal/OSHA from a list of all eligible firms. This random selection enabled a particularly strong research design. Researchers found that among single-establishment firms, the inspections helped reduce workers' compensation injuries by 9.4% and workers' compensation costs by 26%. They also found no impact (neither negative nor significantly positive) regarding a variety of business factors, including workplace survival, employment, payroll, or sales.

The Haviland study, based on Pennsylvania workers'

compensation data from 1998 to 2005, provides additional evidence that OSHA inspections help reduce workplace injuries. Unlike the Levine study, no control group was available to compare inspected firms against. Haviland's study relied on before-and-after inspection comparisons. Similar to the Levine study, the Haviland study was limited to single-establishment firms with 10 or more employees. Both studies also used workers' compensation data instead of Bureau of Labor Statistics data, and were limited to one state each (Haviland used Pennsylvania and Levine used California). The Haviland study also had the additional limitation of including only manufacturing firms. However, the Haviland study did include both planned and complaint-related inspections and explored the impact of inspections with and without associated penalties assessed.

Interestingly, Haviland only found significant improvement following inspections with penalties among establishments with between 20 and 250 employees. Among this group, researchers found an average of 19% to 24% improvement that persisted for about two years. No benefit was found if the establishments were not penalized or had fewer than 20 employees or more than 250 employees. They also found that planned inspections resulted in greater reductions than complaint-driven inspections.

Looking at both studies together provides promising evidence that planned inspections, particularly those with fines, positively influence safety for at least two years.

Haviland, A.M., Burns, R.M., Gray, W.B., Ruder, T., & Mendeloff, J. (2012). A new estimate of the impact of OSHA inspections on manufacturing injury rates. American Journal of Industrial Medicine. Downloaded, prepublication from wileyonlinelibrary.com.

Levine, D.I., Toffel, M.W., & Johnson, M.S. (2012). Randomized government safety inspections reduce worker injuries with no detectable job loss. Science. Vol. 336, No. 6083, pp. 907-911.

U.S. Government Accountability Office. (2002). OSHA can strengthen enforcement through improved program management. GAO-03-45. Washington, DC: Author.

U.S. Government Accountability Office. (2009). Enhancing OSHA's records audits process could improve the accuracy of worker injury and illness data. GAO-10-10. Washington, DC: Author.

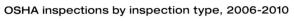

OSHA inspections by inspection type, 2006-2010

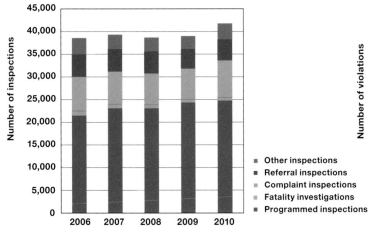

OSHA violations by violation type, 2006-2010

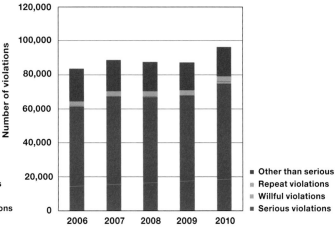

According to the Bureau of Labor Statistics, sprains and strains were the most common type of injury involving days away from work in 2010, accounting for 40% of the total 933,200 injuries in private industry. Soreness or pain was the second most common type of injury, followed by cuts, lacerations, or punctures. Overall, the education and health services, retail trade, and manufacturing industry sectors had the greatest number of injuries, combining to make up 48% of the total.

Number of nonfatal occupational injuries and illnesses involving days away from work[a] by nature of injury and industry sector, private industry, United States, 2010

Nature of injury	Private sector[b,c,d]	Industry sector								
		Education and health services	Retail trade	Manufacturing	Transportation and warehousing[d]	Leisure and hospitality	Professional and business services	Construction	Wholesale trade	All other sectors[b,d,e]
Total[c]	933,200	186,830	131,380	127,140	89,540	88,740	75,890	74,950	58,060	100,640
Sprains or strains	370,130	89,370	53,640	41,990	43,300	27,390	27,170	25,630	24,730	36,910
Fractures	69,380	10,380	8,130	10,960	5,240	4,790	6,540	8,870	4,450	10,020
Cuts, lacerations, or punctures	79,120	6,450	13,280	14,570	3,750	15,480	6,440	9,120	3,950	6,090
Bruises or contusions	76,960	17,020	12,950	9,170	7,780	8,340	5,000	4,130	4,800	7,750
Heat burns	14,620	1,890	1,470	2,240	200	6,340	350	750	450	950
Chemical burns	4,210	590	530	1,070	270	360	280	460	310	330
Amputations	5,260	110	450	2,290	230	350	360	590	310	570
Carpal tunnel syndrome	8,490	840	910	3,180	350	200	760	610	510	1,130
Tendonitis	4,010	870	680	900	180	250	250	50	140	680
Multiple injuries	41,620	9,330	5,190	4,640	3,590	3,110	3,810	3,220	2,540	6,170
With fractures	*7,600*	*790*	*600*	*1,510*	*600*	*550*	*890*	*950*	*410*	*1,300*
With sprains	*15,410*	*4,840*	*2,010*	*1,140*	*1,670*	*1,330*	*1,250*	*510*	*750*	*1,920*
Soreness or pain	101,290	24,520	13,370	10,860	10,800	9,520	8,840	7,690	5,610	10,080
Back pain	*33,240*	*8,640*	*4,440*	*3,430*	*3,390*	*2,500*	*2,230*	*3,020*	*2,020*	*3,540*
All other natures	158,120	25,460	20,790	25,280	13,850	12,600	16,080	13,820	10,260	19,990

Source: Bureau of Labor Statistics Occupational Injuries/Illnesses Fatal Injuries Profiles, accessed July 12, 2012 from http://data.bls.gov/gqt/InitialPage.
[a]*Days-away-from-work cases include those that result in days away from work with or without job transfer or restriction.*
[b]*Excludes farms with fewer than 11 employees.*
[c]*Data may not sum to row and column totals because of rounding and exclusion of nonclassifiable responses.*
[d]*Data for transportation and mining do not reflect the changes OSHA made to its recordkeeping requirements effective Jan. 1, 2002; therefore, estimates for these industries are not comparable with estimates for other industries.*
[e]*Includes agriculture, forestry, fishing, and hunting; financial activities; information; mining (including oil and gas extraction); other services (except public administration); and utilities.*

Percent of injuries involving days away from work by nature of injury, private industry, United States, 2010

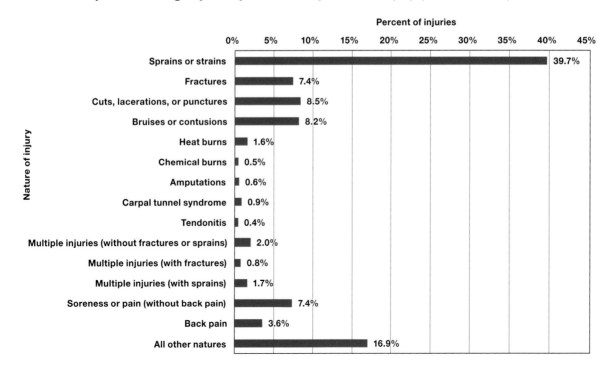

According to the Bureau of Labor Statistics, the back was the body part most frequently affected in injuries involving days away from work in 2010, accounting for 20% of the total 933,200 injuries in private industry. Multiple-part injuries were the second most common, followed by knee, finger, and shoulder injuries. Overall, the education and health services, retail trade, and manufacturing industry sectors had the highest number of injuries, combining to make up 48% of the total.

Number of nonfatal occupational injuries and illnesses involving days away from work[a] by part of body affected and industry sector, private industry, United States, 2010

Part of body affected	Private sector[b,c,d]	Industry sector								
		Education and health services	Retail trade	Manufacturing	Transportation and warehousing[d]	Leisure and hospitality	Professional and business services	Construction	Wholesale trade	All other sectors[b,d,e]
Total[c]	933,200	186,830	131,380	127,140	89,540	88,740	75,890	74,950	58,060	100,640
Head	61,830	10,750	9,430	9,700	5,630	5,370	5,400	5,220	3,520	6,820
Eye	*22,370*	*2,560*	*3,080*	*5,340*	*2,040*	*1,260*	*1,320*	*3,000*	*1,270*	*2,500*
Neck	12,950	3,440	1,590	1,250	1,490	570	990	1,370	1,180	1,060
Trunk	310,400	73,170	46,510	39,410	34,470	21,820	21,870	21,690	20,750	30,710
Shoulder	*68,040*	*14,180*	*9,390*	*10,400*	*9,050*	*4,680*	*4,450*	*4,990*	*4,130*	*6,780*
Back	*185,270*	*49,110*	*29,030*	*19,920*	*18,980*	*13,120*	*12,220*	*12,300*	*12,610*	*17,980*
Upper extremities	209,600	29,180	29,130	41,650	13,070	29,980	17,210	17,540	11,790	19,880
Wrist	*39,110*	*7,640*	*4,930*	*7,360*	*2,520*	*3,320*	*3,490*	*3,720*	*2,120*	*4,000*
Hand (except finger)	*39,510*	*4,640*	*5,420*	*6,470*	*2,340*	*7,570*	*4,030*	*3,490*	*1,770*	*3,790*
Finger	*75,440*	*7,730*	*11,170*	*18,470*	*3,810*	*11,770*	*5,680*	*6,050*	*4,530*	*6,210*
Lower extremities	212,080	37,020	29,060	23,490	22,730	21,090	18,990	19,910	13,480	26,290
Knee	*82,980*	*15,880*	*11,120*	*8,860*	*8,370*	*8,500*	*7,710*	*6,640*	*5,050*	*10,860*
Foot (except toe)	*31,710*	*5,110*	*5,670*	*4,200*	*3,270*	*2,840*	*2,550*	*3,140*	*2,060*	*2,860*
Toe	*8,360*	*1,140*	*2,000*	*1,120*	*760*	*750*	*580*	*630*	*690*	*690*
Body systems	16,390	2,980	1,980	1,800	1,240	1,470	1,860	1,330	1,120	2,600
Multiple parts	104,020	29,220	12,590	9,320	10,380	7,360	9,070	7,540	5,770	12,770

Source: Bureau of Labor Statistics Occupational Injuries/Illnesses and Fatal Injuries Profiles, accessed July 12, 2012 from http://data.bls.gov/gqt/InitialPage.
[a]Days-away-from-work cases include those that result in days away from work with or without job transfer or restriction.
[b]Excludes farms with fewer than 11 employees.
[c]Data may not sum to row and column totals because of rounding and exclusion of nonclassifiable responses.
[d]Data for transportation and mining do not reflect the changes OSHA made to its recordkeeping requirements effective Jan. 1, 2002; therefore, estimates for these industries are not comparable with estimates for other industries.
[e]Includes agriculture, forestry, fishing, and hunting; financial activities; information; mining (including oil and gas extraction); other services (except public administration); and utilities.

Percent of injuries involving days away from work by part of body affected, private industry, United States, 2010

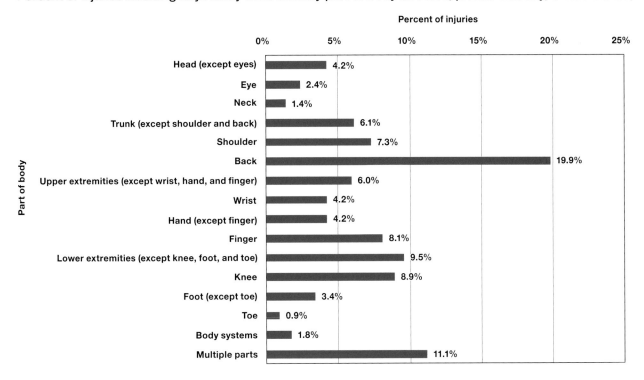

Percent of injuries

Head (except eyes) 4.2%
Eye 2.4%
Neck 1.4%
Trunk (except shoulder and back) 6.1%
Shoulder 7.3%
Back 19.9%
Upper extremities (except wrist, hand, and finger) 6.0%
Wrist 4.2%
Hand (except finger) 4.2%
Finger 8.1%
Lower extremities (except knee, foot, and toe) 9.5%
Knee 8.9%
Foot (except toe) 3.4%
Toe 0.9%
Body systems 1.8%
Multiple parts 11.1%

Safety professionals in business and industry often want to compare, or benchmark, the occupational injury and illness incidence rates of their establishments with the national average rates compiled by the Bureau of Labor Statistics (BLS) through its annual Survey of Occupational Injuries and Illnesses.[a] The incidence rates published on the following pages are for 2011 and were compiled under the revised OSHA recordkeeping requirements that went into effect in 2002.

Step 1

The first step in benchmarking is to calculate the incidence rates for the establishment. The basic formula for computing incidence rates is $(N \times 200,000)/EH$, or the number of cases (N) multiplied by $200,000$ then divided by the number of hours worked (EH) by all employees during the time period, where $200,000$ is the base for 100 full-time workers (working 40 hours per week, 50 weeks per year). Because BLS rates are based on reports from entire establishments, both the OSHA 300 log and the number of hours worked should cover the whole establishment being benchmarked. The hours worked and the log also should cover the same time period (e.g., a month, quarter, or full year). The following rates may be calculated.

Total cases – The incidence rate of total OSHA recordable cases per 200,000 hours worked. For this rate, N is the total number of cases on the OSHA 300 log.

Cases with days away from work or job transfer or restriction – The incidence rate of cases with days away from work, or job transfer, or restriction. N is the count of cases with a check in column H or column I of the OSHA 300 log.

Cases with days away from work – The incidence rate of cases with days away from work. N is the count of cases with a check in column H of the OSHA 300 log.

Cases with job transfer or restriction – The incidence rate of cases with job transfer or restriction, but no days away from work. N is the count of cases with a check in column I of the OSHA 300 log.

Other recordable cases – The incidence rate of recordable cases without days away from work or job transfer or restriction. N is the count of cases with a check in column J of the OSHA 300 log.

In the flow chart on the opposite page, post the number of cases to each box in the top row and the number of employee hours worked in its box. Then use the formula to calculate the rates and write them in the last row of boxes in Step 1.

An alternative approach is to use the Incidence Rate Calculator and Comparison Tool available on BLS's website at *http://data.bls.gov/IIRC/*. This tool will calculate your rate and provide a report comparing your rate to your industry.

Step 2

After computing one or more of the rates, the next step is to determine the North American Industry Classification System (NAICS) code for the establishment.[b] (NAICS replaced the Standard Industrial Classification [SIC] code beginning in 2003.) This code is used to find the appropriate BLS rate for comparison. NAICS codes can be found at *www.census.gov/naics*. The website also contains a crosswalk between NAICS and SIC codes. Otherwise, call a regional BLS office for assistance.

Write the establishment's NAICS code in the box in Step 2 of the flow chart.

Step 3

Once the NAICS code is known, the national average incidence rates may be found by (a) consulting the table of rates on pages 80-82, (b) visiting BLS's website, or (c) by calling a regional BLS office. Note that some tables on the website provide incidence rates by size of establishment and rate quartiles within each NAICS code. These rates may be useful for a more precise comparison. Note that the incidence rates for 2001 and earlier years were compiled under the old OSHA recordkeeping requirements in effect at that time. Caution must be used in comparing rates computed for 2002 and later years with earlier years – keeping in mind the differences in recordkeeping requirements.

In the flow chart on the opposite page, post the rates from the BLS survey to the boxes in Step 3. Now compare these with the rates calculated in Step 1.

An alternative way of benchmarking is to compare the current incidence rates for an establishment to its own prior historical rates to determine if the rates are improving and if progress is satisfactory (using criteria set by the organization).

[a]*Bureau of Labor Statistics. (1997). BLS Handbook of Methods. Washington, DC: U.S. Government Printing Office (Or at www.bls.gov/opub/hom/home.htm).*
[b]*Executive Office of the President, Office of Management and Budget. (2002). North American Industry Classification System, United States, 2002. Springfield, VA: National Technical Information Service.*

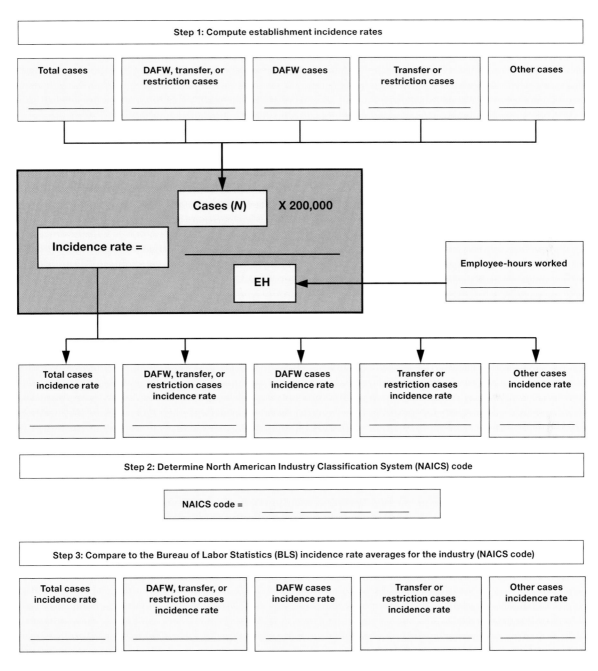

Step 1: Compute establishment incidence rates

Total cases	DAFW, transfer, or restriction cases	DAFW cases	Transfer or restriction cases	Other cases
_____	_____	_____	_____	_____

$$\text{Incidence rate} = \frac{\text{Cases } (N) \times 200{,}000}{\text{EH}}$$

Employee-hours worked
_____

Total cases incidence rate	DAFW, transfer, or restriction cases incidence rate	DAFW cases incidence rate	Transfer or restriction cases incidence rate	Other cases incidence rate
_____	_____	_____	_____	_____

Step 2: Determine North American Industry Classification System (NAICS) code

NAICS code = _____ _____ _____ _____

Step 3: Compare to the Bureau of Labor Statistics (BLS) incidence rate averages for the industry (NAICS code)

Total cases incidence rate	DAFW, transfer, or restriction cases incidence rate	DAFW cases incidence rate	Transfer or restriction cases incidence rate	Other cases incidence rate
_____	_____	_____	_____	_____

See page 76 for detailed instructions.
DAFW = Days away from work.

Trends in Occupational Incidence Rates

◆ *Incidence rates continue to level out.*

Four of the five private-sector occupational injury and illness incidence rates published by the Bureau of Labor Statistics (BLS) for 2011 were unchanged from 2010, while the remaining incidence rate decreased. The incidence rate for total recordable cases was 3.5 per 100 full-time workers; the incidence rate for total cases with days away from work, job transfer, or restriction was 1.8; the rate for cases with days away from work was 1.1; and the rate for other recordable cases was 1.7 – all unchanged from 2010. The incidence rate for cases with job transfer or restriction was 0.7 in 2011, down from 0.8 in 2010.

There have been several changes that affect comparability of incidence rates from year to year. The North American Industry Classification System replaced the Standard Industrial Classification system beginning with the 2003 survey of occupational injuries and illnesses. Revisions to the Occupational Safety and Health Administration's occupational injury and illness recordkeeping requirements went into effect in 2002. Beginning with 1992, BLS revised its annual survey to include only nonfatal cases and stopped publishing the incidence rate of lost workdays.

Occupational injury and illness incidence rates, private industry, United States, 1990-2011

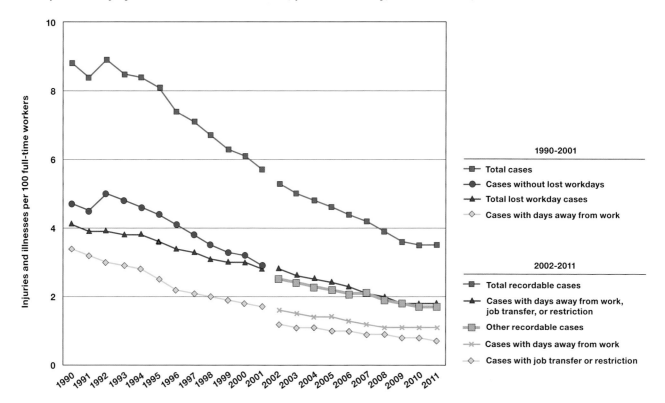

Source: Bureau of Labor Statistics.
Note: Beginning with 1992, all rates are for nonfatal cases only.
Changes in OSHA recordkeeping requirements in 2002 affect comparison with earlier years.

The tables below and on pages 80-82 present the results of the 2011 Survey of Occupational Injuries and Illnesses conducted by the Bureau of Labor Statistics (BLS). The survey collects data on injuries and illnesses (from the OSHA 300 log) and employee-hours worked from a nationwide sample of about 230,000 private-industry establishments, as well as state and local governments. The survey excludes private households, the self-employed, and farms with fewer than 11 employees. The incidence rates give the number of cases per 100 full-time workers per year using 200,000 employee-hours as the equivalent. Definitions of the terms are given in the Glossary on page 205.

Beginning with 1992 data, BLS revised its annual survey to include only nonfatal cases and stopped publishing incidence rates of lost workdays. Beginning with 2003 data, BLS adopted the North American Industry Classification System for publication of the incidence rates by industry.

Bureau of Labor Statistics estimates of nonfatal occupational injury and illness incidence rates and number of injuries and illnesses by industry sector, 2011

| Industry sector | Total recordable cases | Cases with days away from work, job transfer, or restriction | | | |
		Total	Cases with days away from work	Cases with job transfer or restriction	Other recordable cases
Incidence rate per 100 full-time workers[c]					
All industries, including state and local government[d]	**3.8**	**1.9**	**1.2**	**0.7**	**1.9**
Private sector[d]	**3.5**	**1.8**	**1.1**	**0.7**	**1.7**
Goods producing[d]	4.2	2.3	1.2	1.1	1.9
Agriculture, forestry, fishing, and hunting[d]	5.5	3.2	1.8	1.4	2.3
Mining	2.2	1.4	0.9	0.5	0.9
Construction	3.9	2.1	1.5	0.7	1.8
Manufacturing	4.4	2.4	1.1	1.3	2.0
Service providing	3.3	1.6	1.0	0.6	1.6
Wholesale trade	3.2	1.9	1.1	0.9	1.3
Retail trade	3.9	2.2	1.2	1.0	1.7
Transportation and warehousing	5.0	3.4	2.3	1.1	1.6
Utilities	3.5	1.9	1.0	0.9	1.6
Information	1.6	0.9	0.6	0.3	0.7
Financial activities	1.4	0.6	0.4	0.2	0.7
Professional and business services	1.7	0.8	0.5	0.3	0.9
Education and health services	4.7	2.1	1.3	0.9	2.5
Leisure and hospitality	4.0	1.6	1.0	0.6	2.4
Other services	2.6	1.3	0.9	0.4	1.2
State and local government[d]	**5.7**	**2.5**	**1.9**	**0.6**	**3.2**
Number of injuries and illnesses (in thousands)					
All industries, including state and local government[d]	**3,807.4**	**1,903.8**	**1,181.3**	**722.5**	**1,903.6**
Private sector[d]	**2,986.5**	**1,538.7**	**908.3**	**630.4**	**1,447.8**
Goods producing[d]	758.4	415.7	223.9	191.7	342.8
Agriculture, forestry, fishing, and hunting[d]	48.3	28.3	16.2	12.0	20.0
Mining	17.2	10.6	7.1	3.5	6.6
Construction	190.2	103.3	71.6	31.7	86.9
Manufacturing	502.7	273.5	129.0	144.5	229.2
Service providing	2,228.1	1,123.0	684.4	438.7	1,105.1
Wholesale trade	171.2	102.6	57.2	45.5	68.5
Retail trade	424.6	235.1	126.5	108.5	189.6
Transportation and warehousing	193.2	130.5	88.0	42.4	62.7
Utilities	19.3	10.4	5.7	4.7	8.9
Information	37.9	21.4	14.0	7.4	16.5
Financial activities	89.9	40.6	27.4	13.2	49.3
Professional and business services	216.4	104.4	71.2	33.1	112.0
Education and health services	668.7	306.9	182.3	124.6	361.8
Leisure and hospitality	333.1	133.0	85.3	47.6	200.1
Other services	73.8	38.2	26.7	11.5	35.7
State and local government[d]	**820.9**	**365.1**	**273.0**	**92.1**	**455.8**

Source: Bureau of Labor Statistics.
[a]*Industry sector and two- and three-digit NAICS code totals on pages 80-82 include data for industries not shown separately.*
[b]*North American Industry Classification System, 2002 edition, for industries shown on pages 80-82.*
[c]*Incidence rate =* $\dfrac{\text{Number of injuries and illnesses} \times 200{,}000}{\text{Total hours worked by all employees during period covered}}$

where 200,000 is the base for 100 full-time workers (working 40 hours per week, 50 weeks per year). The "Total recordable cases" rate is based on the number of cases with check marks in columns (G), (H), (I), and (J) of the OSHA 300 log. The "Cases with days away from work, job transfer, or restriction – total" rate is based on columns (H) and (I). The "Cases with days away from work" rate is based on column (H). The "Cases with job transfer or restriction" rate is based on column (I). The "Other recordable cases" rate is based on column (J).
[d]*Excludes farms with fewer than 11 employees.*
[e]*Data do not meet publication guidelines.*
[f]*Industry scope changed in 2009.*
[g]*Data too small to be displayed.*

Bureau of Labor Statistics estimates of nonfatal occupational injury and illness incidence rates for selected industries, 2011

Industry[a]	NAICS code[b]	Total recordable cases	Cases with days away from work, job transfer, or restriction			Other recordable cases
			Total	Cases with days away from work	Cases with job transfer or restriction	
All industries, including state and local government[d]		3.8	1.9	1.2	0.7	1.9
Private sector[e]		3.5	1.8	1.1	0.7	1.7
Goods producing[e]		4.2	2.3	1.2	1.1	1.9
Natural resources and mining[e]		4.0	2.4	1.4	0.9	1.6
Agriculture, forestry, fishing, and hunting[e]	11	5.5	3.2	1.8	1.4	2.3
Crop production	111	5.5	3.2	1.7	1.5	2.2
Animal production	112	6.7	4.1	2.3	1.8	2.6
Forestry and logging	113	5.0	3.3	2.9	0.3	1.8
Fishing, hunting, and trapping	114	4.8	1.6	1.1	([e])	3.2
Support activities for agriculture and forestry	115	4.8	2.7	1.5	1.1	2.2
Mining	21	2.2	1.4	0.9	0.5	0.9
Oil and gas extraction	211	0.9	0.5	0.4	0.1	0.4
Mining (except oil and gas)	212	3.0	1.9	1.5	0.5	1.1
Coal mining	2121	3.7	2.5	2.2	0.3	1.3
Metal ore mining	2122	2.3	1.5	0.9	0.5	0.9
Nonmetallic mineral mining and quarrying	2123	2.4	1.6	0.9	0.7	0.9
Support activities for mining	213	2.3	1.4	0.8	0.6	0.9
Construction		3.9	2.1	1.5	0.7	1.8
Construction of buildings	236	3.6	1.9	1.2	0.7	1.7
Residential building construction	2361	4.3	2.3	1.6	([e])	2.0
Nonresidential building construction	2362	3.1	1.7	0.9	0.7	1.4
Heavy and civil engineering construction	237	3.5	2.0	1.2	0.7	1.5
Utility system construction	2371	2.9	1.8	1.1	0.6	1.2
Land subdivision	2372	3.2	1.9	1.2	([e])	1.3
Highway, street, and bridge construction	2373	4.4	2.4	1.5	0.8	2.0
Other heavy and civil engineering construction	2379	3.6	1.9	1.0	0.9	1.6
Specialty trade contractors	238	4.1	2.2	1.6	0.6	1.9
Foundation, structure, and building exterior contractors	2381	5.1	3.0	2.0	0.9	2.2
Building equipment contractors	2382	4.1	2.0	1.5	0.6	2.1
Building finishing contractors	2383	3.7	2.3	1.7	0.6	1.4
Other specialty trade contractors	2389	3.6	1.9	1.5	0.4	1.7
Manufacturing		4.4	2.4	1.1	1.3	2.0
Food manufacturing	311	5.6	3.5	1.5	2.1	2.1
Animal food manufacturing	3111	4.9	2.4	1.2	1.2	2.5
Grain and oilseed milling	3112	3.3	1.8	1.0	0.8	1.6
Sugar and confectionery product manufacturing	3113	5.1	2.7	1.4	1.3	2.4
Fruit and vegetable preserving and specialty food manufacturing	3114	5.3	3.4	1.6	1.7	1.9
Dairy product manufacturing	3115	5.9	3.8	2.0	1.9	2.1
Animal slaughtering and processing	3116	6.4	4.3	1.2	3.1	2.2
Seafood product preparation and packaging	3117	7.4	4.5	2.6	1.8	3.0
Bakeries and tortilla manufacturing	3118	5.0	3.1	1.5	1.6	1.9
Other food manufacturing	3119	4.9	3.0	1.6	1.4	1.9
Beverage and tobacco product manufacturing	312	6.9	5.3	([e])	2.5	1.6
Beverage manufacturing	3121	7.3	5.6	([e])	2.7	1.6
Tobacco manufacturing	3122	3.3	2.0	1.3	0.7	1.3
Textile mills	313	3.5	2.0	0.9	1.1	1.5
Fiber, yarn, and thread mills	3131	2.5	1.4	0.6	0.8	1.1
Fabric mills	3132	3.5	2.0	1.1	0.9	1.4
Textile and fabric finishing and fabric coating mills	3133	4.3	2.4	0.9	1.5	1.9
Textile product mills	314	3.5	1.9	0.9	1.0	1.5
Textile furnishings mills	3141	2.4	1.6	0.6	1.0	0.8
Other textile product mills	3149	4.5	2.3	1.2	1.1	2.2
Apparel manufacturing	315	2.5	1.1	0.6	0.6	1.4
Apparel knitting mills	3151	2.9	1.5	0.7	0.7	1.4
Cut and sew apparel manufacturing	3152	2.3	1.0	0.5	0.6	1.3
Apparel accessories and other apparel manufacturing	3159	3.7	1.3	1.2	0.1	2.3
Leather and allied product manufacturing	316	6.1	3.4	1.7	1.7	2.7
Footwear manufacturing	3162	5.7	3.0	1.5	1.5	2.8
Other leather and allied product manufacturing	3169	6.0	3.5	1.6	1.9	2.5
Wood product manufacturing	321	6.5	3.5	1.9	1.6	3.0
Sawmills and wood preservation	3211	6.4	3.4	2.2	1.2	3.0
Veneer, plywood, and engineered wood product manufacturing	3212	4.8	2.3	1.3	1.1	2.5
Other wood product manufacturing	3219	7.1	3.9	1.9	2.0	3.2
Paper manufacturing	322	3.4	1.9	1.0	0.9	1.5
Pulp, paper, and paperboard mills	3221	2.7	1.4	0.9	0.6	1.3
Converted paper product manufacturing	3222	3.7	2.1	1.0	1.0	1.6
Printing and related support activities	323	2.9	1.6	0.8	0.8	1.3
Petroleum and coal products manufacturing	324	2.0	1.0	0.5	0.6	0.9
Chemical manufacturing	325	2.4	1.4	0.7	0.7	1.0
Basic chemical manufacturing	3251	2.1	1.2	0.6	0.5	1.0
Resin, synthetic rubber, and artificial and synthetic fibers and filaments manufacturing	3252	2.8	1.8	0.8	1.0	1.1
Pesticide, fertilizer, and other agricultural chemical manufacturing	3253	3.1	1.7	0.7	1.0	1.5
Pharmaceutical and medicine manufacturing	3254	2.0	1.2	0.5	0.6	0.8
Paint, coating, and adhesive manufacturing	3255	2.5	1.5	0.8	0.7	1.0
Soap, cleaning compound, and toilet preparation manufacturing	3256	2.5	1.6	0.7	0.8	0.9
Other chemical product and preparation manufacturing	3259	3.4	2.0	1.1	0.8	1.4

See source and footnotes on page 79.

Bureau of Labor Statistics estimates of nonfatal occupational injury and illness incidence rates for selected industries, 2011 (cont.)

Industry[a]	NAICS code[b]	Total recordable cases	Incidence rates[c]			Other recordable cases
			Cases with days away from work, job transfer, or restriction			
			Total	Cases with days away from work	Cases with job transfer or restriction	
Plastics and rubber products manufacturing	326	4.9	2.8	1.3	1.5	2.1
Plastics product manufacturing	3261	4.7	2.7	1.3	1.4	2.1
Rubber product manufacturing	3262	5.6	3.3	1.5	1.8	2.3
Nonmetallic mineral product manufacturing	327	5.4	3.0	1.7	1.4	2.4
Clay product and refractory manufacturing	3271	5.7	2.9	1.3	1.6	2.8
Glass and glass product manufacturing	3272	5.1	2.8	1.1	1.6	2.3
Cement and concrete product manufacturing	3273	6.1	3.6	2.3	1.5	2.5
Lime and gypsum product manufacturing	3274	4.4	2.1	1.2	0.9	2.3
Other nonmetallic mineral product manufacturing	3279	4.3	2.3	1.3	1.0	2.1
Primary metal manufacturing	331	6.1	3.5	1.8	1.7	2.7
Iron and steel mills and ferroalloy manufacturing	3311	3.2	1.7	0.9	0.9	1.5
Steel product manufacturing from purchased steel	3312	7.1	4.1	2.1	2.0	2.9
Alumina and aluminum production and processing	3313	4.3	2.4	1.0	1.4	1.9
Nonferrous metal (except aluminum) production and processing	3314	4.7	2.7	1.5	1.2	1.9
Foundries	3315	9.6	5.4	2.8	2.7	4.2
Fabricated metal product manufacturing	332	5.6	2.6	1.3	1.3	3.0
Forging and stamping	3321	7.0	3.4	1.6	1.7	3.6
Cutlery and hand tool manufacturing	3322	5.2	2.2	1.1	1.0	3.0
Architectural and structural metals manufacturing	3323	6.8	3.2	1.6	1.7	3.6
Boiler, tank, and shipping container manufacturing	3324	6.1	2.7	1.4	1.2	3.4
Hardware manufacturing	3325	4.3	2.5	1.1	1.4	1.8
Spring and wire product manufacturing	3326	5.1	2.7	1.3	1.4	2.4
Machine shops; turned product; and screw, nut, and bolt manufacturing	3327	5.2	2.2	1.3	0.8	3.0
Coating, engraving, heat treating, and allied activities	3328	5.4	2.9	1.3	1.6	2.6
Other fabricated metal product manufacturing	3329	4.4	2.1	1.0	1.1	2.3
Machinery manufacturing	333	4.4	2.0	1.0	1.0	2.3
Agriculture, construction, and mining machinery manufacturing	3331	4.4	2.1	1.1	1.0	2.3
Industrial machinery manufacturing	3332	4.3	1.8	1.2	0.7	2.4
Commercial and service machinery manufacturing	3333	3.2	1.6	0.7	0.9	1.6
Ventilation, heating, air conditioning, and commercial refrigeration equipment manufacturing	3334	4.7	2.5	1.0	1.5	2.2
Metalworking machinery manufacturing	3335	5.3	2.3	1.3	0.9	3.0
Engine, turbine, and power transmission equipment manufacturing	3336	3.8	1.8	0.9	1.0	2.0
Other general purpose machinery manufacturing	3339	4.2	1.9	0.9	1.0	2.3
Computer and electronic product manufacturing	334	1.4	0.7	0.4	0.3	0.7
Computer and peripheral equipment manufacturing	3341	0.7	0.4	0.2	0.2	0.3
Communications equipment manufacturing	3342	1.3	0.7	0.3	0.4	0.6
Audio and video equipment manufacturing	3343	2.1	1.4	0.4	1.0	0.7
Semiconductor and other electronic component manufacturing	3344	1.6	0.8	0.5	0.4	0.8
Navigational, measuring, electromedical, and control instruments manufacturing	3345	1.5	0.6	0.4	0.3	0.8
Manufacturing and reproducing magnetic and optical media	3346	1.5	0.9	0.4	0.6	0.5
Electrical equipment, appliance, and component manufacturing	335	3.1	1.6	0.6	1.0	1.5
Electric lighting equipment manufacturing	3351	3.7	1.9	0.8	1.1	1.8
Household appliance manufacturing	3352	2.9	1.6	0.6	1.0	1.3
Electrical equipment manufacturing	3353	2.9	1.5	0.6	0.9	1.4
Other electrical equipment and component manufacturing	3359	3.1	1.7	0.7	1.0	1.4
Transportation equipment manufacturing	336	5.2	2.7	1.1	1.6	2.5
Motor vehicle manufacturing	3361	7.5	3.8	1.6	2.2	3.7
Motor vehicle body and trailer manufacturing	3362	8.6	4.0	1.8	2.3	4.5
Motor vehicle parts manufacturing	3363	5.2	2.7	1.0	1.7	2.5
Aerospace product and parts manufacturing	3364	3.3	1.8	0.6	1.2	1.5
Railroad rolling stock manufacturing	3365	4.8	2.6	1.1	1.5	2.2
Ship and boat building	3366	7.5	4.5	2.5	2.0	3.0
Other transportation equipment manufacturing	3369	4.2	2.0	0.9	1.0	2.3
Furniture and related product manufacturing	337	5.3	2.7	1.3	1.5	2.6
Household and institutional furniture and kitchen cabinet manufacturing	3371	5.5	2.9	1.3	1.5	2.7
Office furniture (including fixtures) manufacturing	3372	5.2	2.4	1.2	1.2	2.7
Other furniture-related product manufacturing	3379	4.6	2.6	0.9	1.7	2.0
Miscellaneous manufacturing	339	3.3	1.7	0.8	0.9	1.5
Medical equipment and supplies manufacturing	3391	2.5	1.3	0.6	0.7	1.2
Other miscellaneous manufacturing	3399	4.2	2.2	1.1	1.1	1.9
Service providing		**3.3**	**1.6**	**1.0**	**0.6**	**1.6**
Trade, transportation, and utilities		**3.9**	**2.3**	**1.3**	**1.0**	**1.6**
Wholesale trade	42	3.2	1.9	1.1	0.9	1.3
Merchant wholesalers, durable goods	423	2.8	1.5	0.9	0.7	0.3
Merchant wholesalers, nondurable goods	424	4.4	2.9	1.6	1.3	1.5
Wholesale electronic markets and agents and brokers	425	1.9	1.0	0.6	(e)	0.9
Retail trade	44-45	3.9	2.2	1.2	1.0	1.7
Motor vehicle and parts dealers	441	3.9	1.9	1.3	0.6	2.0
Furniture and home furnishings stores	442	4.0	2.4	1.5	0.9	1.5
Electronics and appliance stores	443	2.1	0.8	0.5	0.3	1.3

See source and footnotes on page 79.

Bureau of Labor Statistics estimates of nonfatal occupational injury and illness incidence rates for selected industries, 2011 (cont.)

Industry[a]	NAICS code[b]	Total recordable cases	Cases with days away from work, job transfer, or restriction			Other recordable cases
			Total	Cases with days away from work	Cases with job transfer or restriction	
Building material and garden equipment and supplies dealers	444	5.4	3.5	1.7	1.8	1.9
Food and beverage stores	445	4.7	2.7	1.4	1.2	2.0
Health and personal care stores	446	2.2	0.9	0.6	0.3	1.3
Gasoline stations	447	2.5	1.1	0.7	0.4	1.4
Clothing and clothing accessories stores	448	2.6	0.9	0.7	0.3	1.6
Sporting goods, hobby, book, and music stores	451	2.6	1.2	0.6	0.6	1.3
General merchandise stores	452	4.6	3.0	1.3	1.7	1.7
Miscellaneous store retailers	453	4.0	1.6	0.9	0.7	2.4
Nonstore retailers	454	2.9	1.7	1.1	0.6	1.2
Transportation and warehousing	48-49	5.0	3.4	2.3	1.1	1.6
Air transportation	481	7.3	5.5	4.3	1.2	1.8
Rail transportation	482	1.9	1.4	1.3	0.1	0.5
Water transportation	483	2.0	1.6	1.2	0.3	0.4
Truck transportation	484	4.9	3.2	2.3	0.9	1.7
Transit and ground passenger transportation	485	4.7	2.9	2.1	0.8	1.8
Pipeline transportation	486	1.5	1.2	(e)	0.2	0.4
Scenic and sightseeing transportation	487	3.5	2.1	1.7	0.5	1.3
Support activities for transportation	488	3.8	2.5	1.6	0.8	1.3
Couriers and messengers	492	6.6	4.5	2.6	1.9	2.1
Warehousing and storage	493	5.5	3.8	1.8	1.9	1.7
Utilities	22	3.5	1.9	1.0	0.9	1.6
Electric power generation, transmission, and distribution	2211	3.2	1.6	0.9	0.7	1.6
Natural gas distribution	2212	4.0	2.5	0.9	1.5	1.6
Water, sewage, and other systems	2213	5.2	3.3	2.3	1.1	1.9
Information		**1.6**	**0.9**	**0.6**	**0.3**	**0.7**
Publishing industries (except Internet)	511	1.3	0.7	0.4	0.2	0.6
Motion picture and sound recording industries	512	2.1	0.6	0.3	0.2	1.5
Broadcasting (except Internet)	515	1.9	1.2	0.6	0.5	0.7
Telecommunications	517	2.1	1.4	1.0	0.4	0.7
Data processing, hosting, and related services[f]	518	0.6	0.3	0.2	0.1	0.4
Other information services	519	0.6	0.3	0.2	0.1	0.3
Financial activities		**1.4**	**0.6**	**0.4**	**0.2**	**0.7**
Finance and insurance	52	0.8	0.3	0.2	0.1	0.6
Monetary authorities	521	1.0	0.4	0.3	(e)	0.6
Credit intermediation and related activities	522	1.1	0.3	0.3	0.1	0.7
Securities, commodity contracts, and other financial investments and related activities	523	(e)	0.1	0.1	(g)	0.2
Insurance carriers and related activities	524	0.7	0.2	0.2	(g)	0.5
Funds, trusts, and other financial activities	525	0.6	0.2	0.1	0.1	0.4
Real estate and rental and leasing	53	3.0	1.7	1.1	0.6	1.3
Real estate	531	2.8	1.6	1.1	0.5	1.2
Rental and leasing services	532	3.7	2.2	1.1	1.1	1.5
Lessors of nonfinancial intangible assets (except copyrighted works)	533	0.6	0.2	0.2	(e)	0.4
Professional and business services		**1.7**	**0.8**	**0.5**	**0.3**	**0.9**
Professional, scientific, and technical services	54	1.0	0.4	0.3	0.1	0.7
Management of companies and enterprises	55	1.4	0.6	0.4	0.2	0.8
Administrative and support and waste management and remediation services	56	2.7	1.5	1.0	0.5	1.2
Administrative and support services	561	2.5	1.4	1.0	0.4	1.2
Waste management and remediation services	562	4.9	3.0	2.0	1.0	1.9
Education and health services		**4.7**	**2.1**	**1.3**	**0.9**	**2.5**
Educational services	61	2.1	0.9	0.6	0.3	1.2
Health care and social assistance	62	5.0	2.3	1.4	1.0	2.7
Ambulatory health care services	621	2.7	0.9	0.7	0.3	1.7
Hospitals	622	6.8	2.7	1.6	1.1	4.1
Nursing and residential care facilities	623	7.8	4.7	2.5	2.2	3.1
Social assistance	624	3.6	1.9	1.2	0.7	1.7
Leisure and hospitality		**4.0**	**1.6**	**1.0**	**0.6**	**2.4**
Arts, entertainment, and recreation	71	4.5	2.2	1.2	0.9	2.4
Accommodation and food services	72	3.9	1.5	1.0	0.5	2.4
Accommodation	721	5.1	2.8	1.5	1.3	2.3
Food services and drinking places	722	3.6	1.2	0.8	0.3	2.4
Other services, except public administration		**2.6**	**1.3**	**0.9**	**0.4**	**1.2**
Repair and maintenance	811	3.2	1.7	1.3	0.4	1.5
Personal and laundry services	812	2.4	1.4	0.8	0.5	1.0
Religious, grantmaking, civic, professional, and similar organizations	813	2.0	0.8	0.5	0.3	1.2
State and local government[d]		**5.7**	**2.5**	**1.9**	**0.6**	**3.2**
State government[d]		**4.6**	**2.3**	**1.8**	**0.5**	**2.3**
Local government[d]		**6.1**	**2.6**	**1.9**	**0.7**	**3.5**

See source and footnotes on page 79.

Bureau of Labor Statistics estimates of nonfatal occupational injury and illness incidence rates[a] for selected industries, 2011

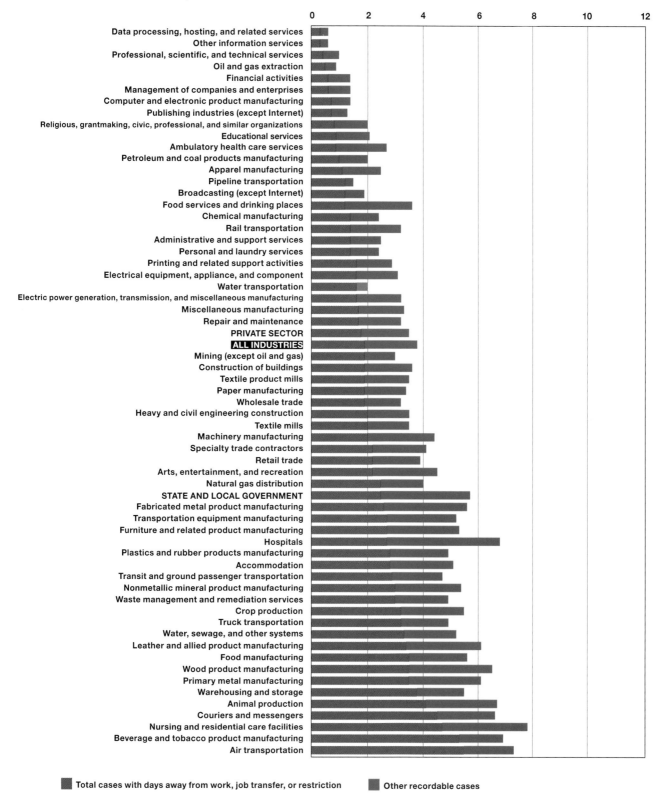

Data processing, hosting, and related services
Other information services
Professional, scientific, and technical services
Oil and gas extraction
Financial activities
Management of companies and enterprises
Computer and electronic product manufacturing
Publishing industries (except Internet)
Religious, grantmaking, civic, professional, and similar organizations
Educational services
Ambulatory health care services
Petroleum and coal products manufacturing
Apparel manufacturing
Pipeline transportation
Broadcasting (except Internet)
Food services and drinking places
Chemical manufacturing
Rail transportation
Administrative and support services
Personal and laundry services
Printing and related support activities
Electrical equipment, appliance, and component
Water transportation
Electric power generation, transmission, and miscellaneous manufacturing
Miscellaneous manufacturing
Repair and maintenance
PRIVATE SECTOR
ALL INDUSTRIES
Mining (except oil and gas)
Construction of buildings
Textile product mills
Paper manufacturing
Wholesale trade
Heavy and civil engineering construction
Textile mills
Machinery manufacturing
Specialty trade contractors
Retail trade
Arts, entertainment, and recreation
Natural gas distribution
STATE AND LOCAL GOVERNMENT
Fabricated metal product manufacturing
Transportation equipment manufacturing
Furniture and related product manufacturing
Hospitals
Plastics and rubber products manufacturing
Accommodation
Transit and ground passenger transportation
Nonmetallic mineral product manufacturing
Waste management and remediation services
Crop production
Truck transportation
Water, sewage, and other systems
Leather and allied product manufacturing
Food manufacturing
Wood product manufacturing
Primary metal manufacturing
Warehousing and storage
Animal production
Couriers and messengers
Nursing and residential care facilities
Beverage and tobacco product manufacturing
Air transportation

■ Total cases with days away from work, job transfer, or restriction   ■ Other recordable cases

Note: Industries are shown at the two-, three-, or four-digit NAICS level.
[a]Total cases with days away from work, job transfer, or restriction plus other recordable cases equals total recordable cases per 200,000 hours worked.

The tables on pages 85-100 present data on the characteristics of injured and ill workers and the injuries and illnesses that affected them. These data indicate how many workers died from on-the-job injuries and how many were affected by non-fatal injuries and illnesses. The data may be used to help set priorities for occupational safety and health programs and for benchmarking.

The fatality information covers only deaths due to injuries and comes from the Bureau of Labor Statistics (BLS) Census of Fatal Occupational Injuries. The data are for calendar year 2010 and include wage and salary workers, the self-employed, and unpaid family workers in all types of businesses and industries.

The data on nonfatal cases cover both occupational injuries and illnesses and come from the BLS Survey of Occupational Injuries and Illnesses for 2010. The survey also is used to produce the incidence rates shown on the preceding pages. The estimates on the following pages are the number of cases involving days away from work (with or without days of restricted work activity). The nonfatal cases presented on pages 85-99 do not cover the self-employed; unpaid family workers; or federal, state, or local government employees. Nonfatal cases involving state and local government employees are presented on page 100.

Data are presented for the sex, age, occupation, and race or ethnic origin of the worker and for the nature of the injury or illness, the part of body affected, the source of the injury or illness, and the event or exposure that produced the injury or illness.

The text at the top of each page describes the kind of establishments that are included in the industry sector and gives the total number of workers in the industry in 2010 and the number working in the private sector.

How to benchmark

Incidence rates, percent distributions, or ranks may be used for benchmarking purposes. The results of the calculations described here may be compared to similar rates, percent distributions, and rankings based on data for a company.

For nonfatal incidence rates, multiply the number of cases by 1,000 and then divide by the private-sector employment given in the text at the top of the page. This will give the number of cases with days away from work per 1,000 employees per year. For fatality rates, multiply the number of fatalities by 100,000 then divide by the total employment given at the top of the page. This will give the number of deaths per 100,000 employees per year.

To compute percent distributions, divide the number of cases for each characteristic by the total number of cases found on the first line of the table. Multiply the quotient by 100 and round to one decimal place. Percent distributions may not add to 100% because of unclassifiable cases not shown.

Ranks are determined by arranging the characteristics from largest to smallest within each group and then numbering consecutively starting with one for the largest.

Industry sectors

Page 85 shows nonfatal injury and illness data for the private sector of the economy (excluding government entities) and fatal injury data for all industries (including government). Pages 86-99 present the data for industry sectors based on the North American Industry Classification System. Page 100 presents the fatal injury data for all government and nonfatal cases for state and local government (the BLS survey does not cover federal government entities).

The nonfatal occupational injury and illness data cover only private sector employees and exclude employees in federal, state, and local government entities and the self-employed. The fatal injury data cover all workers in both the private sector and government.

There were 140,298,000 people employed in 2010, of which 118,014,000 worked in the private sector.

Number of nonfatal occupational injuries and illness involving days away from work[a] and fatal occupational injuries by selected worker and case characteristics, private industry, United States, 2010

Characteristic	Private industry[b,c] nonfatal cases	All industries fatalities
Total	933,200	4,690
Sex		
Men	563,850	4,322
Women	365,610	368
Age		
Younger than 16	200	16
16 to 19	22,140	74
20 to 24	87,370	245
25 to 34	201,710	785
35 to 44	208,520	868
45 to 54	239,100	1,169
55 to 64	132,900	948
65 and older	27,680	582
Occupation		
Management, business, and financial	24,230	571
Professional and related	81,410	94
Service	239,510	825
Sales and related	65,920	280
Office and administrative support	66,390	70
Farming, fishing, and forestry	11,850	276
Construction and extractive	74,190	780
Installation, maintenance, and repair	80,650	363
Production	107,670	225
Transportation and material moving	180,240	1,160
Military occupations	–	46
Race or ethnic origin[d]		
White, non-Hispanic	391,850	3,360
Black, non-Hispanic	73,140	412
Hispanic	122,970	707
Other, multiple, and not reported	345,240	211
Nature of injury or illness		
Sprains or strains	370,130	15
Fractures	69,380	38
Cuts, lacerations, or punctures	79,120	603
Bruises or contusions	76,960	5
Heat burns	14,620	93
Chemical burns	4,210	–
Amputations	5,260	14
Carpal tunnel syndrome	8,490	–
Tendonitis	4,010	–
Multiple injuries	41,620	1,714
Soreness or pain	101,290	–
Back pain	33,240	–
All other	158,120	2,204

Characteristic	Private industry[b,c] nonfatal cases	All industries fatalities
Part of body affected		
Head	61,830	970
Eye	22,370	–
Neck	12,950	143
Trunk	310,400	721
Back	185,270	49
Shoulder	68,040	–
Upper extremities	209,600	20
Finger	75,440	–
Hand, except finger	39,510	–
Wrist	39,110	–
Lower extremities	212,080	71
Knee	82,980	9
Foot or toe	40,060	8
Body systems	16,390	796
Multiple	104,020	1,969
All other	5,930	–
Source of injury or illness		
Chemicals or chemical products	13,600	160
Containers	112,880	62
Furniture or fixtures	37,590	19
Machinery	52,320	355
Parts and materials	78,990	310
Worker motion or position	128,230	–
Floor or ground surfaces	193,910	635
Handtools	42,140	70
Vehicles	77,300	1,932
Health care patient	55,150	–
All other	122,660	1,141
Event or exposure		
Contact with object or equipment	241,160	738
Struck by object	119,130	404
Struck against object	67,170	13
Caught in object, equipment, or material	41,040	319
Fall to lower level	59,440	522
Fall on same level	139,660	100
Slips or trips	29,140	–
Overexertion	223,970	6
Overexertion in lifting	112,170	–
Repetitive motion	30,080	–
Exposed to harmful substance	42,780	414
Transportation incidents	38,330	1,857
Highway incident	24,060	1,044
Nonhighway incident, except air, rail, and water	4,920	276
Pedestrian or nonpassenger struck by vehicle or mobile equipment	6,510	280
Fires or explosions	1,510	191
Assault or violent act	23,410	832
Assault by person	16,910	518
Other	6,500	314
All other	103,720	29

Source: National Safety Council tabulations of Bureau of Labor Statistics (BLS) data.
Note: Because of rounding and data exclusion of nonclassifiable responses, data may not sum to the totals. Dashes (–) indicate data that do not meet publication guidelines.
[a]Days away from work include those that result in days away from work with or without restricted work activity or job transfer.
[b]Excludes farms with fewer than 11 employees.

[c]Data for mining operators in coal, metal, and nonmetal mining and for employees in railroad transportation are provided to BLS by the Mine Safety and Health Administration (MSHA), U.S. Department of Labor; and the Federal Railroad Administration (FRA), U.S. Department of Transportation. Independent mining contractors are excluded from the coal, metal, and nonmetal mining industries. MSHA and FRA data do not reflect the changes in OSHA recordkeeping requirements in 2002.
[d]In the fatalities column, non-Hispanic categories include cases with Hispanic origin not reported.

The Agriculture, Forestry, Fishing and Hunting industry sector includes growing crops; raising animals; harvesting timber; and harvesting fish and other animals from a farm, ranch, or their natural habitats; and agricultural support services.

Employment in Agriculture, Forestry, Fishing, and Hunting totaled 2,207,000 in 2010, of which 2,159,000 were private sector employees.

Number of nonfatal occupational injuries and illnesses involving days away from work[a] and fatal occupational injuries by selected worker and case characteristics, private industry, United States, Agriculture, Forestry, Fishing, and Hunting, 2010

Characteristic	Nonfatal cases[b]	Fatalities
Total	14,010	621
Sex		
Men	11,020	596
Women	2,930	25
Age		
Younger than 16	20	13
16 to 19	620	22
20 to 24	1,700	18
25 to 34	3,560	52
35 to 44	2,980	85
45 to 54	2,870	106
55 to 64	1,650	136
65 and older	270	188
Occupation		
Management, business, and financial	250	322
Professional and related	220	–
Service	530	6
Sales and related	90	–
Office and administrative support	150	–
Farming, fishing, and forestry	9,910	255
Construction and extractive	40	–
Installation, maintenance, and repair	690	5
Production	510	–
Transportation and material moving	1,550	28
Military occupations	–	–
Race or ethnic origin[c]		
White, non-Hispanic	3,530	499
Black, non-Hispanic	300	23
Hispanic	7,540	82
Other, multiple, and not reported	2,640	17
Nature of injury or illness		
Sprains or strains	4,610	–
Fractures	1,780	–
Cuts, lacerations, or punctures	1,350	24
Bruises or contusions	1,260	–
Heat burns	170	7
Chemical burns	130	–
Amputations	70	–
Carpal tunnel syndrome	50	–
Tendonitis	60	–
Multiple injuries	950	194
Soreness or pain	920	–
Back pain	290	–
All other	2,670	388

Characteristic	Nonfatal cases[b]	Fatalities
Part of body affected		
Head	1,190	105
Eye	470	–
Neck	150	18
Trunk	3,890	129
Back	2,050	6
Shoulder	900	–
Upper extremities	3,610	–
Finger	1,510	–
Hand, except finger	890	–
Wrist	410	–
Lower extremities	3,400	10
Knee	1,080	–
Foot or toe	570	–
Body systems	210	155
Multiple	1,440	202
All other	110	–
Source of injury or illness		
Chemicals or chemical products	280	15
Containers	1,350	6
Furniture or fixtures	160	–
Machinery	1,030	94
Parts and materials	1,270	14
Worker motion or position	1,680	–
Floor or ground surfaces	2,780	31
Handtools	890	–
Vehicles	1,020	317
Health care patient	–	–
All other	3,420	142
Event or exposure		
Contact with object or equipment	4,580	190
Struck by object	2,130	109
Struck against object	1,180	–
Caught in object, equipment, or material	1,090	79
Fall to lower level	1,160	28
Fall on same level	1,720	–
Slips or trips	560	–
Overexertion	2,250	–
Overexertion in lifting	1,120	–
Repetitive motion	440	–
Exposed to harmful substance	700	47
Transportation incidents	430	301
Highway incident	140	78
Nonhighway incident, except air, rail, and water	130	155
Pedestrian or nonpassenger struck by vehicle or mobile equipment	140	24
Fires or explosions	120	11
Assault or violent act	760	41
Assault by person	20	7
Other	740	34
All other	1,290	–

Source: National Safety Council tabulations of Bureau of Labor Statistics data.
Note: Because of rounding and data exclusion of nonclassifiable responses, data may not sum to the totals. Dashes (–) indicate data that do not meet publication guidelines.
[a]*Days away from work include those that result in days away from work with or without restricted work activity or job transfer.*
[b]*Excludes farms with less than 11 employees.*
[c]*In the fatalities column, non-Hispanic categories include cases with Hispanic origin not reported.*

The Mining industry sector includes extraction of naturally occurring mineral solids, such as coal and ores; liquid minerals, such as crude petroleum; and gases, such as natural gas. It also includes quarrying, well operations, beneficiating, other preparation customarily performed at the site, and mining support activities.

Mining employment in 2010 totaled 729,000 workers, of which 727,000 were private sector employees.

Number of nonfatal occupational injuries and illnesses involving days away from work[a] and fatal occupational injuries by selected worker and case characteristics, private industry, United States, Mining, 2010

Characteristic	Nonfatal cases[b]	Fatalities
Total	**6,910**	**172**
Sex		
Men	6,800	170
Women	120	–
Age		
Younger than 16	–	–
16 to 19	130	–
20 to 24	810	12
25 to 34	1,650	51
35 to 44	1,740	37
45 to 54	1,550	34
55 to 64	950	29
65 and older	50	9
Occupation		
Management, business, and financial	130	5
Professional and related	100	–
Service	180	–
Sales and related	–	–
Office and administrative support	30	–
Farming, fishing, and forestry	–	–
Construction and extractive	3,780	107
Installation, maintenance, and repair	710	10
Production	640	8
Transportation and material moving	1,340	37
Military occupations	–	–
Race or ethnic origin[c]		
White, non-Hispanic	1,740	142
Black, non-Hispanic	80	5
Hispanic	430	25
Other, multiple, and not reported	4,660	–
Nature of injury or illness		
Sprains or strains	2,590	–
Fractures	1,210	–
Cuts, lacerations, or punctures	460	–
Bruises or contusions	610	–
Heat burns	110	10
Chemical burns	50	–
Amputations	130	–
Carpal tunnel syndrome	–	–
Tendonitis	–	–
Multiple injuries	360	91
Soreness or pain	260	–
Back pain	*80*	*–*
All other	1,130	69
Part of body affected		
Head	450	26
Eye	*110*	*–*
Neck	100	–
Trunk	2,270	15
Back	*1,050*	*–*
Shoulder	*680*	*–*
Upper extremities	1,460	–
Finger	*750*	*–*
Hand, except finger	*200*	*–*
Wrist	*170*	*–*
Lower extremities	1,770	–
Knee	*710*	*–*
Foot or toe	*380*	*–*
Body systems	100	30
Multiple	750	101
All other	20	–

Characteristic	Nonfatal cases[b]	Fatalities
Source of injury or illness		
Chemicals or chemical products	440	–
Containers	720	–
Furniture or fixtures	80	–
Machinery	760	24
Parts and materials	1,170	17
Worker motion or position	270	–
Floor or ground surfaces	1,230	8
Handtools	430	–
Vehicles	530	57
Health care patient	–	–
All other	1,270	59
Event or exposure		
Contact with object or equipment	3,000	41
Struck by object	*1,560*	*25*
Struck against object	*630*	*–*
Caught in object, equipment, or material	*760*	*16*
Fall to lower level	390	9
Fall on same level	780	–
Slips or trips	90	–
Overexertion	1,820	–
Overexertion in lifting	*770*	*–*
Repetitive motion	40	–
Exposed to harmful substance	260	11
Transportation incidents	190	51
Highway incident	*110*	*40*
Nonhighway incident, except air, rail, and water	*40*	*–*
Pedestrian or nonpassenger struck by vehicle or mobile equipment	*30*	*5*
Fires or explosions	50	56
Assault or violent act	–	–
Assault by person	*–*	*–*
Other	*–*	*–*
All other	310	–

Source: National Safety Council tabulations of Bureau of Labor Statistics (BLS) data.

Note: Because of rounding and data exclusion of nonclassifiable responses, data may not sum to the totals. Dashes (–) indicate data that do not meet publication guidelines.

[a]Days away from work include those that result in days away from work with or without restricted work activity or job transfer.

[b]Data for mining operators in coal, metal, and nonmetal mining are provided to BLS by the Mine Safety and Health Administration (MSHA), U.S. Department of Labor. Independent mining contractors are excluded from the coal, metal, and nonmetal mining industries. MSHA data do not reflect the changes in OSHA recordkeeping requirements in 2002.

[c]In the fatalities column, non-Hispanic categories include cases with Hispanic origin not reported.

The Construction industry sector includes establishments engaged in construction of buildings, heavy construction other than buildings, and specialty trade contractors such as plumbing, electrical, carpentry, etc.

In 2010, employment in the Construction industry totaled 9,077,000 workers, of which 8,634,000 were private sector employees.

Number of nonfatal occupational injuries and illnesses involving days away from work[a] and fatal occupational injuries by selected worker and case characteristics, private industry, United States, Construction, 2010

Characteristic	Nonfatal cases	Fatalities		Characteristic	Nonfatal cases	Fatalities
Total	**74,950**	**774**		**Part of body affected**		
Sex				Head	5,220	173
Men	72,800	771		*Eye*	*3,000*	*–*
Women	2,140	–		Neck	1,370	18
Age				Trunk	21,690	102
Younger than 16	–	–		*Back*	*12,300*	*12*
16 to 19	1,110	12		*Shoulder*	*4,990*	*–*
20 to 24	5,320	45		Upper extremities	17,540	–
25 to 34	20,380	147		*Finger*	*6,050*	*–*
35 to 44	18,550	159		*Hand, except finger*	*3,490*	*–*
45 to 54	20,560	232		*Wrist*	*3,720*	*–*
55 to 64	7,160	125		Lower extremities	19,910	7
65 and older	1,170	53		*Knee*	*6,640*	*–*
Occupation				*Foot or toe*	*3,770*	*–*
Management, business, and financial	2,030	40		Body systems	1,330	167
Professional and related	270	10		Multiple	7,540	305
Service	650	–		All other	350	–
Sales and related	410	–		**Source of injury or illness**		
Office and administrative support	500	–		Chemicals or chemical products	860	28
Farming, fishing, and forestry	100	–		Containers	2,760	12
Construction and extractive	56,680	603		Furniture or fixtures	1,460	5
Installation, maintenance, and repair	8,780	47		Machinery	4,960	79
Production	2,230	17		Parts and materials	15,210	90
Transportation and material moving	3,320	51		Worker motion or position	9,790	–
Military occupations	–	–		Floor or ground surfaces	16,090	263
Race or ethnic origin[b]				Handtools	6,330	10
White, non-Hispanic	43,070	526		Vehicles	4,620	170
Black, non-Hispanic	2,710	42		Health care patient	–	–
Hispanic	13,380	181		All other	12,520	116
Other, multiple, and not reported	15,790	25		**Event or exposure**		
Nature of injury or illness				Contact with object or equipment	24,710	138
Sprains or strains	25,630	–		*Struck by object*	*11,910*	*64*
Fractures	8,870	5		*Struck against object*	*6,610*	*–*
Cuts, lacerations, or punctures	9,120	18		*Caught in object, equipment, or material*	*4,170*	*70*
Bruises or contusions	4,130	–		Fall to lower level	10,050	255
Heat burns	750	12		Fall on same level	7,170	7
Chemical burns	460	–		Slips or trips	2,590	–
Amputations	590	–		Overexertion	14,360	–
Carpal tunnel syndrome	610	–		*Overexertion in lifting*	*7,450*	*–*
Tendonitis	50	–		Repetitive motion	1,520	–
Multiple injuries	3,220	289		Exposed to harmful substance	3,170	126
Soreness or pain	7,690	–		Transportation incidents	2,930	188
Back pain	*3,020*	*–*		*Highway incident*	*1,680*	*98*
All other	13,820	443		*Nonhighway incident, except air, rail, and water*	*340*	*29*
				Pedestrian or nonpassenger struck by vehicle or mobile equipment	*650*	*45*
				Fires or explosions	220	26
				Assault or violent act	300	30
				Assault by person	*80*	*8*
				Other	*220*	*22*
				All other	7,930	–

Source: National Safety Council tabulations of Bureau of Labor Statistics data.
Note: Because of rounding and data exclusion of nonclassifiable responses, data may not sum to the totals. Dashes (–) indicate data that do not meet publication guidelines.
[a]*Days away from work include those that result in days away from work with or without restricted work activity or job transfer.*
[b]*In the fatalities column, non-Hispanic categories include cases with Hispanic origin not reported.*

The Manufacturing industry sector includes establishments engaged in the mechanical or chemical transformation of materials, substances, or components into new products. It includes durable and nondurable goods such as food, textiles, apparel, lumber, wood products, paper and paper products, printing, chemicals and pharmaceuticals, petroleum and coal products, rubber and plastics products, metals and metal products, machinery, electrical equipment, and transportation equipment.

Manufacturing employment in 2010 was 14,081,000 workers, of which 13,976,000 were private sector employees.

Number of nonfatal occupational injuries and illnesses involving days away from work[a] and fatal occupational injuries by selected worker and case characteristics, private industry, United States, Manufacturing, 2010

Characteristic	Nonfatal cases	Fatalities
Total	127,140	329
Sex		
Men	100,020	311
Women	27,090	18
Age		
Younger than 16	70	–
16 to 19	1,920	–
20 to 24	9,230	17
25 to 34	25,110	52
35 to 44	29,960	71
45 to 54	35,790	91
55 to 64	20,450	74
65 and older	2,740	23
Occupation		
Management, business, and financial	1,200	29
Professional and related	1,920	18
Service	2,830	8
Sales and related	610	6
Office and administrative support	4,120	8
Farming, fishing, and forestry	530	7
Construction and extractive	4,350	9
Installation, maintenance, and repair	9,410	49
Production	79,010	127
Transportation and material moving	22,910	68
Military occupations	–	–
Race or ethnic origin[b]		
White, non-Hispanic	64,840	244
Black, non-Hispanic	10,330	24
Hispanic	21,230	50
Other, multiple, and not reported	30,740	11
Nature of injury or illness		
Sprains or strains	41,990	–
Fractures	10,960	–
Cuts, lacerations, or punctures	14,570	20
Bruises or contusions	9,170	–
Heat burns	2,240	17
Chemical burns	1,070	–
Amputations	2,290	–
Carpal tunnel syndrome	3,180	–
Tendonitis	900	–
Multiple injuries	4,640	106
Soreness or pain	10,860	–
Back pain	3,430	–
All other	25,280	182

Characteristic	Nonfatal cases	Fatalities
Part of body affected		
Head	9,700	84
Eye	5,340	–
Neck	1,250	12
Trunk	39,410	42
Back	19,920	–
Shoulder	10,400	–
Upper extremities	41,650	–
Finger	18,470	–
Hand, except finger	6,470	–
Wrist	7,360	–
Lower extremities	23,490	6
Knee	8,860	–
Foot or toe	5,320	–
Body systems	1,800	59
Multiple	9,320	125
All other	520	–
Source of injury or illness		
Chemicals or chemical products	3,020	14
Containers	14,810	5
Furniture or fixtures	3,460	–
Machinery	15,660	47
Parts and materials	22,160	55
Worker motion or position	21,150	–
Floor or ground surfaces	17,820	41
Handtools	7,710	–
Vehicles	6,330	87
Health care patient	–	–
All other	14,240	73
Event or exposure		
Contact with object or equipment	45,500	93
Struck by object	19,080	48
Struck against object	9,600	–
Caught in object, equipment, or material	13,700	42
Fall to lower level	5,720	32
Fall on same level	13,140	10
Slips or trips	2,710	–
Overexertion	27,890	–
Overexertion in lifting	13,370	–
Repetitive motion	8,800	–
Exposed to harmful substance	7,110	30
Transportation incidents	2,650	84
Highway incident	890	55
Nonhighway incident, except air, rail, and water	590	7
Pedestrian or nonpassenger struck by vehicle or mobile equipment	1,040	13
Fires or explosions	190	33
Assault or violent act	290	45
Assault by person	140	14
Other	150	31
All other	13,150	–

Source: National Safety Council tabulations of Bureau of Labor Statistics data.
Note: Because of rounding and data exclusion of nonclassifiable responses, data may not sum to the totals. Dashes (–) indicate data that do not meet publication guidelines.
[a]Days away from work include those that result in days away from work with or without restricted work activity or job transfer.
[b]In the fatalities column, non-Hispanic categories include cases with Hispanic origin not reported.

Establishments in Wholesale Trade generally sell merchandise to other businesses. The merchandise includes the outputs of agriculture, mining, manufacturing, and certain information industries, such as publishing.

Wholesale Trade employed 3,805,000 people in 2010, of which 3,790,000 were private sector employees.

Number of nonfatal occupational injuries and illnesses involving days away from work[a] and fatal occupational injuries by selected worker and case characteristics, private industry, United States, Wholesale Trade, 2010

Characteristic	Nonfatal cases	Fatalities
Total	58,060	191
Sex		
Men	49,510	187
Women	8,530	–
Age		
Younger than 16	–	–
16 to 19	1,260	5
20 to 24	4,650	7
25 to 34	12,490	25
35 to 44	14,600	40
45 to 54	15,230	48
55 to 64	7,570	45
65 and older	1,530	21
Occupation		
Management, business, and financial	710	5
Professional and related	290	–
Service	810	6
Sales and related	5,700	39
Office and administrative support	5,180	6
Farming, fishing, and forestry	640	5
Construction and extractive	650	–
Installation, maintenance, and repair	6,340	19
Production	5,760	14
Transportation and material moving	31,920	93
Military occupations	–	–
Race or ethnic origin[b]		
White, non-Hispanic	30,700	145
Black, non-Hispanic	3,880	12
Hispanic	9,920	24
Other, multiple, and not reported	13,560	10
Nature of injury or illness		
Sprains or strains	24,730	–
Fractures	4,450	–
Cuts, lacerations, or punctures	3,950	23
Bruises or contusions	4,800	–
Heat burns	450	–
Chemical burns	310	–
Amputations	310	–
Carpal tunnel syndrome	510	–
Tendonitis	140	–
Multiple injuries	2,540	76
Soreness or pain	5,610	–
Back pain	2,020	–
All other	10,260	90

Characteristic	Nonfatal cases	Fatalities
Part of body affected		
Head	3,520	32
Eye	1,270	–
Neck	1,180	12
Trunk	20,750	35
Back	12,610	–
Shoulder	4,130	–
Upper extremities	11,970	–
Finger	4,530	–
Hand, except finger	1,770	–
Wrist	2,120	–
Lower extremities	13,480	–
Knee	5,050	–
Foot or toe	2,740	–
Body systems	1,120	28
Multiple	5,770	83
All other	270	–
Source of injury or illness		
Chemicals or chemical products	600	–
Containers	12,140	14
Furniture or fixtures	1,090	–
Machinery	2,920	16
Parts and materials	6,730	16
Worker motion or position	8,360	–
Floor or ground surfaces	9,490	15
Handtools	1,430	–
Vehicles	7,430	92
Health care patient	–	–
All other	6,680	33
Event or exposure		
Contact with object or equipment	15,200	48
Struck by object	7,800	24
Struck against object	3,870	–
Caught in object, equipment, or material	2,780	23
Fall to lower level	3,160	12
Fall on same level	7,150	–
Slips or trips	1,780	–
Overexertion	15,650	–
Overexertion in lifting	9,100	–
Repetitive motion	1,750	–
Exposed to harmful substance	2,200	7
Transportation incidents	3,750	81
Highway incident	2,580	64
Nonhighway incident, except air, rail, and water	630	–
Pedestrian or nonpassenger struck by vehicle or mobile equipment	450	8
Fires or explosions	90	6
Assault or violent act	400	35
Assault by person	160	22
Other	250	13
All other	6,910	–

Source: National Safety Council tabulations of Bureau of Labor Statistics data.
Note: Because of rounding and data exclusion of nonclassifiable responses, data may not sum to the totals. Dashes (–) indicate data that do not meet publication guidelines.
[a]Days away from work include those that result in days away from work with or without restricted work activity or job transfer.
[b]In the fatalities column, non-Hispanic categories include cases with Hispanic origin not reported.

Establishments in Retail Trade generally sell merchandise in small quantities for personal or household consumption. This sector includes both store and nonstore retailers.

Retail Trade employed 15,933,000 people in 2010, of which 15,833,000 were private sector employees.

Number of nonfatal occupational injuries and illnesses involving days away from work[a] and fatal occupational injuries by selected worker and case characteristics, private industry, United States, Retail Trade, 2010

Characteristic	Nonfatal cases	Fatalities
Total	131,380	311
Sex		
Men	74,470	272
Women	56,850	39
Age		
Younger than 16	30	–
16 to 19	5,280	–
20 to 24	17,560	23
25 to 34	26,950	45
35 to 44	25,780	54
45 to 54	28,480	69
55 to 64	19,020	63
65 and older	6,420	51
Occupation		
Management, business, and financial	2,190	6
Professional and related	1,390	–
Service	13,490	14
Sales and related	49,460	185
Office and administrative support	15,530	10
Farming, fishing, and forestry	100	–
Construction and extractive	900	–
Installation, maintenance, and repair	14,340	24
Production	6,730	8
Transportation and material moving	27,100	60
Military occupations	–	–
Race or ethnic origin[b]		
White, non-Hispanic	49,470	208
Black, non-Hispanic	6,630	21
Hispanic	11,870	44
Other, multiple, and not reported	63,410	38
Nature of injury or illness		
Sprains or strains	53,640	–
Fractures	8,130	5
Cuts, lacerations, or punctures	13,280	143
Bruises or contusions	12,950	–
Heat burns	1,470	–
Chemical burns	530	–
Amputations	450	–
Carpal tunnel syndrome	910	–
Tendonitis	680	–
Multiple injuries	5,190	49
Soreness or pain	13,370	–
Back pain	4,440	–
All other	20,790	107

Characteristic	Nonfatal cases	Fatalities
Part of body affected		
Head	9,430	93
Eye	3,080	–
Neck	1,590	11
Trunk	46,510	83
Back	29,030	–
Shoulder	9,390	–
Upper extremities	29,130	–
Finger	11,170	–
Hand, except finger	5,420	–
Wrist	4,930	–
Lower extremities	29,060	8
Knee	11,120	–
Foot or toe	7,680	–
Body systems	1,980	27
Multiple	12,590	87
All other	1,090	–
Source of injury or illness		
Chemicals or chemical products	1,670	9
Containers	26,300	–
Furniture or fixtures	9,320	–
Machinery	7,890	6
Parts and materials	10,790	10
Worker motion or position	17,770	–
Floor or ground surfaces	24,310	35
Handtools	6,190	13
Vehicles	10,850	75
Health care patient	20	–
All other	13,670	158
Event or exposure		
Contact with object or equipment	38,910	24
Struck by object	21,650	15
Struck against object	10,350	–
Caught in object, equipment, or material	4,860	8
Fall to lower level	6,720	21
Fall on same level	18,600	17
Slips or trips	3,660	–
Overexertion	34,060	–
Overexertion in lifting	21,520	–
Repetitive motion	3,840	–
Exposed to harmful substance	3,840	16
Transportation incidents	3,990	62
Highway incident	1,970	45
Nonhighway incident, except air, rail, and water	480	–
Pedestrian or nonpassenger struck by vehicle or mobile equipment	1,300	12
Fires or explosions	220	7
Assault or violent act	1,320	163
Assault by person	990	135
Other	330	28
All other	16,230	–

Source: National Safety Council tabulations of Bureau of Labor Statistics data.
Note: Because of rounding and data exclusion of nonclassifiable responses, data may not sum to the totals. Dashes (–) indicate data that do not meet publication guidelines.
[a]Days away from work include those that result in days away from work with or without restricted work activity or job transfer.
[b]In the fatalities column, non-Hispanic categories include cases with Hispanic origin not reported.

This industry sector includes transportation of cargo and passengers, warehousing and storage of goods, scenic and sightseeing transportation, and support activities related to transportation by rail, highway, air, water, or pipeline.

Employment in the Transportation and Warehousing industry sector totaled 5,881,000 in 2010, of which 4,800,000 were private sector employees.

Number of nonfatal occupational injuries and illnesses involving days away from work[a] and fatal occupational injuries by selected worker and case characteristics, private industry, United States, Transportation and Warehousing[b], 2010

Characteristic	Nonfatal cases	Fatalities
Total	**89,540**	**661**
Sex		
Men	68,530	629
Women	17,630	32
Age		
Younger than 16	–	–
16 to 19	570	5
20 to 24	4,490	22
25 to 34	14,880	95
35 to 44	23,080	116
45 to 54	28,450	195
55 to 64	14,400	173
65 and older	2,840	54
Occupation		
Management, business, and financial	610	6
Professional and related	290	–
Service	6,670	–
Sales and related	200	–
Office and administrative support	7,920	5
Farming, fishing, and forestry	40	–
Construction and extractive	940	–
Installation, maintenance, and repair	6,370	20
Production	1,610	–
Transportation and material moving	64,740	620
Military occupations	–	–
Race or ethnic origin[c]		
White, non-Hispanic	25,090	444
Black, non-Hispanic	5,350	92
Hispanic	5,710	91
Other, multiple, and not reported	53,390	34
Nature of injury or illness		
Sprains or strains	43,300	–
Fractures	5,240	–
Cuts, lacerations, or punctures	3,750	47
Bruises or contusions	7,780	–
Heat burns	200	28
Chemical burns	270	–
Amputations	230	–
Carpal tunnel syndrome	350	–
Tendonitis	180	–
Multiple injuries	3,590	324
Soreness or pain	10,800	–
Back pain	3,390	–
All other	13,850	255

Characteristic	Nonfatal cases	Fatalities
Part of body affected		
Head	5,630	109
Eye	2,040	–
Neck	1,490	9
Trunk	34,470	94
Back	18,980	–
Shoulder	9,050	–
Upper extremities	13,070	–
Finger	3,810	–
Hand, except finger	2,340	–
Wrist	2,520	–
Lower extremities	22,730	7
Knee	8,370	–
Foot or toe	4,030	–
Body systems	1,240	75
Multiple	10,380	366
All other	530	–
Source of injury or illness		
Chemicals or chemical products	900	21
Containers	17,630	6
Furniture or fixtures	1,700	–
Machinery	1,900	13
Parts and materials	7,730	22
Worker motion or position	12,250	–
Floor or ground surfaces	16,910	41
Handtools	1,670	6
Vehicles	18,920	479
Health care patient	140	–
All other	8,710	72
Event or exposure		
Contact with object or equipment	19,280	63
Struck by object	8,580	32
Struck against object	6,090	–
Caught in object, equipment, or material	3,230	30
Fall to lower level	6,640	29
Fall on same level	11,040	10
Slips or trips	3,130	–
Overexertion	24,370	–
Overexertion in lifting	11,770	–
Repetitive motion	1,680	–
Exposed to harmful substance	2,470	27
Transportation incidents	8,610	451
Highway incident	5,820	328
Nonhighway incident, except air, rail, and water	1,100	8
Pedestrian or nonpassenger struck by vehicle or mobile equipment	820	48
Fires or explosions	50	10
Assault or violent act	580	66
Assault by person	370	44
Other	210	22
All other	11,680	–

Source: National Safety Council tabulations of Bureau of Labor Statistics (BLS) data.
Note: Because of rounding and data exclusion of nonclassifiable responses, data may not sum to the totals. Dashes (–) indicate data that do not meet publication guidelines.
[a]Days away from work include those that result in days away from work with or without restricted work activity or job transfer.
[b]Data for employees in railroad transportation are provided to BLS by the Federal Railroad Administration (FRA), U.S. Department of Transportation. FRA data do not reflect the changes in OSHA recordkeeping requirements in 2002.
[c]In the fatalities column, non-Hispanic categories include cases with Hispanic origin not reported.

The Utilities sector includes establishments that provide electric power generation, transmission, and distribution; natural gas distribution; steam supply; water treatment and distribution; and sewage collection, treatment, and disposal.

The Utilities sector employed 1,253,000 people in 2010, of which 908,000 were private sector employees.

Number of nonfatal occupational injuries and illnesses involving days away from work[a] and fatal occupational injuries by selected worker and case characteristics, private industry, United States, Utilities, 2010

Characteristic	Nonfatal cases	Fatalities
Total	5,650	26
Sex		
Men	4,990	26
Women	670	–
Age		
Younger than 16	–	–
16 to 19	20	–
20 to 24	200	–
25 to 34	1,140	–
35 to 44	1,270	5
45 to 54	1,790	11
55 to 64	1,130	5
65 and older	100	–
Occupation		
Management, business, and financial	150	–
Professional and related	180	–
Service	120	–
Sales and related	60	–
Office and administrative support	790	–
Farming, fishing, and forestry	–	–
Construction and extractive	580	–
Installation, maintenance, and repair	2,970	13
Production	520	–
Transportation and material moving	280	–
Military occupations	–	–
Race or ethnic origin[b]		
White, non-Hispanic	2,710	22
Black, non-Hispanic	190	–
Hispanic	270	–
Other, multiple, and not reported	2,480	–
Nature of injury or illness		
Sprains or strains	2,690	–
Fractures	540	–
Cuts, lacerations, or punctures	310	–
Bruises or contusions	360	–
Heat burns	20	–
Chemical burns	20	–
Amputations	30	–
Carpal tunnel syndrome	100	–
Tendonitis	20	–
Multiple injuries	150	6
Soreness or pain	370	–
Back pain	110	–
All other	1,040	20

Characteristic	Nonfatal cases	Fatalities
Part of body affected		
Head	240	–
Eye	50	–
Neck	80	–
Trunk	1,940	–
Back	1,070	–
Shoulder	490	–
Upper extremities	1,090	–
Finger	290	–
Hand, except finger	210	–
Wrist	210	–
Lower extremities	1,810	–
Knee	930	–
Foot or toe	170	–
Body systems	50	14
Multiple	400	7
All other	30	–
Source of injury or illness		
Chemicals or chemical products	100	–
Containers	280	–
Furniture or fixtures	30	–
Machinery	240	–
Parts and materials	780	9
Worker motion or position	1,300	–
Floor or ground surfaces	1,190	–
Handtools	510	–
Vehicles	420	5
Health care patient	–	–
All other	750	6
Event or exposure		
Contact with object or equipment	950	–
Struck by object	480	–
Struck against object	240	–
Caught in object, equipment, or material	170	–
Fall to lower level	360	–
Fall on same level	770	–
Slips or trips	210	–
Overexertion	1,210	–
Overexertion in lifting	390	–
Repetitive motion	350	–
Exposed to harmful substance	360	12
Transportation incidents	310	6
Highway incident	240	5
Nonhighway incident, except air, rail, and water	20	–
Pedestrian or nonpassenger struck by vehicle or mobile equipment	20	–
Fires or explosions	20	–
Assault or violent act	90	–
Assault by person	–	–
Other	90	–
All other	1,020	–

Source: National Safety Council tabulations of Bureau of Labor Statistics data.
Note: Because of rounding and data exclusion of nonclassifiable responses, data may not sum to the totals. Dashes (–) indicate data that do not meet publication guidelines.
[a]Days away from work include those that result in days away from work with or without restricted work activity or job transfer.
[b]In the fatalities column, non-Hispanic categories include cases with Hispanic origin not reported.

The Information sector includes establishments that produce and distribute information and cultural products, provide the means to transmit or distribute these products as well as data or communications, and process data. Included are both traditional and Internet publishing and broadcasting, motion pictures and sound recordings, telecommunications, Internet service providers, Web search portals, data processing, and information services.

The Information sector employed 3,150,000 people in 2010, of which 2,962,000 were private sector employees.

Number of nonfatal occupational injuries and illnesses involving days away from work[a] and fatal occupational injuries by selected worker and case characteristics, private industry, United States, Information, 2010

Characteristic	Nonfatal cases	Fatalities
Total	19,330	43
Sex		
Men	14,220	37
Women	5,110	6
Age		
Younger than 16	–	–
16 to 19	290	–
20 to 24	700	–
25 to 34	4,270	9
35 to 44	5,720	10
45 to 54	5,110	12
55 to 64	2,710	7
65 and older	300	–
Occupation		
Management, business, and financial	580	–
Professional and related	2,350	–
Service	760	–
Sales and related	960	–
Office and administrative support	2,900	–
Farming, fishing, and forestry	–	–
Construction and extractive	140	–
Installation, maintenance, and repair	9,490	18
Production	890	–
Transportation and material moving	1,260	9
Military occupations	–	–
Race or ethnic origin[b]		
White, non-Hispanic	4,660	35
Black, non-Hispanic	860	–
Hispanic	830	–
Other, multiple, and not reported	12,980	–
Nature of injury or illness		
Sprains or strains	9,230	–
Fractures	1,100	–
Cuts, lacerations, or punctures	800	–
Bruises or contusions	1,590	–
Heat burns	80	–
Chemical burns	–	–
Amputations	20	–
Carpal tunnel syndrome	230	–
Tendonitis	70	–
Multiple injuries	1,160	21
Soreness or pain	1,600	–
Back pain	540	–
All other	3,460	18

Characteristic	Nonfatal cases	Fatalities
Part of body affected		
Head	1,050	9
Eye	380	–
Neck	250	–
Trunk	7,020	–
Back	4,310	–
Shoulder	1,430	–
Upper extremities	3,060	–
Finger	840	–
Hand, except finger	480	–
Wrist	830	–
Lower extremities	4,610	–
Knee	1,820	–
Foot or toe	700	–
Body systems	450	6
Multiple	2,820	22
All other	80	–
Source of injury or illness		
Chemicals or chemical products	140	–
Containers	1,030	–
Furniture or fixtures	870	–
Machinery	670	–
Parts and materials	1,250	5
Worker motion or position	4,220	–
Floor or ground surfaces	5,130	6
Handtools	510	–
Vehicles	1,640	21
Health care patient	–	–
All other	3,580	6
Event or exposure		
Contact with object or equipment	3,420	–
Struck by object	1,710	–
Struck against object	1,160	–
Caught in object, equipment, or material	310	–
Fall to lower level	1,600	–
Fall on same level	3,660	–
Slips or trips	700	–
Overexertion	3,620	–
Overexertion in lifting	1,560	–
Repetitive motion	1,010	–
Exposed to harmful substance	640	–
Transportation incidents	1,130	21
Highway incident	890	20
Nonhighway incident, except air, rail, and water	70	–
Pedestrian or nonpassenger struck by vehicle or mobile equipment	50	–
Fires or explosions	–	–
Assault or violent act	280	11
Assault by person	50	–
Other	230	9
All other	3,270	–

Source: National Safety Council tabulations of Bureau of Labor Statistics data.
Note: Because of rounding and data exclusion of nonclassifiable responses, data may not sum to the totals. Dashes (–) indicate data that do not meet publication guidelines.
[a]Days away from work include those that result in days away from work with or without restricted work activity or job transfer.
[b]In the fatalities column, non-Hispanic categories include cases with Hispanic origin not reported.

Financial Activities includes the Finance and Insurance sector and the Real Estate and Rental and Leasing sector. Included are banks and other savings institutions; securities and commodities brokers, dealers, exchanges, and services; insurance carriers, brokers, and agents; real estate operators, developers, agents, and brokers; and establishments that rent and lease goods, such as automobiles, computers, and household and industrial machinery and equipment.

Financial Activities had 9,350,000 workers in 2010, of which 9,130,000 were private sector employees.

Number of nonfatal occupational injuries and illnesses involving days away from work[a] and fatal occupational injuries by selected worker and case characteristics, private industry, United States, Financial Activities, 2010

Characteristic	Nonfatal cases	Fatalities
Total	**27,480**	**113**
Sex		
Men	14,280	92
Women	13,200	21
Age		
Younger than 16	–	–
16 to 19	180	–
20 to 24	1,250	–
25 to 34	5,120	13
35 to 44	6,480	15
45 to 54	8,460	40
55 to 64	4,390	21
65 and older	850	19
Occupation		
Management, business, and financial	3,730	32
Professional and related	670	–
Service	5,730	14
Sales and related	2,090	24
Office and administrative support	7,750	–
Farming, fishing, and forestry	100	–
Construction and extractive	570	6
Installation, maintenance, and repair	3,540	20
Production	240	–
Transportation and material moving	3,040	11
Military occupations	–	–
Race or ethnic origin[b]		
White, non-Hispanic	11,040	78
Black, non-Hispanic	1,900	11
Hispanic	3,880	19
Other, multiple, and not reported	10,660	5
Nature of injury or illness		
Sprains or strains	9,260	–
Fractures	3,200	–
Cuts, lacerations, or punctures	1,360	33
Bruises or contusions	1,850	–
Heat burns	100	–
Chemical burns	30	–
Amputations	60	–
Carpal tunnel syndrome	560	–
Tendonitis	470	–
Multiple injuries	1,720	29
Soreness or pain	3,340	–
Back pain	1,190	–
All other	5,540	51

Characteristic	Nonfatal cases	Fatalities
Part of body affected		
Head	1,580	28
Eye	260	–
Neck	160	6
Trunk	8,160	21
Back	4,830	–
Shoulder	1,860	–
Upper extremities	5,290	–
Finger	1,210	–
Hand, except finger	830	–
Wrist	1,430	–
Lower extremities	7,430	–
Knee	3,280	–
Foot or toe	840	–
Body systems	970	20
Multiple	3,780	36
All other	110	–
Source of injury or illness		
Chemicals or chemical products	350	–
Containers	2,070	–
Furniture or fixtures	1,720	–
Machinery	2,320	–
Parts and materials	630	9
Worker motion or position	4,290	–
Floor or ground surfaces	7,860	20
Handtools	1,010	–
Vehicles	2,440	28
Health care patient	110	–
All other	3,090	41
Event or exposure		
Contact with object or equipment	4,790	–
Struck by object	2,040	–
Struck against object	1,410	–
Caught in object, equipment, or material	820	–
Fall to lower level	3,210	18
Fall on same level	5,110	–
Slips or trips	930	–
Overexertion	5,370	–
Overexertion in lifting	2,900	–
Repetitive motion	1,770	–
Exposed to harmful substance	930	10
Transportation incidents	1,460	29
Highway incident	910	18
Nonhighway incident, except air, rail, and water	100	–
Pedestrian or nonpassenger struck by vehicle or mobile equipment	140	–
Fires or explosions	20	–
Assault or violent act	1,150	49
Assault by person	890	32
Other	260	17
All other	2,750	–

Source: National Safety Council tabulations of Bureau of Labor Statistics data.
Note: Because of rounding and data exclusion of nonclassifiable responses, data may not sum to the totals. Dashes (–) indicate data that do not meet publication guidelines.
[a]Days away from work include those that result in days away from work with or without restricted work activity or job transfer.
[b]In the fatalities column, non-Hispanic categories include cases with Hispanic origin not reported.

The Professional and Business Services sector includes legal, accounting, architectural, engineering, computer, consulting, research, advertising, photographic, translation and interpretation, veterinary, and other professional scientific and technical services. Also included are business management and administrative and support activities and waste management and remediation services.

Professional and Business Services employed 15,252,000 people in 2010, of which 14,843,000 were private sector employees.

Number of nonfatal occupational injuries and illnesses involving days away from work[a] and fatal occupational injuries by selected worker and case characteristics, private industry, United States, Professional and Business Services, 2010

Characteristic	Nonfatal cases	Fatalities
Total	75,890	364
Sex		
Men	47,640	347
Women	28,240	17
Age		
Younger than 16	–	–
16 to 19	710	–
20 to 24	7,460	36
25 to 34	17,090	72
35 to 44	16,590	74
45 to 54	19,060	101
55 to 64	10,580	50
65 and older	2,180	28
Occupation		
Management, business, and financial	3,550	22
Professional and related	7,600	21
Service	29,970	201
Sales and related	1,640	5
Office and administrative support	8,050	–
Farming, fishing, and forestry	220	–
Construction and extractive	3,250	12
Installation, maintenance, and repair	4,620	18
Production	4,320	17
Transportation and material moving	12,440	61
Military occupations	–	–
Race or ethnic origin[b]		
White, non-Hispanic	30,000	247
Black, non-Hispanic	5,230	45
Hispanic	13,040	63
Other, multiple, and not reported	27,620	9
Nature of injury or illness		
Sprains or strains	27,170	–
Fractures	6,540	–
Cuts, lacerations, or punctures	6,440	36
Bruises or contusions	5,000	–
Heat burns	350	–
Chemical burns	280	–
Amputations	360	–
Carpal tunnel syndrome	760	–
Tendonitis	250	–
Multiple injuries	3,810	149
Soreness or pain	8,840	–
Back pain	2,230	–
All other	16,080	171

Characteristic	Nonfatal cases	Fatalities
Part of body affected		
Head	5,400	73
Eye	1,320	–
Neck	990	11
Trunk	21,870	46
Back	12,220	–
Shoulder	4,450	–
Upper extremities	17,210	–
Finger	5,680	–
Hand, except finger	4,030	–
Wrist	3,490	–
Lower extremities	18,990	7
Knee	7,710	–
Foot or toe	3,140	–
Body systems	1,860	67
Multiple	9,070	159
All other	500	–
Source of injury or illness		
Chemicals or chemical products	940	14
Containers	7,440	–
Furniture or fixtures	2,090	–
Machinery	4,090	35
Parts and materials	4,750	19
Worker motion or position	11,150	–
Floor or ground surfaces	19,430	63
Handtools	4,260	6
Vehicles	7,500	139
Health care patient	860	–
All other	11,680	83
Event or exposure		
Contact with object or equipment	19,030	59
Struck by object	9,650	42
Struck against object	5,570	–
Caught in object, equipment, or material	2,810	17
Fall to lower level	6,290	54
Fall on same level	12,740	6
Slips or trips	2,410	–
Overexertion	13,210	–
Overexertion in lifting	6,690	–
Repetitive motion	2,470	–
Exposed to harmful substance	3,080	44
Transportation incidents	4,310	144
Highway incident	2,780	64
Nonhighway incident, except air, rail, and water	620	28
Pedestrian or nonpassenger struck by vehicle or mobile equipment	800	37
Fires or explosions	90	–
Assault or violent act	3,000	48
Assault by person	880	20
Other	2,120	28
All other	9,260	5

Source: National Safety Council tabulations of Bureau of Labor Statistics data.
Note: Because of rounding and data exclusion of nonclassifiable responses, data may not sum to the totals. Dashes (–) indicate data that do not meet publication guidelines.
[a]Days away from work include those that result in days away from work with or without restricted work activity.
[b]In the fatalities column, non-Hispanic categories include cases with Hispanic origin not reported.

Educational Services includes instruction and training through schools, colleges, universities, and training centers. Health Services includes ambulatory health care facilities, hospitals, nursing and residential care facilities, and social assistance for individuals, families, and communities.

Educational and Health Services employed 32,063,000 people in 2010, of which 21,383,000 were private sector employees.

Number of nonfatal occupational injuries and illnesses involving days away from work[a] and fatal occupational injuries by selected worker and case characteristics, private industry, United States, Educational and Health Services, 2010

Characteristic	Nonfatal cases	Fatalities
Total	**186,830**	**171**
Sex		
Men	36,970	102
Women	149,740	69
Age		
Younger than 16	20	–
16 to 19	2,170	–
20 to 24	15,270	–
25 to 34	41,710	32
35 to 44	41,000	41
45 to 54	47,670	34
55 to 64	30,490	34
65 and older	5,890	26
Occupation		
Management, business, and financial	5,420	13
Professional and related	61,560	–
Service	100,030	105
Sales and related	460	–
Office and administrative support	10,410	–
Farming, fishing, and forestry	40	–
Construction and extractive	1,020	–
Installation, maintenance, and repair	2,800	–
Production	1,630	–
Transportation and material moving	3,360	38
Military occupations	–	–
Race or ethnic origin[b]		
White, non-Hispanic	79,190	137
Black, non-Hispanic	26,300	19
Hispanic	15,200	9
Other, multiple, and not reported	66,140	6
Nature of injury or illness		
Sprains or strains	89,370	–
Fractures	10,380	8
Cuts, lacerations, or punctures	6,450	27
Bruises or contusions	17,020	–
Heat burns	1,890	–
Chemical burns	590	–
Amputations	110	–
Carpal tunnel syndrome	840	–
Tendonitis	870	–
Multiple injuries	9,330	74
Soreness or pain	24,520	–
Back pain	8,640	–
All other	25,460	60

Characteristic	Nonfatal cases	Fatalities
Part of body affected		
Head	10,750	34
Eye	2,560	–
Neck	3,440	
Trunk	73,170	11
Back	49,110	–
Shoulder	14,180	–
Upper extremities	29,180	–
Finger	7,730	–
Hand, except finger	4,640	–
Wrist	7,640	–
Lower extremities	37,020	6
Knee	15,880	–
Foot or toe	6,250	–
Body systems	2,980	28
Multiple	29,220	86
All other	1,070	–
Source of injury or illness		
Chemicals or chemical products	2,270	17
Containers	9,730	–
Furniture or fixtures	9,590	–
Machinery	4,070	–
Parts and materials	2,200	8
Worker motion or position	21,480	–
Floor or ground surfaces	42,970	26
Handtools	2,410	6
Vehicles	10,180	81
Health care patient	53,800	–
All other	22,920	29
Event or exposure		
Contact with object or equipment	28,190	–
Struck by object	13,560	–
Struck against object	9,770	–
Caught in object, equipment, or material	3,560	–
Fall to lower level	7,480	14
Fall on same level	35,970	12
Slips or trips	6,260	–
Overexertion	61,380	–
Overexertion in lifting	25,020	–
Repetitive motion	3,840	–
Exposed to harmful substance	7,460	22
Transportation incidents	6,490	77
Highway incident	5,150	35
Nonhighway incident, except air, rail, and water	390	–
Pedestrian or nonpassenger struck by vehicle or mobile equipment	550	9
Fires or explosions	90	–
Assault or violent act	12,920	38
Assault by person	11,970	22
Other	960	16
All other	16,760	–

Source: National Safety Council tabulations of Bureau of Labor Statistics data.
Note: Because of rounding and data exclusion of nonclassifiable responses, data may not sum to the totals. Dashes (–) indicate data that do not meet publication guidelines.
[a]Days away from work include those that result in days away from work with or without restricted work activity.
[b]In the fatalities column, non-Hispanic categories include cases with Hispanic origin not reported.

The Leisure sector includes establishments that provide arts, entertainment, and recreation experiences such as theatre, dance, music, and spectator sports, museums, zoos, amusement and theme parks, casinos, golf courses, ski areas, marinas, and fitness and sports centers. The Hospitality sector includes hotels and other traveler accommodations, food services, and drinking places.

The Leisure and Hospitality sector employed 12,530,000 people in 2010, of which 12,128,000 were private sector employees.

Number of nonfatal occupational injuries and illnesses involving days away from work[a] and fatal occupational injuries by selected worker and case characteristics, private industry, United States, Leisure and Hospitality, 2010

Characteristic	Nonfatal cases	Fatalities
Total	88,740	238
Sex		
Men	43,640	195
Women	45,040	43
Age		
Younger than 16	40	–
16 to 19	7,260	5
20 to 24	15,260	21
25 to 34	21,060	44
35 to 44	15,870	31
45 to 54	16,290	63
55 to 64	9,290	46
65 and older	2,480	27
Occupation		
Management, business, and financial	2,320	34
Professional and related	3,070	–
Service	72,620	152
Sales and related	2,430	6
Office and administrative support	1,680	–
Farming, fishing, and forestry	20	–
Construction and extractive	800	–
Installation, maintenance, and repair	2,160	11
Production	960	–
Transportation and material moving	2,630	30
Military occupations	–	–
Race or ethnic origin[b]		
White, non-Hispanic	30,670	140
Black, non-Hispanic	6,750	29
Hispanic	16,440	49
Other, multiple, and not reported	34,880	20
Nature of injury or illness		
Sprains or strains	27,390	–
Fractures	4,790	–
Cuts, lacerations, or punctures	15,480	79
Bruises or contusions	8,340	–
Heat burns	6,340	–
Chemical burns	360	–
Amputations	350	–
Carpal tunnel syndrome	200	–
Tendonitis	250	–
Multiple injuries	3,110	58
Soreness or pain	9,520	–
Back pain	2,500	–
All other	12,600	93

Characteristic	Nonfatal cases	Fatalities
Part of body affected		
Head	5,370	44
Eye	1,260	–
Neck	570	5
Trunk	21,820	52
Back	13,120	–
Shoulder	4,680	–
Upper extremities	29,980	–
Finger	11,770	–
Hand, except finger	7,570	–
Wrist	3,320	–
Lower extremities	21,090	6
Knee	8,500	–
Foot or toe	3,590	–
Body systems	1,470	38
Multiple	7,360	92
All other	1,080	–
Source of injury or illness		
Chemicals or chemical products	1,460	14
Containers	14,160	–
Furniture or fixtures	4,980	–
Machinery	5,080	6
Parts and materials	1,660	7
Worker motion or position	10,850	–
Floor or ground surfaces	21,600	25
Handtools	7,500	12
Vehicles	2,960	68
Health care patient	30	–
All other	15,960	104
Event or exposure		
Contact with object or equipment	26,910	11
Struck by object	15,890	6
Struck against object	8,120	–
Caught in object, equipment, or material	1,960	–
Fall to lower level	4,140	13
Fall on same level	17,610	11
Slips or trips	3,250	–
Overexertion	13,870	–
Overexertion in lifting	7,940	–
Repetitive motion	1,970	–
Exposed to harmful substance	9,370	26
Transportation incidents	1,030	67
Highway incident	390	25
Nonhighway incident, except air, rail, and water	340	12
Pedestrian or nonpassenger struck by vehicle or mobile equipment	280	13
Fires or explosions	110	–
Assault or violent act	1,310	104
Assault by person	1,140	84
Other	180	20
All other	9,180	–

Source: National Safety Council tabulations of Bureau of Labor Statistics data.
Note: Because of rounding and data exclusion of nonclassifiable responses, data may not sum to the totals. Dashes (–) indicate data that do not meet publication guidelines.
[a]Days away from work include those that result in days away from work with or without restricted work activity or job transfer.
[b]In the fatalities column, non-Hispanic categories include cases with Hispanic origin not reported.

The Other Services sector includes repair and maintenance of equipment and machinery and personal and household goods; personal care and laundry services; and religious, grant making, civic, professional, and similar organizations.

The Other Services sector employed 6,769,000 people in 2010, of which 6,741,000 were private sector employees.

Number of nonfatal occupational injuries and illnesses involving days away from work[a] and fatal occupational injuries by selected worker and case characteristics, private industry, United States, Other Services (except Public Administration), 2010

Characteristic	Nonfatal cases	Fatalities
Total	**27,260**	**192**
Sex		
Men	18,960	168
Women	8,300	24
Age		
Younger than 16	–	–
16 to 19	630	–
20 to 24	3,480	8
25 to 34	6,300	34
35 to 44	4,900	45
45 to 54	7,770	38
55 to 64	3,110	37
65 and older	850	26
Occupation		
Management, business, and financial	1,350	33
Professional and related	1,520	–
Service	5,130	43
Sales and related	1,800	5
Office and administrative support	1,390	–
Farming, fishing, and forestry	160	–
Construction and extractive	500	–
Installation, maintenance, and repair	8,430	80
Production	2,610	11
Transportation and material moving	4,370	16
Military occupations	–	–
Race or ethnic origin[b]		
White, non-Hispanic	15,150	125
Black, non-Hispanic	2,630	19
Hispanic	3,230	32
Other, multiple, and not reported	6,250	16
Nature of injury or illness		
Sprains or strains	8,530	–
Fractures	2,190	–
Cuts, lacerations, or punctures	1,810	44
Bruises or contusions	2,080	–
Heat burns	470	–
Chemical burns	100	–
Amputations	260	–
Carpal tunnel syndrome	190	–
Tendonitis	60	–
Multiple injuries	1,830	65
Soreness or pain	3,590	–
Back pain	1,330	–
All other	6,150	78

Characteristic	Nonfatal cases	Fatalities
Part of body affected		
Head	2,310	37
Eye	1,230	–
Neck	320	13
Trunk	7,430	32
Back	4,670	6
Shoulder	1,420	–
Upper extremities	5,370	–
Finger	1,610	–
Hand, except finger	1,180	–
Wrist	950	–
Lower extremities	7,270	–
Knee	3,040	–
Foot or toe	900	–
Body systems	820	25
Multiple	3,580	81
All other	160	–
Source of injury or illness		
Chemicals or chemical products	570	7
Containers	2,480	–
Furniture or fixtures	1,040	–
Machinery	740	12
Parts or materials	2,650	18
Worker motion or position	3,670	–
Floor or ground surfaces	7,110	21
Handtools	1,290	–
Vehicles	2,470	72
Health care patient	170	–
All other	4,180	57
Event or exposure		
Contact with object or equipment	6,710	28
Struck by object	3,090	17
Struck against object	2,550	–
Caught in object, equipment, or material	830	11
Fall to lower level	2,520	17
Fall on same level	4,200	–
Slips or trips	880	–
Overexertion	4,900	–
Overexertion in lifting	2,580	–
Repetitive motion	620	–
Exposed to harmful substance	1,200	8
Transportation incidents	1,040	58
Highway incident	510	35
Nonhighway incident, except air, rail, and water	70	8
Pedestrian or nonpassenger struck by vehicle or mobile equipment	240	14
Fires or explosions	240	14
Assault or violent act	1,000	63
Assault by person	230	42
Other	770	21
All other	3,970	–

Source: National Safety Council tabulations of Bureau of Labor Statistics data.
Note: Because of rounding and data exclusion of nonclassifiable responses, data may not sum to the totals. Dashes (–) indicate data that do not meet publication guidelines.
[a]Days away from work include those that result in days away from work with or without restricted work activity or job transfer.
[b]In the fatalities column, non-Hispanic categories include cases with Hispanic origin not reported.

Government includes public employees at all levels from federal (civilian and military) to state, county, and municipal.

Total government employment was 22,284,000 in 2010, of which 18,424,000 were state and local government employees.

Number of nonfatal occupational injuries and illnesses involving days away from work[a] and fatal occupational injuries by selected worker and case characteristics, United States, Government, 2010

Characteristic	State and local government nonfatal cases[b]	All government fatalities
Total	**257,900**	**484**
Sex		
Men	148,230	419
Women	106,910	65
Age		
Younger than 16	20	–
16 to 19	1,550	9
20 to 24	9,250	29
25 to 34	42,110	111
35 to 44	65,270	85
45 to 54	79,410	95
55 to 64	47,180	103
65 and older	6,880	52
Occupation		
Management, business, and financial	4,820	20
Professional and related	54,210	22
Service	131,900	263
Sales and related	1,110	–
Office and administrative support	12,780	25
Farming, fishing, and forestry	430	–
Construction and extractive	14,470	31
Installation, maintenance, and repair	12,450	27
Production	4,130	9
Transportation and material moving	19,900	38
Military occupations	–	46
Race or ethnic origin[c]		
White, non-Hispanic	100,400	368
Black, non-Hispanic	21,210	66
Hispanic	16,190	33
Other, multiple, and not reported	120,100	17
Nature of injury or illness		
Sprains or strains	103,880	–
Fractures	16,110	7
Cuts, lacerations, or punctures	13,080	103
Bruises or contusions	23,420	–
Heat burns	1,760	5
Chemical burns	450	–
Amputations	280	–
Carpal tunnel syndrome	1,570	–
Tendonitis	810	–
Multiple injuries	16,030	183
Soreness or pain	32,780	–
Back pain	7,680	–
All other	47,740	179

Characteristic	State and local government nonfatal cases[b]	All government fatalities
Part of body affected		
Head	14,630	121
Eye	2,850	
Neck	4,030	21
Trunk	76,150	53
Back	42,460	8
Shoulder	19,000	–
Upper extremities	43,850	–
Finger	12,550	–
Hand, except finger	8,770	–
Wrist	8,030	–
Lower extremities	62,130	11
Knee	27,060	–
Foot or toe	9,040	–
Body systems	6,760	57
Multiple	47,450	217
All other	2,900	–
Source of injury or illness		
Chemicals or chemical products	2,530	8
Containers	16,330	–
Furniture or fixtures	10,840	–
Machinery	6,390	13
Parts and materials	9,170	11
Worker motion or position	36,850	–
Floor or ground surfaces	63,650	39
Handtools	7,020	–
Vehicles	24,670	241
Health care patient	17,600	–
All other	35,460	484
Event or exposure		
Contact with object or equipment	42,980	32
Struck by object	19,400	18
Struck against object	16,200	–
Caught in object, equipment, or material	4,290	12
Fall to lower level	14,080	15
Fall on same level	42,740	16
Slips or trips	9,560	–
Overexertion	49,200	–
Overexertion in lifting	21,240	–
Repetitive motion	4,840	–
Exposed to harmful substance	9,950	24
Transportation incidents	17,260	237
Highway incident	12,400	134
Nonhighway incident, except air, rail, and water	2,610	13
Pedestrian or nonpassenger struck by vehicle or mobile equipment	1,240	48
Fires or explosions	1,500	15
Assault or violent act	25,640	136
Assault by person	23,400	86
Other	2,240	50
All other	40,140	7

Source: National Safety Council tabulations of Bureau of Labor Statistics (BLS) data.
Note: Because of rounding and data exclusion of nonclassifiable responses, data may not sum to the totals. Dashes (–) indicate data that do not meet publication guidelines or that data is not available.
[a]Days away from work include those that result in days away from work with or without restricted work activity.
[b]Data for government entities is only collected for state and local governments in the BLS National Survey of Occupational Injuries and Illnesses.
[c]In the fatalities column, non-Hispanic categories include cases with Hispanic origin not reported.

More than 33,000 new skin diseases or disorders cases were diagnosed in 2011.

Approximately 207,500 occupational illnesses were recognized or diagnosed by employers in 2011, according to the Bureau of Labor Statistics (BLS). The all-industry illness data published by BLS now includes data for state and local governments in addition to the private sector. The overall incidence rate of occupational illness for all workers was 20.6 per 10,000 full-time workers. The highest overall incidence rates for all illnesses were for manufacturing and utilities at 40.8 and 38.7 cases per 10,000 full-time workers, respectively – each more than double the rate for private industry of 18.0.

Workers in the utilities industry had the highest incidence rate for skin diseases and disorders, while those in state and local government had the highest incidence rates for respiratory conditions and "all other occupational illnesses." Workers in agriculture, forestry, fishing, and hunting had the highest rate for poisoning, while those in manufacturing had the highest rate for hearing loss.

State and local government, manufacturing, and education and health services accounted for more than 67% of all new illness cases in 2011. Skin diseases or disorders were the most common with 33,300 new cases, followed by hearing loss with 20,700, respiratory conditions with 18,100, and poisonings with 2,500.

The table below shows the number of occupational illnesses and the incidence rate per 10,000 full-time workers as measured by the 2011 BLS survey. To convert these to incidence rates per 100 full-time workers, which are comparable to other published BLS rates, divide the rates in the table by 100. The BLS survey records illnesses only for the year in which they are recognized or diagnosed as work-related. Because only recognized cases are included, the figures underestimate the incidence of occupational illness.

Nonfatal occupational illness incidence rates and number of illnesses by type of illness and industry sector, 2011

Industry sector	All illnesses	Skin diseases or disorders	Respiratory conditions	Poisoning	Hearing loss	All other occupational illnesses
Incidence rate per 10,000 full-time workers						
All industries, including state and local government[a]	**20.6**	**3.3**	**1.8**	**0.3**	**2.1**	**13.2**
Private industry[a]	**18.0**	**2.8**	**1.5**	**0.2**	**2.1**	**11.3**
Goods producing[a]	31.0	4.0	1.5	0.2	8.1	17.2
Agriculture, forestry, fishing, and hunting[a]	30.2	9.2	1.8	0.8	1.3	17.2
Mining[b,c]	7.9	1.3	1.4	(d)	1.4	3.7
Construction	11.3	2.0	1.0	0.2	0.4	7.6
Manufacturing	40.8	4.6	1.7	0.1	12.3	22.1
Service providing	14.6	2.5	1.5	0.2	0.5	9.8
Wholesale trade	8.5	1.9	0.5	0.3	0.8	5.1
Retail trade	10.5	1.5	1.1	0.2	0.1	7.7
Transportation and warehousing	20.9	1.4	1.1	0.4	4.5	13.6
Utilities	38.7	9.3	1.7	(d)	9.8	17.3
Information	9.3	0.7	0.3	0.1	0.6	7.6
Financial activities	7.9	0.6	(d)	0.1	(d)	5.7
Professional and business services	8.4	1.8	0.9	0.2	0.3	5.1
Education and health services	28.0	4.6	2.8	0.2	0.1	20.3
Leisure and hospitality	14.5	4.2	1.5	0.5	0.1	8.2
Other services	8.4	1.1	2.1	(d)	0.2	4.9
State and local government[a]	**36.3**	**6.3**	**3.7**	**0.4**	**1.6**	**24.3**
Number of Illnesses (in thousands)						
All industries, including state and local government[a]	**207.5**	**33.3**	**18.1**	**2.5**	**20.7**	**132.9**
Private industry[a]	**155.4**	**24.3**	**12.8**	**1.9**	**18.4**	**98.0**
Goods producing[a]	55.9	7.2	2.7	0.4	14.7	31.0
Agriculture, forestry, fishing, and hunting[a]	2.7	0.8	0.2	0.1	0.1	1.5
Mining[b,c]	0.6	0.1	0.1	(d)	0.1	0.3
Construction	5.5	1.0	0.5	0.1	0.2	3.7
Manufacturing	47.1	5.3	1.9	0.2	14.2	25.5
Service providing	99.5	17.1	10.1	1.6	3.7	67.1
Wholesale trade	4.5	1.0	0.2	0.1	0.4	2.7
Retail trade	11.5	1.6	1.2	0.3	0.1	8.3
Transportation and warehousing	8.1	0.5	0.4	0.1	1.8	5.3
Utilities	2.1	0.5	0.1	(d)	0.5	0.9
Information	2.2	0.2	0.1	(e)	0.1	1.8
Financial activities	5.3	0.4	(d)	0.1	(d)	3.8
Professional and business services	11.0	2.4	1.2	0.3	0.4	6.7
Education and health services	40.2	6.6	4.0	0.3	0.2	29.2
Leisure and hospitality	12.2	3.6	1.3	0.4	0.1	6.9
Other services	2.4	0.3	0.6	(d)	0.1	1.4
State and local government[a]	**52.1**	**9.0**	**5.3**	**0.6**	**2.4**	**34.9**

Source: Bureau of Labor Statistics. Components may not add to totals due to rounding.
[a]Excludes farms with fewer than 11 employees.
[b]Data for mining do not reflect the changes OSHA made to its recordkeeping requirements effective Jan. 1, 2002; therefore, estimates for this industry are not comparable with estimates for other industries.
[c]Mining includes quarrying and oil and gas extraction.
[d]Data do not meet publication guidelines.
[e]Data too small to be displayed.

Motor Vehicle

Between 1912 and 2011, motor vehicle deaths per 10,000 registered vehicles decreased 96%, from 33 to less than 1.4. In 1912, 3,100 fatalities occurred when the number of registered vehicles totaled only 950,000. In 2011, 34,600 fatalities occurred, but registrations soared to 249 million. While mileage data were not available in 1912, the 2011 mileage death rate of 1.18 per 100,000,000 vehicle miles was down 1% from the revised 2010 rate of 1.19, and is the lowest on record.

Beginning with the 2011 edition of *Injury Facts*, the concept of medically consulted injury was adopted to replace disabling injury as the measure of nonfatal injuries. A medically consulted injury is an injury serious enough that a medical professional was consulted. Medically consulted injuries reported in this edition are not comparable to previous disabling injury estimates. Please see the Technical Appendix for a detailed description of this change. Medically consulted injuries in motor vehicle incidents totaled 3,700,000 in 2011, and total motor vehicle costs were estimated at $263.8 billion. Costs include wage and productivity losses, medical expenses, administrative expenses, motor vehicle property damage, and employer costs.

Motor vehicle deaths decreased 2% from 2010 to 2011 following a similar 2% decline from 2009 to 2010. Miles traveled was down 1%, the number of registered vehicles increased 0.5%, and the population increased 1%. As a result, the mileage and registration death rates were each down 1% and the population death rate was down 3% from 2010 to 2011.

Compared to 2002, 2011 motor vehicle deaths decreased by about 24%. Mileage, registration, and population death rates also were sharply lower in 2011 compared with 2002 (see chart on next page).

The National Safety Council avoids using the word "accident." To some people, the word "accident" may imply a sense of inevitability. In contrast, the safety practice continually strives to decrease and ultimately prevent all unintentional injuries. NSC uses the terms "collision" and "crashes" in place of the word "accident."

Deaths... 34,600
Medically consulted injuries... 3,700,000
Cost... $263.8 billion
Motor vehicle mileage ....2,931 billion
Registered vehicles in the United States 248,900,000
Licensed drivers in the United States 211,600,000
Death rate per 100,000,000 vehicle miles.. 1.18
Death rate per 10,000 registered vehicles..1.39
Death rate per 100,000 population 11.10

Motor vehicle crash outcomes, United States, 2011

Severity	Deaths or injuries	Crashes	Drivers (vehicles) involved
Fatal (within 1 year)	34,600	31,800	46,700
Medically consulted injury	3,700,000	2,600,000	4,700,000
Property damage (including unreported) and nondisabling injury		8,100,000	14,100,000
Total		**10,700,000**	**18,800,000**
Fatal (within 30 days)	32,367	29,757	43,668
Injury (disabling and nondisabling)	2,217,000	1,530,000	2,750,000
Police-reported property damage		3,778,000	6,596,000
Total		**5,308,000**	**9,390,000**

Source: National Safety Council estimates (top half) and National Highway Traffic Safety Administration (bottom half, with the exception of "Drivers (vehicles) involved," which are National Safety Council estimates).

Travel, deaths, and death rates, United States, 1925-2011

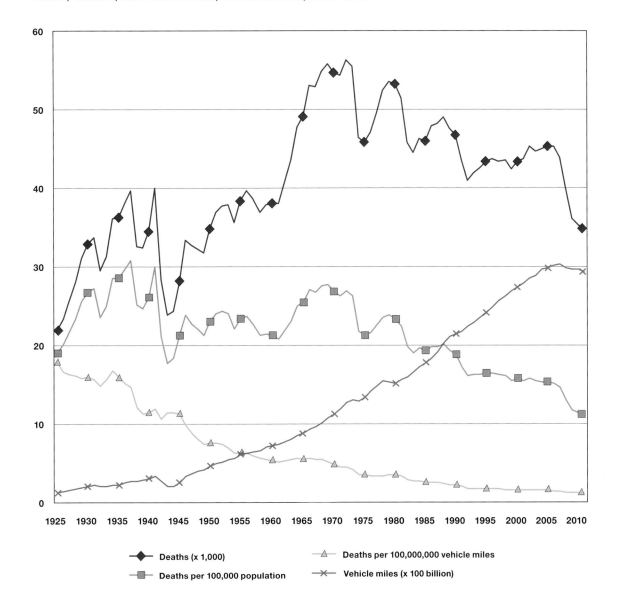

Deaths (x 1,000)

Deaths per 100,000 population

Deaths per 100,000,000 vehicle miles

Vehicle miles (x 100 billion)

Type of crash and age of victim

All motor vehicle crashes

Includes deaths involving mechanically or electrically powered highway-transport vehicles in motion (except those on rails), both on and off the highway or street.

	Total	Change from 2010	Death rate[a]
Deaths	34,600	-2%	11.1
Nonfatal injuries[b]	3,700,000		

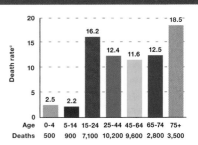

Age	0-4	5-14	15-24	25-44	45-64	65-74	75+
Deaths	500	900	7,100	10,200	9,600	2,800	3,500

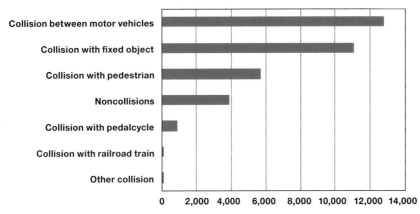

Collision between motor vehicles

Includes deaths from collisions of two or more motor vehicles. Motorized bicycles and scooters, trolley buses, and farm tractors or road machinery traveling on highways are motor vehicles.

	Total	Change from 2010	Death rate[a]
Deaths	12,800	-5%	4.1
Nonfatal injuries[b]	2,750,000		

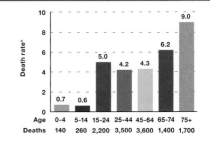

Age	0-4	5-14	15-24	25-44	45-64	65-74	75+
Deaths	140	260	2,200	3,500	3,600	1,400	1,700

Collision with fixed object

Includes deaths from collisions in which the first harmful event is the striking of a fixed object such as a guardrail, abutment, impact attenuator, etc.

	Total	Change from 2010	Death rate[a]
Deaths	11,100	-3%	3.6
Nonfatal injuries[b]	510,000		

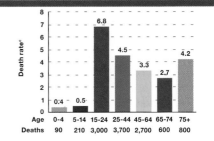

Age	0-4	5-14	15-24	25-44	45-64	65-74	75+
Deaths	90	210	3,000	3,700	2,700	600	800

Collision with pedestrian

Includes all deaths of people struck by motor vehicles, either on or off a street or highway, regardless of the circumstances of the incident.

	Total	Change from 2010	Death rate[a]
Deaths	5,700	+4%	1.8
Nonfatal injuries[b]	160,000		

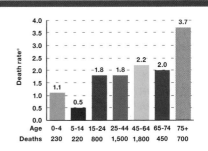

Age	0-4	5-14	15-24	25-44	45-64	65-74	75+
Deaths	230	220	800	1,500	1,800	450	700

See footnotes on page 107.

Noncollisions

Includes deaths from noncollisions in which the first injury or damage-producing event was an overturn, jackknife, or other type of noncollision.

	Total	Change from 2010	Death rate[a]
Deaths	3,900	0%	1.3
Nonfatal injuries[b]	160,000		

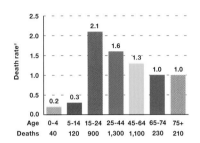

Collision with pedalcycle

Includes deaths of pedalcyclists and motor vehicle occupants from collisions between pedalcycles and motor vehicles on streets, highways, private driveways, parking lots, etc.

	Total	Change from 2010	Death rate[a]
Deaths	900	+12%	0.3
Nonfatal injuries[b]	110,000		

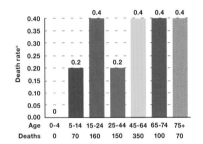

Collision with railroad train

Includes deaths from collisions of motor vehicles (moving or stalled) and railroad vehicles at public or private grade crossings. In other types of incidents, classification requires motor vehicle to be in motion.

	Total	Change from 2010	Death rate[a]
Deaths	100	-28%	[d]
Nonfatal injuries[b]	1,000		

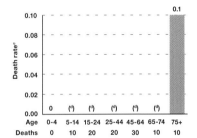

Other collision

Includes deaths from motor vehicle collisions not specified in other categories above. Most of the deaths arose from collisions involving animals or animal-drawn vehicles.

	Total	Change from 2010	Death rate[a]
Deaths	100	0%	[d]
Nonfatal injuries[b]	9,000		

Note: Procedures and benchmarks for estimating deaths by type of incident and age were changed in 1990. Estimates for 1987 and later years are not comparable to earlier years. The noncollision and fixed-object categories were most affected by the changes.
[a]Deaths per 100,000 population.
[b]Nonfatal injury is defined as medically consulted injuries and is not comparable to estimates provided in earlier editions that used the definition of disabling injury. Please see the Technical Appendix for more information regarding medically consulted injuries.
[c]Deaths per 100,000 population in each age group.
[d]Death rate was less than 0.05.

Motor vehicle crashes were the leading cause of death for people ages 2-5 and 11-31 in 2009. Motor vehicle crashes also were the leading cause of unintentional-injury-related death for people for each single year of age from 3 to 27 and from ages 59 to 68. This is a summary of the most important issues that affect traffic safety.

Occupant protection. Safety belt use was a record-high 86% overall in 2012, a statistically significant increase from the 84% use rate in 2011. Forty-nine states and the District of Columbia have mandatory safety belt use laws in effect, with laws in 32 of the states and the District of Columbia allowing standard (primary) enforcement. In 2012, safety belt use was significantly higher in states with standard (primary) enforcement (90%) than in states with secondary enforcement or no safety belt use law (78%). More than half (52%) of the passenger vehicle occupants killed in 2011 were unrestrained, with 62% of occupants killed during the night unrestrained compared to 43% during the day. Safety belt use was significantly lower in 2010 among occupants 16-24 years old than for other age groups. Reported helmet use rates for fatally injured motorcyclists in 2010 were 58% for operators and 49% for passengers, compared with the corresponding rates of 57% and 43%, respectively, in 2009.

Alcohol. From 2010 to 2011, traffic fatalities in alcohol-impaired crashes as a percentage of total traffic fatalities decreased by 1.9% to 30.5%. Overall, 9,878 people were killed in alcohol-impaired crashes in 2011, a reduction of 2.5% from the 10,136 in 2010. In 2011, while drivers ages 25-35 constituted 19% of all drivers in fatal crashes, they were over-represented among the drivers with BACs of 0.08 g/dL or higher, comprising 27% of such drivers involved in fatal crashes. All states and the District of Columbia have 21-year-old minimum-drinking-age laws and have created a threshold by law making it illegal to drive while impaired by alcohol (i.e., with a BAC of 0.08 g/dL or higher).

Speeding. Excessive speed was a factor in 31% of all traffic fatalities in 2011, down from 32% in 2010. Alcohol involvement is highly prevalent among drivers in speeding-related crashes. In 2011, 46% of speeding-related fatalities involved at least one drunk driver, compared with 24% of non-speeding fatalities. It has been estimated that speeding-related crashes cost the nation more than $40 billion annually. A recent study using data from states that record "driving too fast for conditions" and "in excess of posted speed limit" separately found that more severe crashes are more often associated with exceeding the posted speed limit, while less-severe crashes are associated with driving too fast for conditions.

Distracted driving. Recent epidemiological studies have found that cell phone use while driving is associated with a fourfold increase in crash risk. The results also showed no significant difference between handheld and hands-free phone use. A review of 33 cell phone driving studies concluded that cell phone use while driving lengthens driver reaction time by about 0.25 seconds – again with no significant difference

between handheld and hands-free phones. The National Safety Council estimates that 24% of all traffic crashes are associated with drivers using cell phones and text messaging (21% cell phones and 3% text messaging). Although the research cited above indicates there is no safety advantage of hands-free over handheld cell phone use, the 10 states and District of Columbia that have implemented bans impacting all drivers have focused on handheld bans.

Large trucks. In 2011, 3,757 fatalities resulted from traffic crashes involving a large truck (gross vehicle weight rating greater than 10,000 pounds), a 1.9% increased from 3,686 in 2010. The majority of these deaths (72%) were occupants of vehicles other than the large truck. Fatalities among other vehicle occupants in large truck crashes declined 3.6% from 2010 to 2011, while fatalities among truck occupants and non-occupants increased 20% and 19%, respectively. Large trucks are more likely to be involved in a multiple-vehicle fatal crash than passenger vehicles – 78% versus 35%, respectively, in 2011.

Motorcycles. Fatalities among motorcycle riders and passengers increased 41% between 2002 and 2011, from 3,270 to 4,612. Nonfatal injuries have increased as well, from 65,000 to 81,000 over the same period. The number of motorcycle fatalities increased 2% from 2010 to 2011, while injuries decreased by 1%. The latest available mileage data show that motorcycle travel has nearly doubled from 2002 to 2010, increasing from 9.5 billion miles to 18.5 billion over this period. As a result, the death rate has declined 29% from 2002 to 2010, going from 34.23 to 24.39 deaths per 100 million miles traveled. In 2010, speeding was a factor in 35% of motorcycle crashes compared with 23% for fatal passenger car crashes.

Young drivers. There were 4,767 fatalities in crashes involving young drivers ages 15-20 in 2011, a 5% decrease from 2010 and the ninth consecutive yearly decline. Motor vehicle crashes, however, remain the number one cause of death for U.S. teens. Fatalities of young drivers account for more than two-fifths of the overall fatalities associated with young driver crashes; the remainder includes the passengers of young drivers, occupants of other vehicles, and non-occupants. Periods of decreasing young driver-related fatalities between 1988 and 1992 and beginning in 2003 to present appear to coincide with the implementation of 21-year-old minimum-drinking-age laws and improvements in graduated licensing programs, respectively.

Pedestrians. About 5,700 pedestrian deaths and 160,000 medically consulted injuries due to motor vehicle incidents occurred in 2011. Overall, nearly half (49%) of pedestrian deaths and injuries involve no improper action or circumstance. A further 19% of the deaths and injuries result from pedestrians darting or running into the street, 6% involve pedestrians in the roadway improperly (standing, lying, working, or playing), and about 16% are due to other pedestrian actions or circumstances. Pedestrians in age groups beginning with those 10 and older are more likely to exhibit no improper action prior to the incident, while those in younger age groups are more likely to dart or run into the roadway.

Two methods commonly are used to measure the costs of motor vehicle crashes. One is the economic cost framework and the other is the comprehensive cost framework.

Economic costs may be used by a community or state to estimate the economic impact of motor vehicle crashes that occurred within its jurisdiction in a given time period. It is a measure of the productivity lost and expenses incurred because of the crashes. Economic costs, however, should not be used for a cost-benefit analysis because they do not reflect what society is willing to pay to prevent a statistical fatality or injury.

There are five economic cost components: (1) wage and productivity losses, which include wages, fringe benefits, household production, and travel delay; (2) medical expenses, including emergency service costs; (3) administrative expenses, which include the administrative cost of private and public insurance plus police and legal costs; (4) motor vehicle damage, including the value of damage to property; and (5) uninsured employer costs for crashes involving workers.

The information below shows the average economic costs in 2011 per death (**not** per fatal crash), per injury (**not** per injury crash), and per property damage crash.

Economic costs, 2011

Death	**$1,420,000**
Nonfatal disabling injury	**$78,700**
Incapacitating injury[a]	$70,500
Non-incapacitating evident injury[a]	$22,700
Possible injury[a]	$12,800
Property damage crash (including minor injuries)	**$9,100**

Comprehensive costs include not only the economic cost components, but also a measure of the value of lost quality of life associated with the deaths and injuries – that is, what society is willing to pay to prevent them. The values of lost quality of life were obtained through empirical studies of what people actually pay to reduce their safety and health risks, such as through the purchase of air bags or smoke detectors.

Comprehensive costs should be used for a cost-benefit analysis, but because the lost quality of life represents only a dollar equivalence of intangible qualities, they do not represent real economic losses and should not be used to determine the economic impact of past crashes.

The information below shows the average comprehensive costs in 2011 on a per-person basis.

Comprehensive costs, 2011

Death	**$4,459,000**
Incapacitating injury[a]	$225,100
Non-incapacitating evident injury[a]	$57,400
Possible injury[a]	$27,200
No injury	**$2,400**

Source: National Safety Council estimates (see the Technical Appendix) and Children's Safety Network Economics and Insurance Resource Center, Pacific Institute for Research and Evaluation.
Note: The National Safety Council's cost-estimating procedures were extensively revised for the 1993 edition, and additional revisions were made for the 2005-2006 edition. The costs are not comparable to those of prior years.
[a]*Manual on Classification of Motor Vehicle Traffic Accidents, ANSI D16.1-2007 (7th ed.). (2007). Itasca, IL: National Safety Council.*

No state has passed a total ban on cell phone use while driving, although 10 states and the District of Columbia have bans on handheld devices. Mandatory breath alcohol ignition interlock device laws are in effect in 17 states for first-time DUI convictions. Mandatory safety belt use laws are in effect in 49 states and the District of Columbia, of which 19 states and the District of Columbia have primary enforcement for all seating positions. Graduated Driver Licensing is in effect in some form in nearly all states and the District of Columbia, yet relatively few have optimum laws. Please see pages 124-125 for further details regarding young driver issues.

State laws

State	Distracted driving laws			Alcohol law	Mandatory safety belt use law		Graduated Driver Licensing laws				
	Total cell phone ban	Total text messaging ban	Additional novice driver restrictions[b]	Mandatory alcohol ignition interlock device[c]	Enforcement	Seating positions covered by law	Minimum instructional permit period[g]	Minimum hours of supervised driving[h]	No passengers younger than 20	10 p.m. or earlier nighttime driving restriction	Unrestricted license minimum age[i]
Alabama	no	yes	cell phone and texting	yes[d,e]	primary	front	6 mo.	none	no	no	17 yrs.
Alaska	no	yes	no	yes	primary	all	6 mo.	40/10	yes	no	16 yrs., 6 mo.
Arizona	no	no	no	yes	secondary	front[f]	6 mo.	none	no	no	16 yrs., 6 mo.
Arkansas	no	yes	cell phone	yes	primary	front	6 mo.	none	no	no	18 yrs.
California	no[a]	yes	cell phone	no	primary	all	6 mo.	50/10	yes	no	17 yrs.
Colorado	no	yes	cell phone	yes	secondary	front	12 mo.	50/10	yes	no	17 yrs.
Connecticut	no[a]	yes	cell phone	yes	primary	front	4 mo.	40/-	yes	no	18 yrs.
Delaware	no[a]	yes	cell phone	yes[d,e]	primary	all	6 mo.	50/10	no	yes	17 yrs.
District of Columbia	no[a]	yes	cell phone	no	primary	all	6 mo.	40/10	yes	no	18 yrs.
Florida	no	no	no	yes[d,e]	primary	front[f]	12 mo.	50/10	no	no	18 yrs.
Georgia	no	yes	cell phone	yes[e]	primary	front[f]	12 mo.	40/6	yes	no	18 yrs.
Hawaii	no	no	no	yes	primary	front[f]	6 mo.	50/10	no	no	17 yrs.
Idaho	no	yes	no	yes[e]	secondary	all	6 mo.	50/10	no	yes	16 yrs.
Illinois	no	yes	cell phone	yes	primary	all	9 mo.	50/10	no	no	18 yrs.
Indiana	no	yes	cell phone	no	primary	all	6 mo.	50/10	yes	yes	18 yrs.
Iowa	no	yes	cell phone	no	primary	front	6 mo.	20/2	no	no	17 yrs.
Kansas	no	yes	cell phone	yes	primary	all	12 mo.	50/10	no	yes	16 yrs., 6 mo.
Kentucky	no	yes	cell phone	no	primary	all	6 mo.	60/10	no	no	17 yrs.
Louisiana	no	yes	cell phone	yes	primary	all	6 mo.	50/15	no	no	17 yrs.
Maine	no	yes	cell phone	no	primary	all	6 mo.	35/5	yes	no	16 yrs., 9 mo.
Maryland	no[a]	yes	cell phone	yes[d,e]	primary	front	9 mo.	60/10	yes	no	18 yrs.
Massachusetts	no	yes	cell phone	yes[e]	secondary	all	6 mo.	40/-	no	no	18 yrs.
Michigan	no	yes	no	yes[d,e]	primary	front	6 mo.	50/10	no	yes	17 yrs.
Minnesota	no	yes	cell phone	yes[d,e]	primary	all	6 mo.	30/10	no	no	17 yrs.
Mississippi	no	no	texting	no	primary	front	12 mo.	none	no	no	16 yrs., 6 mo.
Missouri	no	no	texting	yes[e]	secondary	front	6 mo.	40/10	no	no	17 yrs., 11 mo.
Montana	no	no	no	yes[e]	secondary	all	6 mo.	50/10	no	no	16 yrs.
Nebraska	no	yes	cell phone	yes	secondary	front	6 mo.	none	no	no	17 yrs.
Nevada	no[a]	yes	no	no	secondary	all	6 mo.	50/10	no	yes	18 yrs.
New Hampshire	no	yes	no	yes[d,e]	no law	no law	none	40/10	no	no	18 yrs.
New Jersey	no[a]	yes	cell phone	yes[d,e]	primary	all	6 mo.	none	no	no	18 yrs.
New Mexico	no	no	cell phone and texting	yes	primary	all	6 mo.	50/10	no	no	16 yrs., 6 mo.
New York	no[a]	yes	no	yes	primary	front	6 mo.	50/15	no	yes	17 yrs.
North Carolina	no	yes	cell phone	yes[d,e]	primary	all	12 mo.	72/16	no	yes	16 yrs., 6 mo.
North Dakota	no	yes	cell phone	no	secondary	front	6 mo.	none	no	yes	16 yrs.
Ohio	no	yes	cell phone	no	secondary	front[f]	6 mo.	50/10	no	no	18 yrs.
Oklahoma	no	no	handheld and texting	yes[d,e]	primary	front	6 mo.	50/10	no	yes	16 yrs., 6 mo.
Oregon	no[a]	yes	cell phone	yes	primary	all	6 mo.	50/-	yes	no	17 yrs.
Pennsylvania	no	yes	no	yes[e]	secondary	front[f]	6 mo.	65/10[h]	no	no	18 yrs.
Rhode Island	no	yes	cell phone	no	primary	all	6 mo.	50/10	no	no	17 yrs., 6 mo.
South Carolina	no	no	no	yes[e]	primary	all	6 mo.	40/10	no	yes	16 yrs., 6 mo.
South Dakota	no	no	no	no	secondary	front	3 mo.	none	no	yes	16 yrs.
Tennessee	no	yes	cell phone	yes[d,e]	primary	front	6 mo.	50/10	no	no	17 yrs.
Texas	no	no	cell phone and texting	yes[e]	primary	all	6 mo.	20/10	no	no	17 yrs.
Utah	no	yes	no	yes	secondary	all	6 mo.	40/10	yes	no	17 yrs.
Vermont	no	yes	cell phone	no	secondary	all	12 mo.	40/10	yes	no	16 yrs., 6 mo.
Virginia	no	yes	cell phone	yes[d,e]	secondary	front	9 mo.	45/15	no	no	18 yrs.
Washington	no[a]	yes	cell phone	yes	primary	all	6 mo.	50/10	yes	no	17 yrs.
West Virginia	no[a]	yes	cell phone and texting	yes[d,e]	secondary	front[f]	6 mo.	none	yes	yes	17 yrs.
Wisconsin	no	yes	cell phone	yes[d,e]	primary	all	6 mo.	30/10	no	no	16 yrs., 9 mo.
Wyoming	no	yes	no	yes[d,e]	secondary	all	10 days	50/10	no	no	16 yrs., 6 mo.

Source: Governors Highway Safety Association data retrieved from www.ghsa.org; Insurance Institute for Highway Safety data retrieved from www.iihs.org. All data retrieved on July 16, 2012.

[a]Statewide handheld ban.

[b]Restrictions specific to novice drivers in addition to any other all-driver ban.

[c]Instruments designed to prevent drivers from starting their cars when breath-alcohol content is at or above a set point.

[d]Mandatory with a conviction for a blood alcohol concentration of at least 0.15 versus the lower limit of 0.08 found in other mandatory states.

[e]Mandatory with repeat convictions or upon reinstatement.

[f]Required for certain ages at all seating positions.

[g]Minimum instructional periods often include time spent in driver's education classes.

[h]Figures shown as follows: Total hours/nighttime hours. For example, 25/5 means 25 hours of supervised driving, 5 of which must be at night. When states (Alabama, Arizona, Connecticut, Nebraska, Oregon, and West Virginia) have lower requirements if driver's education is taken, the lower requirement is reflected in the table. Pennsylvania additionally requires 5 of the total hours of supervised driving to be during inclement weather.

[i]Minimum age to obtain unrestricted license provided driver is crash and violation free. Alcohol restrictions still apply at least until age 21.

Safety belt use hit a record-high 86% overall in 2012, a statistically significant increase from the 84% use rate in 2011. These results are from the National Occupant Protection Use Survey (NOPUS) that is conducted annually by the National Highway Traffic Safety Administration. NOPUS includes the observation of drivers and right-front passengers of passenger vehicles with no commercial or governmental markings.

Significant increases in safety belt use from 2011 to 2012 occurred among drivers of passenger vehicles, whose use rate increased 3 percentage points from 84% to 87%; occupants in states with primary (87% to 90%) and secondary (76% to 78%) enforcement laws; occupants traveling on expressways (89% to 91%) and surface streets (81% to 83%); occupants traveling in slow traffic (76% to 80%); and occupants traveling in moderately dense (82% to 85%) and light (70% to 74%) traffic. Significant increases in safety belt use also were observed for occupants traveling in light fog (93% to 99%) and in clear weather conditions (84% to 86%); occupants in passenger cars (85% to 87%), vans and SUVs (87% to 89%), and pickup trucks (74% to 77%); occupants traveling in the South (80% to 85%) or West (93% to 94%); occupants in rural areas (81% to 84%); and occupants traveling during weekdays overall (83% to 86%) and during weekday rush (83% to 86%) and non-rush (83% to 85%) hours. There were no declines in use observed from 2011 to 2012 for any occupant group.

In 2012, safety belt use was significantly higher for drivers (87%) than right-front passengers (84%), for occupants in states with primary enforcement laws (90%) than those with secondary enforcement laws or no safety belt use law (78%), for occupants traveling on expressways (91%) rather than on surface streets (83%), those traveling in fast (90%) or medium-speed traffic (84%) rather than slow (80%) traffic, those traveling in heavy (89%) rather than moderately dense (85%) or light (74%) traffic, and those traveling in light fog (99%) rather than clear weather conditions (86%) or light precipitation (86%). By vehicle type, safety belt use was significantly higher in vans and SUVs (89%) and in passenger cars (87%) than in pickup trucks (77%). Safety belt use was significantly higher in the West (94%) than in the Midwest (85%), South (85%), or Northeast (80%). Safety belt use in 2012 also was significantly higher in suburban areas (87%) than in urban (86%) or rural (84%) areas.

Safety belt use by state in 2011 ranged from 73.2% in Massachusetts to 97.5% in Washington. Seventeen states and the District of Columbia achieved use rates of 90% or higher, including California, Delaware, Georgia, Hawaii, Illinois, Indiana, Iowa, Maryland, Michigan, Minnesota, Nevada, New Jersey, New Mexico, New York, Oregon, Texas and Washington. Jurisdictions with stronger safety belt laws continue to exhibit generally higher use rates than those with weaker laws.

Results from the NOPUS Controlled Intersection Study show that in 2010 safety belt use continued to be significantly lower among occupants 16-24 years old than other age groups, while safety belt use among occupants 70 and older was significantly higher than other age groups. Safety belt use also continued to be significantly lower among males (83%) than females (88%). Overall, drivers with no passengers were less likely to use safety belts (85%) in 2010 than those with at least one passenger (88%). Similarly, drivers with no passengers were less likely to use safety belts than drivers with passengers younger than 8 (89%), passengers 8 and older (88%), or a mixture of the two age groups (90%).

Child restraint use. Restraint use for child passengers younger than 8 was at 89% in 2010, statistically unchanged from 88% in 2009. Use rates were highest for children from birth to 12 months of age (99%), followed by children ages 1-3 (94%) and ages 4-7 (83%). In 2010, 97% of infants, 99% of children 1-3 years old, and 89% of children ages 4-7 rode in the rear seat. Child passengers in the West had significantly higher restraint use rates than those in other geographical regions.

Safety belt use by the driver strongly influences the restraint status of child passengers. When the driver was belted, a significantly high 92% of child passengers younger than 8 were restrained, compared with only 64% of children when the driver was unbelted.

Children ages 4-7 should be restrained in a front-facing safety seat or booster seat, depending on the child's height and weight. A recent study of national and state data to estimate the effects of early graduation from child restraint seats to booster seats and from booster seats to lap and shoulder belts found that among 3- and 4-year-olds there was evidence of increased risk of injury when restrained in booster seats rather than with the recommended child restraints. Similarly, among 4- to 8-year-olds, there was strong evidence of reduced risk of injury when restrained by a booster seat rather than a lap and shoulder belt.

Source: Pickrell, T.M., & Ye, T.J. (2012, November). Seat belt use in 2012–overall results. Traffic Safety Facts Research Note (DOT HS 811 691). Washington, DC: National Highway Traffic Safety Administration.
Chen, Y.Y., & Ye, T.J. (2012, August). Seat belt use in 2011–use rates in the States and Territories. Traffic Safety Facts Crash Stats (DOT HS 811 651). Washington, DC: National Highway Traffic Safety Administration.
Pickrell, T.M., & Ye, T.J. (2011, November). Occupant Restraint Use in 2010–Results from the National Occupant Protection Use Survey Controlled Intersection Study (DOT HS 811 527). Washington, DC: National Highway Traffic Safety Administration.
Sivinski, R. (2010, July). Booster Seat Effectiveness Estimates Based on CDS and State Data (DOT HS 811 338). Washington, DC: National Highway Traffic Safety Administration.

Safety belt use rate and daytime percent of unrestrained passenger vehicle occupant fatalities, United States, 2000-2012

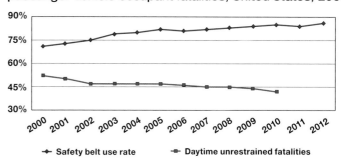

Source: National Occupant Protection Use Survey and the Fatality Analysis Reporting System.

Safety belts

- When used properly, lap/shoulder safety belts reduce the risk of fatal injury to front-seat passenger car occupants by 45% and reduce the risk of moderate-to-critical injury by 50%.
- For light-truck occupants, safety belts reduce the risk of fatal injury by 60% and moderate-to-critical injury by 65%.
- Forty-nine states and the District of Columbia have mandatory safety belt use laws in effect, the only exception being New Hampshire. Seventeen of the states with safety belt use laws in effect in 2011 specified secondary enforcement (i.e., police officers are permitted to write a citation only after a vehicle is stopped for some other traffic infraction). Thirty-two states and the District of Columbia had laws that allowed primary enforcement, enabling officers to stop vehicles and write citations whenever they observe violations of the safety belt law. (See page 110 for additional information on state laws.)
- Safety belts saved an estimated 12,546 lives in 2010 among passenger vehicle occupants older than 4. An additional 3,341 lives could have been saved in 2010 if all passenger vehicle occupants older than 4 wore safety belts. From 1975 through 2010, an estimated 280,486 lives were saved by safety belts.
- A total of 21,253 occupants of passenger vehicles (cars, pickup trucks, vans, and SUVs) were killed in motor vehicle traffic crashes in 2011, 66% of the total traffic fatalities reported for the year. Of this total, 11,028 (52%) were unrestrained. The table below shows the number of passenger vehicle occupant fatalities in crashes by restraint use in 2010.

Passenger vehicle occupants killed, by age and restraint use, 2010

Age group	Restrained		Unrestrained		Unknown		Total		Known restrained (%)	Known unrestrained (%)
	Number	%	Number	%	Number	%	Number	%		
Younger than 4	163	69	58	25	14	6	235	100	74	26
4-7	113	55	77	37	16	8	206	100	59	41
8-12	110	51	85	40	19	9	214	100	56	44
13-15	112	38	151	51	34	11	297	100	43	57
16-20	1,035	37	1,532	54	247	9	2,814	100	40	60
21-24	905	36	1,419	56	209	8	2,533	100	39	61
25-34	1,280	34	2,209	58	320	8	3,809	100	37	63
35-44	1,042	37	1,541	55	196	7	2,779	100	40	60
45-54	1,247	44	1,368	49	200	7	2,815	100	48	25
55-64	1,240	53	918	39	188	8	2,346	100	57	43
65-74	1,027	62	528	32	94	6	1,649	100	66	34
75 and older	1,657	67	648	26	162	7	2,467	100	72	28
Unknown	3	13	13	57	7	30	23	100	19	81
Total	9,934	45	10,547	48	1,706	8	22,187	100	49	51

Air bags

- Air bags, combined with lap/shoulder belts, offer the best available protection for passenger vehicle occupants. Recent analyses indicate a fatality-reducing effectiveness for air bags of 14% when no safety belt was used and 11% when a safety belt was used in conjunction with air bags.
- Lap/shoulder belts should always be used, even in a vehicle with an air bag. Air bags are a supplemental form of protection, and most are designed to deploy only in moderate-to-severe frontal crashes.
- Children in rear-facing child seats should not be placed in the front seat of vehicles equipped with passenger-side air bags. The impact of the deploying air bag could result in injury to the child.
- An estimated 2,306 lives were saved by air bags in 2010, and a total of 32,544 lives were saved from 1975 through 2010.
- Beginning in September 1997, all new passenger cars were required to have driver and passenger-side air bags. In 1998, the same requirement went into effect for light trucks.

Child restraints

- Child restraints saved an estimated 303 lives in 2010 among children younger than 5. An additional 50 lives of such children could have been saved if all had used child safety seats.
- All states and the District of Columbia have had child restraint use laws in effect since 1985.
- Research has shown that child safety seats reduce fatal injury in passenger cars by 71% for infants (younger than 1) and by 54% for toddlers (1-4 years old). For infants and toddlers in light trucks, the corresponding reductions are 58% and 59%, respectively.
- In 2010, there were 235 occupant fatalities among children younger than 4. Of the 221 fatalities among children younger than 4 for which restraint use was known, 58 (26%) were completely unrestrained.
- An estimated 9,611 lives have been saved by child restraints from 1975 through 2010.

Estimated number of lives saved by restraint systems, 1975-2010

Restraint type	1975-2002	2003	2004	2005	2006	2007	2008	2009	2010	Total
Safety belts	164,853	15,095	15,548	15,688	15,458	15,223	13,312	12,763	12,546	280,486
Child restraints	6,754	447	455	424	427	388	286	307	303	9,611
Air bags	11,739[a]	2,519	2,660	2,752	2,824	2,800	2,557	2,387	2,306	32,544

Source: National Center for Statistics and Analysis. (2012, May). Traffic Safety Facts 2010 Data–Occupant Protection (DOT HS 811 619). Washington, DC: National Highway Traffic Safety Administration.
[a]Total is from 1987 to 2002. Frontal air bags did not exist prior to 1987.

Motorcycle helmets

- Motorcycle helmets are estimated to be 37% effective in preventing fatal injuries to motorcycle operators and 41% effective for motorcycle passengers.
- It is estimated that motorcycle helmets saved the lives of 1,550 motorcyclists in 2010. An additional 706 lives could have been saved in 2010 if all motorcyclists had worn helmets.
- Reported helmet use rates for fatally injured motorcyclists in 2010 were 58% for operators and 49% for passengers, compared with the corresponding rates of 57% and 43%, respectively, in 2009.
- As of November 2012, 19 states and the District of Columbia required helmet use by all motorcycle operators and passengers. Helmet use in these states (84%) continued to be significantly higher than states without universal helmet laws (50%) in 2011. However, states without universal helmet laws did show a significant increase in helmet use from 2010 to 2011, rising from 40% to 50%.
- According to the National Occupant Protection Use Survey, use of Department of Transportation-compliant helmets by all motorcyclists (riders and passengers) was at 66% in 2011, a significant increase from the 54% use rate observed in 2010. The use rate for motorcycle riders also increased significantly over the same time period from 55% to 67%.
- The economic cost savings due to helmet use was approximately $2.9 billion in 2008, and an additional $1.3 billion could have been saved if all motorcyclists had worn helmets.

Source: National Center for Statistics and Analysis. (2012, December). Traffic Safety Facts Research Note – 2011 Motor Vehicle Crashes (DOT HS 811 701). Washington, D.C.: National Highway Traffic Safety Administration. National Center for Statistics and Analysis. (2012, May). Traffic Safety Facts 2010 Data – Occupant Protection (DOT HS 811 619). Washington, DC: National Highway Traffic Safety Administration. National Center for Statistics and Analysis. (2012, July). Traffic Safety Facts 2010 Data – Motorcycles (DOT HS 811 639). Washington, DC: National Highway Traffic Safety Administration. National Center for Statistics and Analysis. (2012, April). Traffic Safety Facts Research Note – Motorcycle Helmets Use in 2011 – Overall Results (DOT HS 811 610). Current status of safety belt and motorcycle helmet use laws downloaded Nov. 16, 2012, from the Insurance Institute for Highway Safety at www.iihs.org/laws/default.aspx.

According to studies conducted by the National Highway Traffic Safety Administration, about 9,878 people were killed in alcohol-impaired crashes in 2011, a decline of 2.5% from the 10,136 fatalities in 2010. Alcohol-impaired driving crashes involve at least one driver or motorcycle operator with a blood alcohol concentration (BAC) of 0.08 grams per deciliter (g/dL) or higher. The following data summarize the extent of alcohol involvement in motor vehicle crashes with at least one alcohol-impaired driver or motorcycle operator:

- The cost of alcohol-related motor vehicle crashes in 2011 is estimated by the National Safety Council at $31.0 billion.
- Traffic fatalities in alcohol-impaired driving crashes as a percentage of total traffic fatalities decreased by 1.9% to 30.5% from 2010 to 2011 and decreased by 2.6% from 2002 to 2011 (see corresponding chart on the next page).
- The 9,878 fatalities in alcohol-impaired driving crashes in 2011 represent an average of one alcohol-impaired driving fatality every 53 minutes.
- The percentage of alcohol-impaired-related fatalities was consistently highest among drivers with BAC levels of 0.15 g/dL or higher. Drivers with BAC levels of 0.15 g/dL or higher accounted for 21% to 22% of total motor vehicle fatalities every year since 2006. In contrast, drivers with BAC levels from 0.01 to 0.07 accounted for 5% to 6% of the total fatalities each year (see corresponding chart on the next page).
- Since July 1988, all states and the District of Columbia have had a minimum legal drinking age of 21. The impact these laws had on alcohol-related fatalities was dramatic. Among fatally injured drivers 16-20 years old, the percentage with positive BACs declined from 61% in 1982 to 31% in 1995, a larger decline than for older age groups. These declines occurred among the ages directly affected by increasing the drinking age (ages 18-20) and among young teens not directly affected (ages 16-17).

- In 2011, while people ages 25-34 constituted 19% of all drivers involved in fatal crashes, they were overrepresented among the drivers with a BAC of 0.08 g/dL or higher, comprising 27% of such drivers involved in fatal crashes. Drivers 21-24 years old were similarly overrepresented, accounting for 10% of drivers in fatal crashes and 16% of those with a BAC of 0.08 g/dL or higher. The 35-44 age group also was slightly overrepresented, making up 16% of drivers in fatal crashes and 18% of those with a BAC of 0.08 g/dL or higher.
- Males continue to comprise the majority – 82% in 2011 – of all drivers involved in fatal crashes with a BAC of 0.08 g/dL or higher. Male drivers showed a 1% decrease while female drivers showed a 2% increase in the proportion of drivers involved in fatal crashes who were alcohol-impaired from 2002 to 2011.
- Overall, 21% of drivers involved in fatal crashes in 2011 had a BAC of 0.08 g/dL or higher. The percentages by state varied from a low of 17% in Maine to a high of 44% in Hawaii (see corresponding chart on the next page).
- In 2011, all states and the District of Columbia had by law created a threshold making it illegal to drive with a BAC of 0.08 g/dL or higher.

Percent of alcohol-impaired driving fatalities, United States 1982-2011

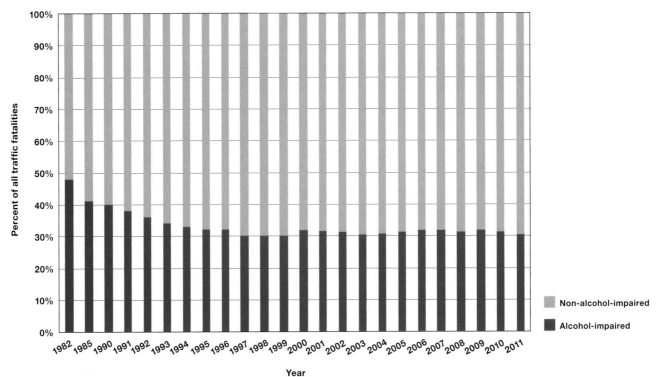

Percent of total motor vehicle fatalities by BAC level, United States, 2006-2010

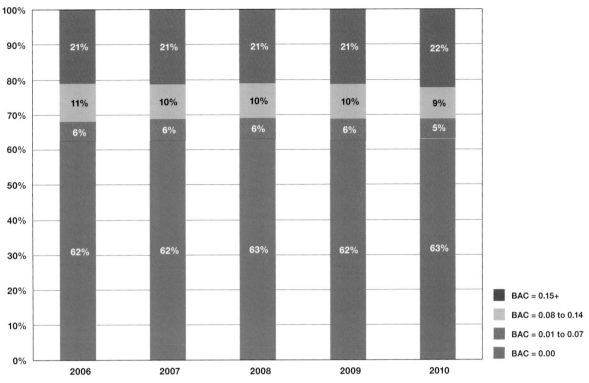

Source: National Center for Statistics and Analysis (August, 2012). Traffic Safety Facts Research Note–Prevalence of High BAC in Alcohol-Impaired-Driving Fatal (DOT HS 811 654). Washington, DC: National Highway Traffic Safety Administration.

Percent of fatalities involved in fatal crashes with BAC of 0.08+, by state, 2011

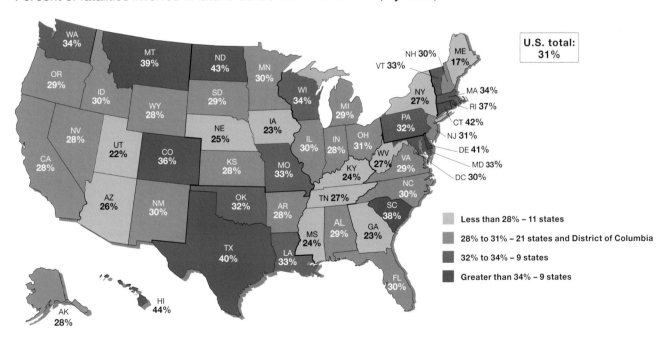

Source: National Center for Statistics and Analysis. (2012). Traffic Safety Facts Research Note: 2011 Motor Vehicle Crashes: Overview. Washington, DC: National Highway Traffic Safety Administration.
National Center for Statistics and Analysis. (2012). Traffic Safety Facts Research Note: Prevalence of High BAC in Alcohol-Impaired-Driving Fatal Crashes.

Washington, DC: National Highway Traffic Safety Administration.
McCartt, A.T., Hellinga, L.A., & Kirley, B.B. (2010). The effect of minimum legal drinking age 21 laws on alcohol-related driving in the United States. Journal of Safety Research, Vol. 41, pp. 173-181.

Although motor vehicle deaths occur more often in collisions between motor vehicles than any other type of incident, this type represents only about 37% of the total. Collisions between a motor vehicle and a fixed object were the next most common type, with about 32% of deaths, followed by pedestrian incidents and noncollisions (rollovers, etc.).

While collisions between motor vehicles accounted for less than half of motor vehicle fatalities, this crash type represented 74% of injuries, 67% of injury crashes, and 71% of all incidents. Single-vehicle crashes involving collisions with fixed objects,

pedestrians, and noncollisions, on the other hand, accounted for a greater proportion of fatalities and fatal crashes compared to less-serious crashes. These three crash types made up 59% of fatalities and 61% of fatal crashes, but only 29% or less of injuries, injury crashes, or all crashes.

Of collisions between motor vehicles, angle collisions cause the greatest number of deaths, about 6,200 in 2011, and also the greatest number of fatal crashes. The table below shows the estimated number of deaths, injuries, fatal crashes, injury crashes, and all crashes for various types of motor vehicle crashes.

Motor vehicle deaths, injuries, and number of crashes by type of crash, 2011

Type of crash	Deaths	Nonfatal injuries[a]	Fatal crashes	Injury crashes	All crashes
Total	34,600	3,700,000	31,800	2,600,000	10,700,000
Collision with...					
Pedestrian	5,700	160,000	4,900	140,000	137,000
Other motor vehicle	12,800	2,750,000	11,400	1,750,000	7,620,000
Angle collision	6,200	1,155,000	5,700	712,000	2,530,000
Head-on collision	3,500	193,000	2,900	102,000	230,000
Rear-end collision	2,100	1,218,000	1,900	813,000	3,600,000
Sideswipe and other two-vehicle collisions	1,000	184,000	900	123,000	1,260,000
Railroad train	100	1,000	100	1,000	3,000
Pedalcycle	900	110,000	800	90,000	110,000
Animal, animal-drawn vehicle	100	9,000	100	9,000	520,000
Fixed or other object	11,100	510,000	11,000	490,000	2,060,000
Noncollision	3,900	160,000	3,500	120,000	250,000

Source: National Safety Council estimates, based on data from the National Highway Traffic Safety Administration Fatality Analysis Reporting System and General Estimates System. Procedures for estimating the number of incidents by type were changed for the 1998 edition and are not comparable to estimates in previous editions (see Technical Appendix).
[a]Nonfatal injury is defined as a medically consulted injury and is not comparable to estimates provided in earlier editions that used the definition of disabling injury. Please see the Technical Appendix for more information regarding medically consulted injuries.

Speeding is one of the major factors contributing to the occurrence of deaths, injuries, and property damage related to motor vehicle crashes. The role of speeding in crash causation can be described in terms of its effect on the driver, the vehicle, and the road. Excessive-speed driving reduces the amount of time the driver has to react in a dangerous situation to avoid a crash. Speeding increases vehicle stopping distance and also reduces the ability of road safety structures such as guardrails, impact attenuators, crash cushions, median dividers, and concrete barriers to protect vehicle occupants in a crash.

The National Highway Traffic Safety Administration (NHTSA) estimates that speeding-related crashes[a] cost the nation $40.4 billion in 2000, or 18% of the entire cost of motor vehicle crashes in the United States. This economic loss is equivalent to $110.7 million per day or $4.6 million per hour.

Speeding was a factor in 31% of all traffic fatalities in 2011, killing an average of 27 people per day for a total of 9,944 speeding-related fatalities. The total number of fatal motor vehicle crashes attributable to speeding was 8,937. Among young drivers, the impact of speeding is even more severe. Forty-one percent of fatalities involving young drivers (ages 15-19) are speeding-related, compared with 29% of fatalities involving drivers older than 19.

Speeding as typically reported by NHTSA combines both "driving too fast for conditions" and "exceeding posted speed limit," as well as other speed-related offenses including racing.

A recent NHTSA study using data from six states whose police incident reports record these components separately found that more-severe crashes are more often associated with exceeding the posted speed limit, while less-severe crashes are associated with driving too fast for conditions:

Fatal crashes:
- 55% attributed to exceeding posted speed limit
- 45% attributed to driving too fast for conditions

Injury crashes:
- 26% attributed to exceeding posted speed limit
- 74% attributed to driving too fast for conditions

Property damage only:
- 18% attributed to exceeding posted speed limit
- 82% attributed to driving too fast for conditions

Alcohol and speeding are a deadly combination, with alcohol involvement highly prevalent among drivers in speeding-related crashes. In 2011, 46% of speeding-related fatalities involved at least one drunk driver, compared with 24% of non-speeding fatalities. Between midnight and 4 a.m., 30% of fatalities involve both speeding and a drunk driver compared to about 3% of the fatalities between 8 a.m. and noon (see chart).

Proportion of fatalities that are alcohol-related by speeding status and time of day, United States, 2011

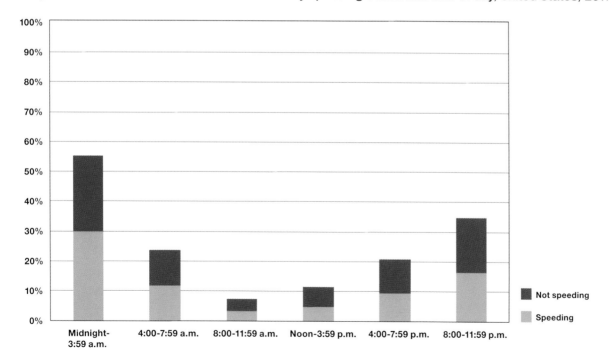

Source: National Safety Council analysis of NHTSA FARS data. National Center for Statistics and Analysis. (2010). An Analysis of Speeding-Related Crashes: Definitions and the Effects of Road Environments. Washington, DC: National Highway Traffic Safety Administration. (DOT HS 811 090.)
[a]A crash is considered speeding-related if the driver was charged with a speeding-related offense or if racing, driving too fast for conditions, or exceeding the posted speed limit was indicated as a contributing factor in the crash.

The term "distracted driving" is not always used consistently. Some reports use the terms "inattention" and "distraction" synonymously. While drowsiness and daydreaming can be categorized as inattention, the term "distraction," as defined by the National Highway Traffic Safety Administration (NHTSA), is a specific type of inattention that occurs when drivers divert their attention away from the driving task to focus on another activity. These distractions can be from electronic sources, such as cell phones or navigation devices, or more conventional distractions such as interacting with passengers or eating. Distracting tasks can affect drivers in different ways, and can be categorized into the following types:

- Visual distraction: Tasks that require the driver to look away from the roadway to visually obtain information
- Manual distraction: Tasks that require the driver to take a hand off the steering wheel and manipulate a device
- Cognitive distraction: Tasks that are defined as the mental workload associated with a task that involves thinking about something other than the driving task

The impact of distraction on driving is determined not only by the type of distraction, but also the frequency and duration of the task. Because of this, even if a task is less distracting, a driver who engages in it frequently or for long durations may increase the crash risk to a level comparable to that of much more difficult tasks performed less often. Text messaging while driving, for example, has been found to pose a greater crash risk than talking on a cell phone. However, because drivers currently talk on cell phones more frequently and for longer durations than they text message, cell phone use accounts for more crashes.

Cell phone driving prevalence

Nationally, about 9% of drivers are using handheld or hands-free cell phones at any given daylight moment. This result from the National Occupant Protection Use Survey (NOPUS)

conducted by NHTSA is the only national estimate of driver cell phone use based on actual driver observations. As shown in the graph below, the percentage of drivers likely to be on either handheld or hands-free cell phones decreased from 11% in 2007 and 2008 to 9% starting in 2009 and continuing in 2010. The corresponding handheld cell phone use estimate remained constant at 5% of drivers in 2009 and 2008. In addition, the percentage of drivers observed manipulating handheld electronic devices increased from 0.6% in 2009 to 0.9% in 2010. Among other activities, this observation would include text messaging as well as manipulating devices such as MP3 players.

A national phone survey conducted by NHTSA in 2010 on distracted driving attitudes and behaviors found that the majority of drivers (77%) reported answering their cell phone while driving and 41% reported making calls. Results also found that drivers rarely mentioned traffic situations, personal safety, or state laws in their decisions about using cell phones while driving.

NHTSA demonstration programs have shown that a combination of high-visibility enforcement and media campaigns reduces the prevalence of handheld cell phone use among drivers. NHTSA awarded cooperative agreements to Connecticut and New York to implement and evaluate the impact of high-visibility enforcement in Syracuse, New York; and Hartford, Connecticut. The campaigns were composed of four waves of media and enforcement activities, of which the first two waves have been conducted and evaluated. In Hartford, the results of Wave 1 showed a significant decrease in handheld cell phone use – from 6.8% before the program to 4.3% following the first wave and 3.1% following the second wave (see graph on next page). A control area in Connecticut that was not impacted by the high-visibility campaign also showed a slight decrease in handheld cell phone use, but this was not statistically significant. In Syracuse, a slightly smaller impact was found representing a 38% overall decrease in handheld cell phone use, compared with a 22% decrease in the control area.

Driver use of cell phones, 2002-2010

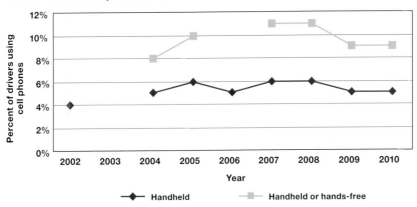

Note: Handheld or hands-free estimate is not available for 2006.
Source: National Occupant Protection Use Survey, National Highway Traffic Safety Administration, 2002-2011

Cell phone driving risk

Two epidemiological studies have found that cell phone use while driving is associated with approximately a quadrupling of crash risk. Researchers in Australia analyzed cell phone records of drivers who went to hospital emergency departments due to injuries sustained in a crash. A second group of researchers in Canada analyzed cell phone records of drivers who reported property damage-only crashes. Both studies compared cell phone use during a 10-minute period prior to the time of the crash and during non-crash periods, and found cell phone use while driving was associated with a slightly more than fourfold increase in crash risk. Results also showed no significant difference between handheld and hands-free cell phone use.

A review of 33 cell phone driving studies representing a total sample size of approximately 2,000 participants revealed the following:

- A cell phone conversation while driving lengthens driver reaction time. The total mean increase in reaction time analysis is 0.25 seconds.
- Use of handheld and hands-free cell phones results in similar increases in reaction time.

The National Safety Council estimates that 24% of all traffic crashes are associated with drivers using cell phones and text messaging (21% cell phone and 3% text messaging). The percent crash estimates are based on a population attributable risk percent calculation that factors in the relative risk of an activity and the prevalence of the activity. The data inputs for the 21% of crashes associated with cell phones included epidemiological studies that have found that cell phone use results in a fourfold increase in the risk of crashes as well as NHTSA's NOPUS results showing that 9% of drivers are talking on cell phones at any given daylight moment. The 3% of crashes associated with text messaging is based on an 8 times relative risk while text messaging estimate and a NOPUS estimate that about 0.9% of drivers at any given daylight moment are observed manipulating handheld electronic devices. For additional details on the National Safety Council's crash estimates, please visit *www.nsc.org/safety_road/Distracted_Driving/Pages/distracted_driving.aspx.*

State laws

Although research findings indicate that there is little to no safety advantage of hands-free over handheld cell phone use, the states that have implemented bans impacting all drivers have focused on handheld bans. As of July 2012, 10 states and the District of Columbia ban handheld devices for all drivers, while 34 states and the District of Columbia have passed total texting ban laws. The only state laws banning any use of cell phones while driving are limited to either young drivers or bus drivers. As of July 2012, 33 states and the District of Columbia ban young or novice drivers from using cell phones while driving. See page 110 for additional information regarding state motor vehicle laws.

McEvoy, S.P., Stevenson, M.R., McCartt, A.T., Woodward, M., Haworth, C., Palamar, P., & Cercarelli, R. (2005). Role of mobile phones in motor vehicle crashes resulting in hospital attendance: A case-crossover study. British Medical Journal. *Online First BMJ, doi:10.1136/bmj.38537.397512.55 (published online July 12, 2005).*

National Highway Traffic Safety Administration. (2002-2010). Traffic Safety Fact Sheets. *Available at www-nrd.nhtsa.dot.gov/cats/index.aspx.*

National Highway Traffic Safety Administration. (2010). Research note: High visibility enforcement demonstration programs in Connecticut and New York reduce hand-held phone use. Available at www-nrd.nhtsa.dot.gov/cats/index.aspx.

National Highway Traffic Safety Administration. (2011). National phone survey on distracted driving attitudes and behaviors. Available at www.nhtsa.gov/staticfiles/nti/pdf/811555.pdf.

National Highway Traffic Safety Administration (2010). Overview of the national highway traffic safety administration's driver distraction program. (DOT HS 811 299.)

National Safety Council (2010). Understanding the distracted brain, why driving while using hands-free cellphones is risky behavior. Downloaded on Sept. 1, 2010 from www.nsc.org/safety_road/Distracted_Driving/Pages/distracted_driving.aspx.

Ranney, T.A. (2008, April). Driver distraction: A review of the current state-of-knowledge (Report No. DOT HS 810 787). Washington, DC: National Highway Traffic Safety Administration.

Redelmeier, D.A., & Tibshirani, R.J. (1997). Association between cellular-telephone calls and motor vehicle collisions, New England Journal of Medicine, *336 (7), 453-458.*

Impact of high-visibility enforcement on driver handheld cell phone use

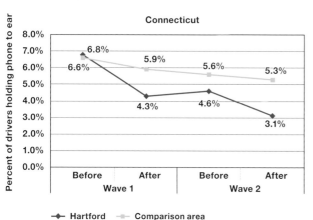

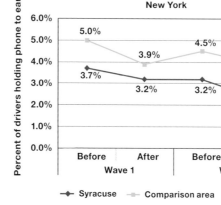

Source: National Highway Traffic Safety Administration, 2010

In most motor vehicle crashes, factors are present relating to the driver, the vehicle, and the road, and it is the interaction of these factors that often sets up the series of events that result in a crash. The table below relates only to the driver, and shows the principal kinds of improper driving in crashes in 2011 as reported by police. The "Other improper driving" category in the table includes driver inattention – however, see page 118 for a discussion of distracted driving issues.

Exceeding the posted speed limit or driving at an unsafe speed was the most common primary error in fatal crashes.

Right-of-way violations predominated in the "Injury crashes" and "All crashes" categories.

While some drivers were under the influence of alcohol or other drugs, this represents the driver's physical condition – not a driving error. See page 114 for a discussion of alcohol involvement in traffic incidents.

Correcting the improper practices listed below could reduce the number of crashes. This does not mean, however, that road and vehicle conditions can be disregarded.

Primary improper driving reported in crashes, 2011

Kind of improper driving	Fatal crashes	Injury crashes	All crashes
Total	100.0%	100.0%	100.0%
Improper driving	**54.6**	**57.0**	**53.5**
Speed too fast or unsafe	13.6	12.0	9.6
Right of way	10.6	15.2	12.6
Failed to yield	6.9	10.3	9.3
Disregarded signal	1.7	2.4	1.7
Passed stop sign	2.0	2.6	1.6
Drove left of center	4.6	0.9	0.7
Made improper turn	4.6	3.3	2.8
Improper overtaking	1.1	0.8	0.9
Followed too closely	1.2	6.5	7.8
Other improper driving	18.9	18.5	19.1
No improper driving stated	**45.4**	**43.0**	**46.5**

Source: Based on reports from 17 state traffic authorities. Percents may not add to totals due to rounding.

Large Trucks

In 2011, 3,757 fatalities resulted from a traffic crash involving a large truck, a 1.9% increase from 3,686 in 2010. About 72% of these deaths were occupants of vehicles other than the large truck (see chart below). Fatalities among other vehicle occupants in large truck crashes declined 3.6% from 2010 to 2011, while fatalities among truck occupants and non-occupants increased 20% and 19%, respectively. A large truck is one with a gross vehicle weight rating greater than 10,000 pounds.

Large trucks are more likely to be involved in a multiple-vehicle fatal crash than passenger vehicles. In 2011, 78% of large truck fatal crashes were multiple-vehicle crashes, compared with 35% of other fatal crashes.

In two-vehicle fatal crashes involving a large truck, 61% of the vehicles were struck in the front compared with 65% in two-vehicle fatal crashes not involving large trucks. The truck was struck in the rear nearly 3 times as often as the other vehicle – 19% and 7%, respectively.

Source: National Safety Council analysis of National Highway Traffic Safety Administration Fatality Analysis Reporting System data.
National Center for Statistics and Analysis. (December 2012). Traffic Safety Facts Research Note: 2011 Motor Vehicle Crashes: Overview. (DOT HS 811 701.) Washington, DC: NHTSA.

Fatalities in crashes involving large trucks, United States, 2011

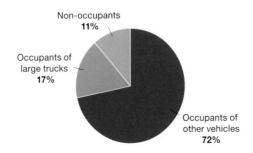

Non-occupants 11%
Occupants of large trucks 17%
Occupants of other vehicles 72%

Although motorcycles make up 3% of all registered vehicles and only 0.6% of all vehicle miles traveled in the United States, motorcyclists accounted for 14% of total traffic fatalities, 17% of all occupant fatalities, and 4% of all occupant injuries in 2011.

Fatalities among motorcycle riders and passengers have increased 41% between 2002 and 2011, from 3,270 to 4,612. Nonfatal injuries have increased as well, from 65,000 to 81,000 during the same period. The number of motorcycle fatalities increased 2% from 2010 to 2011, while injuries decreased by 1%.

Exposure also has increased. From 2002 through 2010 (the latest year available), the number of registered motorcycles increased more than 64% to 8.2 million from 5.0 million. Miles traveled is up 93%, from 9.5 billion to 18.5 billion in 2010 (latest available data). Consequently, the death rate from 2002 to 2010 has decreased 29%, from 34.23 to 24.39 deaths per 100 million miles traveled.

In 2010, speeding was a factor in 35% of fatal motorcycle crashes compared with 23% for fatal passenger car crashes.

Twenty-eight percent of motorcycle operators involved in fatal crashes were alcohol-impaired (blood alcohol concentration greater than or equal to 0.08 g/dL), compared with 23% for passenger cars, 22% for light trucks, and 2% for large trucks.

Motorcycle helmets are estimated to be 37% effective in preventing fatal injuries to motorcycle operators and 41% effective for motorcycle passengers. The National Highway Traffic Safety Administration estimated helmets saved 1,550 motorcyclists' lives in 2010, and an additional 706 lives could have been saved if all motorcyclists wore helmets. Helmet use continues a downward trend from a high of 71% in 2000; the latest occupant protection use survey results show a decrease in helmet use from 67% in 2009 to 54% for 2010.

In 2012, 19 states and the District of Columbia had laws requiring helmet use by all motorcyclists. Other states either required only a subset of motorcyclists to use helmets (such as those younger than 18) or had no helmet requirement.

An analysis by the National Safety Council shows a strong relationship between retail gasoline prices and motorcycle fatalities. After correcting for general inflation, as retail gasoline prices go up, so do motorcycle fatalities. The inverse also appears to be true; when gasoline prices trend down, so do motorcycle fatalities. These trends have been consistent for more than 30 years (see chart below).

Source: National Center for Statistics and Analysis. (2012). Traffic Safety Facts 2010 Data: Motorcycles. (DOT HS 811 639.) Washington, DC: National Highway Traffic Safety Administration.
Insurance Institute for Highway Safety. (November 2012). Motorcycle and bicycle helmet use laws. Downloaded on Nov. 20, 2012 from www.iihs.org/laws/Helmet UseOverview.aspx.
U.S. Department of Energy, Historical Gas Prices. Downloaded on Nov. 20, 2012 from www.eia.gov/forecasts/steo/realprices.

Motorcycle fatality and gasoline price trends, United States, 1976-2011

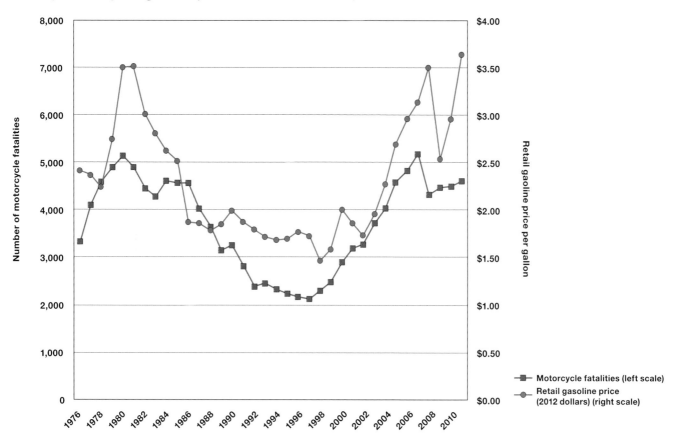

School bus-related crashes killed 123 people nationwide in 2011, according to National Safety Council tabulations of data from the National Highway Traffic Safety Administration (NHTSA).

A school bus-related crash is defined by NHTSA to be any crash in which a vehicle, regardless of body design, used as a school bus is directly or indirectly involved, such as a crash involving school children alighting from a vehicle.

From 2006 to 2011, about 73% of the deaths in school bus-related crashes were occupants of vehicles other than the school bus and 16% were pedestrians. About 5% were school bus passengers, 3% were school bus drivers, and another 3% were pedalcyclists.

Out of the people injured in school bus-related crashes from 2006 to 2011, about 38% were school bus passengers, 9% were school bus drivers, and an additional 45% were occupants of other vehicles. The remainder were pedestrians, pedalcyclists, and other or unknown type persons.

Characteristics of school bus transportation

According to *School Transportation News*, an estimated 440,000 to 480,000 yellow school buses provide transportation service daily nationwide and travel approximately 4.4 billion miles each school year. Approximately 26 million elementary and secondary school children ride school buses to and from school each day throughout the United States. That equates to more than 55 million student trips daily – not including the estimated 5 million daily round-trips for extracurricular activities. This compares to projections from the U.S. Department of Education of enrollments in fall 2011 in grades K-12 of about 49.4 million public school pupils and 5.3 million private school pupils nationwide.

Deaths and injuries in school bus-related crashes, United States, 2006-2011

	2006	2007	2008	2009	2010	2011
Deaths						
Total	150	142	152	118	129	123
School bus driver	3	4	4	2	6	7
School bus passenger	5	1	15	3	10	4
Pedestrian	22	19	21	21	26	20
Pedalcyclist	2	6	8	1	3	4
Occupant of other vehicle	118	112	104	91	83	87
Other non-occupants	0	0	0	0	1	1
Injuries						
Total	13,000	9,000	13,000	13,000	10,000	11,000
School bus driver	2,000	1,000	1,000	1,000	1,000	(a)
School bus passenger	5,000	2,000	6,000	6,000	3,000	4,000
Pedestrian	(a)	(a)	(a)	1,000	(a)	(a)
Pedalcyclist	(a)	(a)	(a)	(a)	(a)	(a)
Occupant of other vehicle	5,000	5,000	5,000	5,000	5,000	6,000
Other non-occupants	(a)	(a)	(a)	(a)	(a)	(a)

Source: Deaths for 2006-2010–National Center for Statistics and Analysis. (2011). Traffic Safety Facts 2010 Data–School Transportation-Related Crashes. (DOT HS 811 659.) Washington, DC: National Highway Traffic Safety Administration. Fatality data for 2011 and pedalcyclist deaths are National Safety Council tabulations of Fatality Analysis Reporting System (FARS) data. Injuries–National Center for Statistics and Analysis. (2006-2010). Traffic Safety Facts, 2006-2010 editions. Washington, DC: National Highway Traffic Safety Administration. Injury data for 2011 are National Safety Council tabulations of General Estimates System data. School bus transportation data accessed Dec. 17, 2012 from School Transportation News at http://stnonline.com/resources/safety/school-bus-safety-data. Student enrollment data from the Digest of Education Statistics: 2011, accessed Dec. 17, 2012 from the National Center for Education Statistics at http://nces.ed.gov/programs/digest/d11/tables/dt11_002.asp?referrer=report.
[a]Fewer than 500.

In 2011, an estimated 5,700 pedestrian deaths and 160,000 medically consulted nonfatal injuries[a] occurred among pedestrians in motor vehicle incidents. More than 19% of these deaths and injuries occurred when pedestrians darted or ran into streets. Pedestrians being in the roadway improperly (standing, working, or playing) accounted for about 6% of pedestrian deaths and injuries, while improper crossing of the roadway or intersection accounted for 4%. Nearly half of pedestrian deaths and injuries involved no improper action or circumstance.

The distribution of pedestrian deaths and injuries by action varies for people of different ages. Darting or running into the road was the leading specified type for individuals younger than 10, varying from about 43% for those younger than 5 to nearly 63% for those ages 5-9. No improper action or circumstance was the leading specified type for all other age groups, ranging from 43% for those 10-14 years old to 64% for those 65 and older.

[a]Medically consulted injuries are not comparable to estimates provided in earlier editions that used the definition of disabling injury. Please see the Technical Appendix for more information regarding medically consulted injuries.

Deaths and injuries of pedestrians by age and action/circumstance, United States, 2011

Action or circumstance	Total[a]	Age of people killed or injured							
		Younger than 5	5-9	10-14	15-19	20-24	25-44	45-64	65 and older
Totals[a]	110.2%	111.6%	120.1%	113.3%	110.3%	115.2%	109.0%	107.9%	106.1%
No improper action or circumstance	49.1%	37.2%	27.9%	43.3%	49.3%	45.6%	44.7%	55.7%	63.8%
Darting or running into roadway	19.3%	42.6%	62.6%	36.2%	26.7%	16.0%	13.1%	12.9%	5.9%
Other action or circumstance	15.9%	11.1%	19.6%	18.5%	13.5%	18.7%	16.3%	15.5%	13.3%
In roadway improperly (standing, lying, working, playing)	6.2%	8.4%	1.6%	3.9%	3.8%	6.6%	7.8%	8.6%	2.7%
Improper crossing of roadway or intersection	4.2%	0.6%	1.5%	2.0%	3.4%	8.6%	6.5%	2.9%	2.0%
Failure to obey traffic signs, signals, or officer	3.6%	6.4%	2.6%	1.4%	2.1%	5.4%	5.0%	2.5%	4.0%
Not visible (dark clothing, no lighting, etc.)	2.6%	0.0%	0.0%	4.6%	1.8%	1.1%	4.5%	0.9%	4.8%
Inattentive – talking, eating, etc.	2.5%	0.0%	2.6%	1.0%	3.3%	3.9%	3.6%	1.7%	0.6%
Not reported/unknown	7.0%	5.3%	1.6%	2.3%	6.3%	9.4%	7.6%	7.2%	9.0%

Source: National Safety Council tabulations of National Highway Traffic Safety Administration General Estimates System data.
[a]Totals are greater than 100% as multiple actions/circumstances may be entered for each case. Columns may not sum to totals because of rounding.

Pedestrian deaths and death rates by sex and age group, United States, 2010

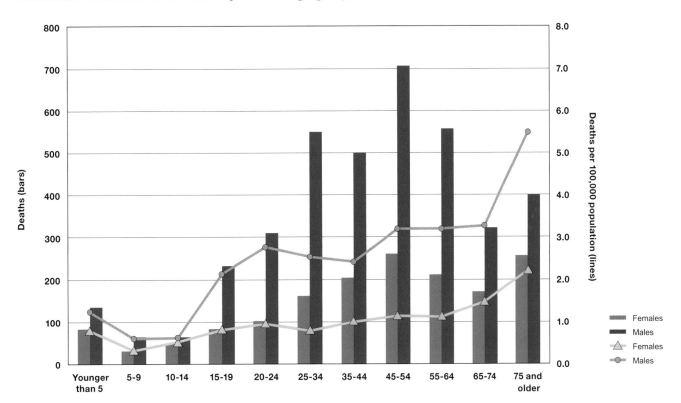

Source: National Safety Council tabulations based on U.S. Census Bureau and National Center for Health Statistics data.

According to the latest data available from the National Highway Traffic Safety Administration, 2011 marked the 10th consecutive year in which the number of teen fatalities in motor vehicle crashes has decreased in the United States, now at 2,638. However, motor vehicle crashes are still the number one cause of death for U.S. teens. National Center for Health Statistics data indicate that more than 1 out of 4 injury deaths among 16- to 20-year-olds is caused by a crash. The death toll among teens ages 13-19 was 2,638 in 2011, and is equivalent to nearly seven deaths per day. Based on mileage estimates from the National Household Travel Survey, the fatal crash rate per 100,000,000 miles driven is 6.1 for drivers 16-19 years old, compared with 1.3 among drivers 35-54 years old.

Mileage-based fatal crash rate per 100,000,000 miles driven by age of driver, United States, 2009

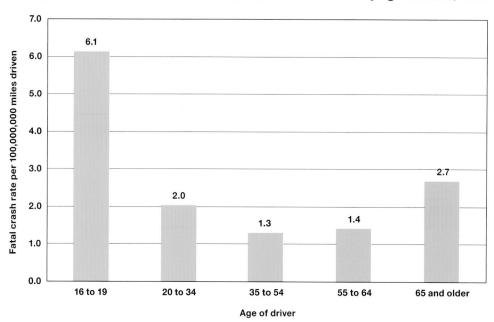

Source: Mileage-based rates estimated by the National Safety Council based on annual average mileage from the 2009 National Household Travel Survey, drivers in fatal crashes from the National Highway Traffic Safety Administration's Fatality Analysis Reporting System, and total licensed drivers estimated from Federal Highway Administration average annual mileage.

Crashes involving young drivers impact people of all ages. The chart below clearly shows that young driver fatalities account for less than half of the overall fatalities associated with young driver crashes. In 2011, there were 1,987 young driver fatalities, 1,191 fatalities among passengers of young drivers, 1,120 fatalities to occupants of all other vehicles, and 469 non-occupant fatalities. Although the number of deaths has dramatically decreased since 1982, the number of young driver deaths per miles driven is still more than 3 times higher than for all drivers of passenger vehicles.

Historical trend of young driver-related fatalities, United States, 1982-2011

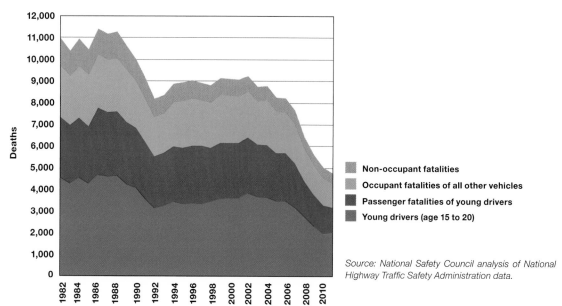

Source: National Safety Council analysis of National Highway Traffic Safety Administration data.

A recent study using the National Highway Traffic Safety Administration's National Motor Vehicle Crash Causation Survey found that driver error among 15- to 18-year-old drivers was by far the most common reason for crashes (95.6%). Among crashes with a driver error, a teen made the error 79.3% of the time. Recognition errors, such as inadequate surveillance, accounted for 46.3% of all teen driving errors, followed by decision errors, including following too closely and too fast for conditions (40.1%), and performance errors such as loss of control (8.0%).

A strategy shown to help prevent young driver crashes is the passage and enforcement of state Graduated Driver Licensing (GDL) programs. GDL programs allow for a gradual phasing in of full driving privileges using a three-step process comprising an initial learner's permit phase; an intermediate, or provisional, license phase; and a full licensure phase.

Not all state GDL programs are equally effective. A recent national study of the impact of state GDL programs found that programs rated "good" were associated with 30% lower fatal crash rates among 15- to 17-year-olds compared with GDL programs rated "poor." Programs rated "fair" yielded fatal crash rates 11% lower.

Although the components of GDL programs vary from state to state, stronger GDL programs consist of five or more of the following components:

1. A minimum age of at least 16 years old for gaining a learner's permit
2. A requirement to hold the learner's permit for at least six months before gaining a license that allows any unsupervised driving
3. A requirement for certification of at least 30 hours of supervised driving practice during the learner's permit stage
4. An intermediate stage of licensing with a minimum entry age of at least 16 years and 6 months
5. A nighttime driving restriction for intermediate license

holders, beginning no later than 10 p.m.
6. A passenger restriction for intermediate license holders, allowing no more than one passenger (except family members)
7. A minimum age of 17 for full licensure

Looking at the adoption of these seven GDL components by states over time shows dramatic advancements in young driver safety. As shown in the chart below, starting in 1991, only 10 states had any programs reflecting GDL components. By 2001, 36 states and the District of Columbia had programs reflecting one or more GDL components. The latest available data show that by the end of 2012 only two states had implemented all seven components and only seven states and the District of Columbia had five or six GDL components. The majority of states have either three or four components implemented.

In addition to these seven components commonly associated with GDL programs, the National Safety Council recommends several additional or more stringent components be included in comprehensive GDL programs:

- Cell phone use ban
- Text messaging ban
- No passengers younger than 18
- Mandatory safety belt use (primary safety belt laws)

Sources: Baker, S.P., Chen, L-H, & Li, G. (2007). National review of graduated driver licensing. Downloaded on Nov. 22, 2011 from www.aaafoundation.org/resources/index.cfm?button=research.
Braitman, K.A., Kirley, B., McCartt, A., & Chaudhary, N. (2008). Crashes of novice teenage drivers: characteristics and contributing factors. Journal of Safety Research, Vol. 39, pp. 27-54.
Curry, A.E., Hafetz, J., Kallan, M.J., Winston, F.K., & Durbin, D.R. (2011). Prevalence of teen driver errors leading to serious motor vehicle crashes. Accident Analysis and Prevention, Vol. 43, pp. 1285-1290.
McCartt, A.T., Teoh, E.R., Fields, M., Braitman, K.A., & Hellinga, L.A. (2010). Graduated licensing laws and fatal crashes of teenage drivers: a national study. Traffic Injury Prevention, Vol. 11, pp. 240-248.

Historical trend of the number of states with GDL components, 1991-2012

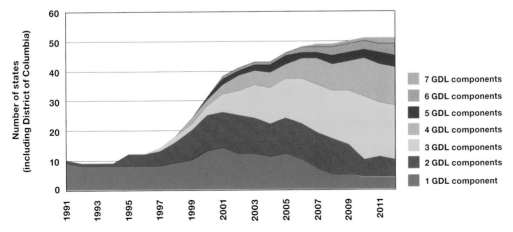

Source: National Safety Council analysis of Insurance Institute for Highway Safety data and review of individual state laws.

The table below shows the total number of licensed drivers and drivers involved in crashes by selected ages and age groups. Also shown is the rate of crash involvement on the basis of the number of drivers in each age group. The fatal crash involvement rates per 100,000 licensed drivers in each age group ranged from a low of 15 for drivers in the 65-74 age group to a high of 42 for drivers age 16. The all-incident involvement rates per 100 drivers in each age group ranged from five for drivers in the 65-74 and 75 and older age groups to 23 for drivers age 16.

On the basis of miles driven by each age group, however, involvement rates (not shown in the table) are highest for young and old drivers. For drivers 16-19 years old, the fatal crash involvement rate per 100 million vehicle miles traveled was about 6.1 in 2009, more than 3 times the overall rate of 1.8 for all drivers in passenger vehicles. The rate declines to about 1.3 for drivers 35-54 years old, and then rises somewhat for drivers 65 and older.

For more details of this mileage-based analysis, please see pages 124 and 125.

Licensed drivers and number in crashes by age of driver, United States, 2011

| Age group | Licensed drivers | | Drivers in ... | | | | | |
| | Number | Percent | Fatal crashes | | | All crashes | | |
			Number	Percent	Rate[a]	Number	Percent	Rate[b]
Total	211,600,000	100.0%	46,700	100.0%	22	18,800,000	100.0%	9
Younger than 16	782,000	0.4	100	0.2	(c)	30,000	0.2	(c)
16	1,196,000	0.6	500	1.1	42	280,000	1.5	23
17	2,002,000	0.9	700	1.5	35	440,000	2.3	22
18	2,685,000	1.3	1,000	2.1	37	580,000	3.1	22
19	3,150,000	1.5	1,200	2.6	38	570,000	3.0	18
19 and younger	9,815,000	4.7	3,500	7.5	36	1,900,000	10.1	19
20	3,561,000	1.7	1,200	2.6	34	570,000	3.0	16
21	3,649,000	1.7	1,300	2.8	36	570,000	3.0	16
22	3,535,000	1.7	1,300	2.8	37	510,000	2.7	14
23	3,455,000	1.6	1,200	2.6	35	580,000	3.1	17
24	3,430,000	1.6	1,100	2.4	32	460,000	2.4	13
20-24	17,630,000	8.3	6,100	13.2	35	2,690,000	14.2	15
25-34	35,829,000	16.9	9,300	19.9	26	3,890,000	20.7	11
35-44	35,871,000	16.9	7,700	16.5	21	3,470,000	18.5	10
45-54	40,823,000	19.3	8,200	17.6	20	3,000,000	16.0	7
55-64	36,852,000	17.4	6,000	12.8	16	2,210,000	11.8	6
65-74	20,916,000	13.9	3,200	6.9	15	1,010,000	5.4	5
75 and older	13,864,000	6.6	2,700	5.8	19	630,000	3.4	5

Source: National Safety Council estimates. Drivers in incidents based on data from the National Highway Traffic Safety Administration's Fatality Analysis Reporting System and General Estimates System. Total licensed drivers and age distribution estimated by the National Safety Council based on data from the Federal Highway Administration.
Note: Percents may not add to total due to rounding.
[a]Drivers in fatal incidents per 100,000 licensed drivers in each age group.
[b]Drivers in all incidents per 100 licensed drivers in each age group.
[c]Rates for drivers younger than 16 are substantially overstated due to the high proportion of unlicensed drivers involved.

Comparing data of long-term motor vehicle deaths and death rates to the backdrop of recession periods reveals several interesting trends. First, during recession periods the number of deaths declines and, to a lesser extent, the mileage-based death rate also tends to decline. The large decline in the number of deaths is partially a result of fewer people driving during poor economic times. As would be expected following the end of recessionary periods, the number of deaths tends to increase. Although the latest 2011 motor vehicle data show a continued decline in the number of fatalities following the last recession, preliminary partial year estimates for 2012 (not included in chart) appear to be showing a modest increase in the number of fatalities. However, the mileage-based death rate does not typically increase following a recession period, but instead stabilizes or continues a slow, steady decline. Given this trend, it appears that even after accounting for recession periods, there is a slow but steady improvement in motor vehicle safety when measured using mileage-based death rates.

Source: Death data are from the National Center for Health Statistics except 1964 and 2011, which are National Safety Council estimates based on data from the National Highway Traffic Safety Administration's Fatality Analysis Reporting System. Motor vehicle rates are based on mileage estimates from the Federal Highway Administration, except 2011, which is a National Safety Council estimate. Recession periods are from the National Bureau of Economic Research.

Historical motor vehicle deaths and death rates, United States, 1950-2011

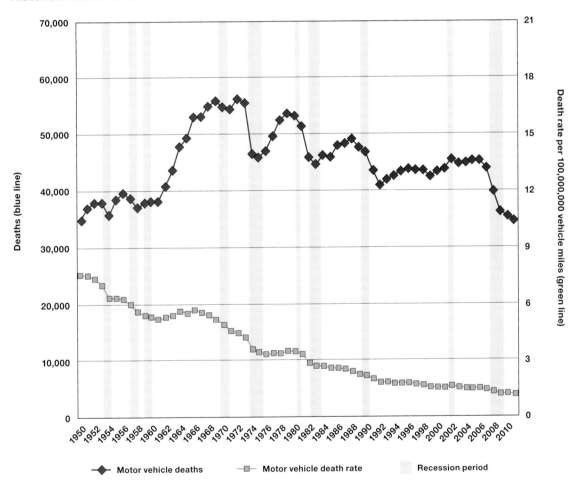

Motor vehicle deaths ◆   Motor vehicle death rate ▫   Recession period

More fatal crashes occurred on Saturday than any other day of the week in 2011, according to data from the National Highway Traffic Safety Administration. More than 18% of fatal crashes occurred on Saturday, compared with about 15% on Fridays and Sundays. For all crashes, Friday had the highest percentage, with more than 17%.

Patterns by hour of day for fatal crashes show peaks during afternoon rush hour for weekdays and, especially, late at night during weekends. For all crashes, primary peaks occurred during afternoon rush hours, with secondary peaks during morning rush hours.

Percent of weekly crashes by hour of day and day of week, United States, 2011

Time of day	Fatal crashes								All crashes							
	Total	Sun.	Mon.	Tues.	Wed.	Thurs.	Fri.	Sat.	Total	Sun.	Mon.	Tues.	Wed.	Thurs.	Fri.	Sat.
All hours	100.0%	15.4%	12.8%	12.3%	12.6%	13.3%	15.3%	18.2%	100.0%	10.0%	14.2%	15.0%	15.3%	15.4%	17.2%	12.8%
Midnight to 3:59 a.m.	17.1%	4.3%	1.6%	1.2%	1.4%	1.7%	2.4%	4.4%	5.6%	1.4%	0.5%	0.5%	0.5%	0.6%	0.8%	1.3%
4:00 to 7:59 a.m.	13.1%	2.0%	1.7%	1.7%	1.7%	1.7%	1.9%	2.3%	10.0%	0.7%	1.6%	1.8%	1.6%	1.7%	1.6%	1.0%
8:00 to 11:59 a.m.	12.2%	1.4%	1.8%	1.8%	1.7%	1.8%	1.9%	1.7%	18.4%	1.5%	2.9%	3.0%	2.9%	3.0%	3.0%	2.2%
Noon to 3:59 p.m.	16.6%	2.2%	2.4%	2.4%	2.4%	2.4%	2.4%	2.4%	26.2%	2.6%	3.7%	3.8%	4.2%	3.9%	4.6%	3.3%
4:00 to 7:59 p.m.	20.4%	2.9%	2.7%	2.8%	2.9%	2.9%	3.0%	3.3%	27.4%	2.3%	3.9%	4.3%	4.6%	4.4%	5.0%	2.9%
8:00 to 11:59 p.m.	19.6%	2.4%	2.4%	2.3%	2.3%	2.8%	3.5%	3.9%	11.7%	1.5%	1.5%	1.5%	1.4%	1.6%	2.2%	2.0%

Source: National Safety Council analysis of data from National Highway Traffic Safety Administraion Fatality Analysis Reporting System and General Estimates System.
Note: Column and row totals may not equal sum of parts due to rounding and unreported time of day or day of week data.

Percent of crashes by time of day and day of week, United States, 2011

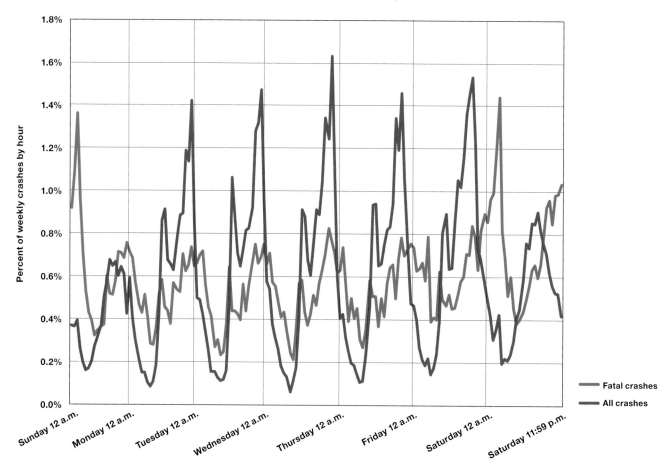

Note: Each daily column represents 24 hours.

Motor vehicle deaths in 2011 were at their lowest level in February and increased to their highest level in July. In 2011, the highest monthly mileage death rate of 1.32 deaths per 100,000,000 vehicle miles occurred in October.

The overall rate for the year was 1.18.

Source: Deaths – National Safety Council estimates. Mileage – Federal Highway Administration, Traffic Volume Trends.

Motor vehicle deaths and mileage death rates by month, United States, 2011

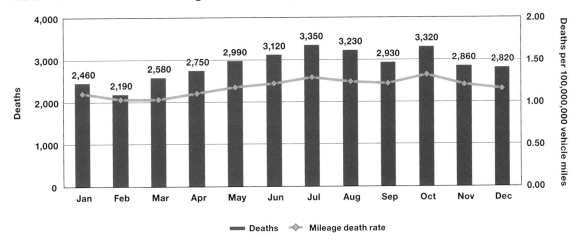

Holidays

Holidays traditionally are a time of travel for families across the United States. Many choose the automobile – with the highest fatality rate of any of the major forms of transportation based on fatalities per passenger mile (see page 156) – as their mode of travel, therefore increasing their risk of dying in a motor vehicle crash. In addition, holidays are often the cause for celebrations that include drinking alcohol, which is a major contributing factor to motor vehicle crashes. Nationwide, alcohol-impaired (blood alcohol concentration of 0.08 g/dL or higher) fatalities in 2011 represented 31% of the total traffic fatalities. The table below shows the number of fatalities for each major holiday period and the percent of those fatalities that were alcohol-impaired.

Motor vehicle deaths and percent alcohol-impaired during holiday periods, United States, 2007-2011

Year	Holiday period[a]											
	New Year's Day		Memorial Day		Independence Day		Labor Day		Thanksgiving Day		Christmas Day	
	Deaths[b]	Alcohol-impaired[c] (%)	Deaths[b]	Alcohol-impaired[c] (%)	Deaths[b]	Alcohol-impaired[c] (%)	Deaths[b]	Alcohol-impaired[c] (%)	Deaths[b]	Alcohol-impaired[c] (%)	Deaths[b]	Alcohol-impaired[c] (%)
2007	387 (3)	40	475 (3)	37	184 (1)	45	508 (3)	42	542 (4)	35	454 (4)	38
2008	407 (4)	41	414 (3)	41	472 (3)	44	473 (3)	40	484 (4)	35	409 (4)	32
2009	458 (4)	40	462 (3)	42	398 (3)	39	351 (3)	38	401 (4)	34	248 (3)	36
2010	286 (3)	48	389 (3)	40	365 (3)	39	390 (3)	36	417 (4)	40	249 (3)	37
2011	304 (3)	–	389 (3)	–	405 (3)	–	373 (3)	–	375 (4)	–	256 (3)	–

Source: Deaths – National Safety Council tabulations of National Highway Traffic Safety Administration (NHTSA) Fatality Analysis Reporting System data. Percent alcohol impaired – NHTSA, Traffic Safety Facts, 2010 edition.
Note: Dashes indicate data not available.
[a]The length of the holiday period depends on the day of the week on which the holiday falls. Memorial Day and Labor Day are always 3.25 days; Thanksgiving is always 4.25 days; and New Year's Day, Independence Day, and Christmas are 3.25 days if the holiday falls on Friday through Monday, 4.25 days if on Tuesday or Thursday, and 1.25 days if on Wednesday.
[b]Number in parentheses refers to the number of whole days in the holiday period.
[c]Highest blood alcohol concentration (BAC) among drivers or motorcycle riders involved in the crash was 0.08 grams per deciliter (g/dL) or higher. The holiday periods used to calculate the percentages conform to the NHTSA holiday period definitions that add another quarter day to the periods noted in footnote (a).

In 2011, 587 people were killed and 38,864 people were injured in work zone crashes (see table below). Of the 587 killed in work zones, 401 were in construction zones, 54 were in maintenance zones, 12 were in utility zones, and 120 were in an unknown type of work zone.

From 2002 through 2011, work zone deaths have ranged from 576 to 1,181 and averaged 875 per year.

According to the Governors Highway Safety Association, nearly all states have laws that increase the penalties for speeding or committing other traffic violations while in a construction work.[a] The penalties often involve doubled fines, but also

can be a fixed dollar amount. In some cases, the penalty is applicable only when workers are present and/or if signs are posted. Presently, 33 states and the District of Columbia double the fine for speeding or other traffic violations in a work zone. Twenty-four states and the District of Columbia require workers to be present in the construction zone for the increased penalties to take effect.

[a]Retrieved Dec. 18, 2012 from www.ghsa.org/html/stateinfo/laws/sanctions_laws.html.

People killed or injured in work zones, United States, 2011

	Total	Vehicle occupants	Pedestrians	Pedalcyclists	Other nonmotorists
Killed	587	479	101	7	0
Injured	38,864	37,892	578	374	20

Source: National Safety Council analysis of data from National Highway Traffic Safety Administration Fatality Analysis Reporting System and General Estimates Systems.

Work zone deaths, United States, 2000-2009

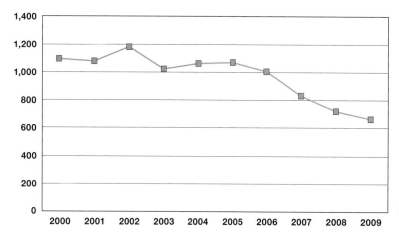

Source: NSC analysis of NHTSA FARS data files.

Emergency Vehicles

Crashes involving emergency vehicles, United States, 2011

	Ambulance		Fire truck/car		Police car	
	Total	Emergency use[a]	Total	Emergency use[a]	Total	Emergency use[a]
Emergency vehicles in fatal crashes	19	9	5	4	76	37
Emergency vehicles in injury crashes	456	126	141	12	3,225	1,279
Emergency vehicles in all crashes	**3,719**	**1,156**	**2,762**	**1,599**	**26,773**	**8,662**
Emergency vehicle drivers killed	0	0	0	0	22	12
Emergency vehicle passengers killed	4	2	0	0	2	0
Other vehicle occupants killed	17	0	6	0	43	0
Nonmotorists killed	0	0	0	0	14	0
Total killed in crashes	**21**	**2**	**6**	**0**	**81**	**12**
Total injured in crashes	**2,746**	**772**	**510**	**245**	**9,593**	**3,305**

Source: National Safety Council analysis of data from National Highway Traffic Safety Administration Fatality Analysis Reporting System and General Estimates Systems.
[a]Vehicle being used as an emergency vehicle at the time of the crash with or without the use of emergency warning equipment.

The National Safety Council (NSC) and the National Highway Traffic Safety Administration (NHTSA) count motor vehicle crash deaths using somewhat different criteria. NSC counts total motor vehicle-related fatalities – both traffic and nontraffic – that occur within one year of the crash. This is consistent with the data compiled from death certificates by the National Center for Health Statistics (NCHS). NCS uses NCHS death certificate data less intentional fatalities as the final count of unintentional deaths from all causes.

NHTSA counts only traffic fatalities that occur within 30 days of the crash in its Fatality Analysis Reporting System (FARS). This means that the FARS count omits about 800 to 1,000 motor vehicle-related deaths each year that occur more than 30 days after the crash. Nontraffic fatalities (those that do not occur on public highways; e.g., parking lots, private roads,

and driveways), which account for 900 to 1,900 deaths annually, also are omitted. By using a 30-day cutoff, NHTSA can issue a "final" count about eight months after the reference year.

Because both the 2009 and 2010 NCHS data were available for this edition of *Injury Facts*, the final counts for both years by cause of death including motor vehicle crashes are included, along with estimates of the totals for 2011. For motor vehicle deaths, these estimates are based on data supplied by traffic authorities in all 50 states and the District of Columbia. See the Technical Appendix for more information on all of the National Safety Council's estimation procedures.

The graph below shows NCHS death certificate counts of unintentional motor vehicle deaths through 2010 and the Council's estimate for 2011 compared to NHTSA FARS counts of traffic deaths.

Motor vehicle deaths: NSC and NHTSA, 1992-2011

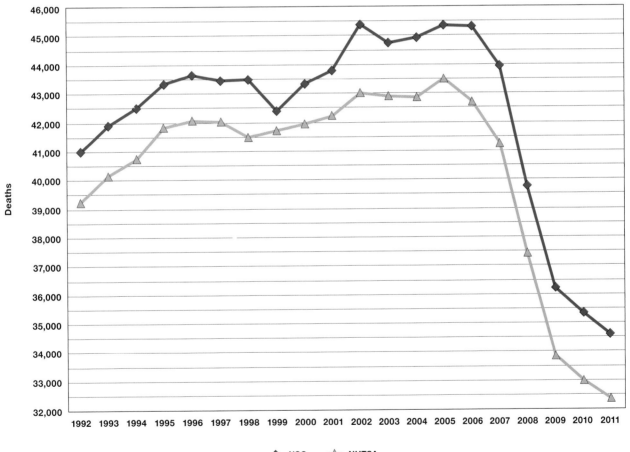

Motor vehicle deaths and rates, United States, 1913-2011

Year	No. of deaths	Estimated no. of vehicles (millions)	Estimated vehicle miles (billions)	Estimated no. of drivers (millions)	Death rates Per 10,000 motor vehicles	Per 100,000,000 vehicle miles	Per 100,000 population
1913	4,200	1.3	(a)	2.0	33.38	(a)	4.4
1914	4,700	1.8	(a)	3.0	26.65	(a)	4.8
1915	6,600	2.5	(a)	3.0	26.49	(a)	6.6
1916	8,200	3.6	(a)	5.0	22.66	(a)	8.1
1917	10,200	5.1	(a)	7.0	19.93	(a)	10.0
1918	10,700	6.2	(a)	9.0	17.37	(a)	10.3
1919	11,200	7.6	(a)	12.0	14.78	(a)	10.7
1920	12,500	9.2	(a)	14.0	13.53	(a)	11.7
1921	13,900	10.5	(a)	16.0	13.25	(a)	12.9
1922	15,300	12.3	(a)	19.0	12.47	(a)	13.9
1923	18,400	15.1	85	22.0	12.18	21.65	16.5
1924	19,400	17.6	104	26.0	11.02	18.65	17.1
1925	21,900	20.1	122	30.0	10.89	17.95	19.1
1926	23,400	22.2	141	33.0	10.54	16.59	20.1
1927	25,800	23.3	158	34.0	11.07	16.33	21.8
1928	28,000	24.7	173	37.0	11.34	16.18	23.4
1929	31,200	26.7	197	40.0	11.69	15.84	25.7
1930	32,900	26.7	206	40.0	12.32	15.97	26.7
1931	33,700	26.1	216	39.0	12.91	15.60	27.2
1932	29,500	24.4	200	36.0	12.09	14.75	23.6
1933	31,363	24.2	201	35.0	12.96	15.60	25.0
1934	36,101	25.3	216	37.0	14.27	16.71	28.6
1935	36,369	26.5	229	39.0	13.72	15.88	28.6
1936	38,089	28.5	252	42.0	13.36	15.11	29.7
1937	39,643	30.1	270	44.0	13.19	14.68	30.8
1938	32,582	29.8	271	44.0	10.93	12.02	25.1
1939	32,386	31.0	285	46.0	10.44	11.35	24.7
1940	34,501	32.5	302	48.0	10.63	11.42	26.1
1941	39,969	34.9	334	52.0	11.45	11.98	30.0
1942	28,309	33.0	268	49.0	8.58	10.55	21.1
1943	23,823	30.9	208	46.0	7.71	11.44	17.8
1944	24,282	30.5	213	45.0	7.97	11.42	18.3
1945	28,076	31.0	250	46.0	9.05	11.22	21.2
1946	33,411	34.4	341	50.0	9.72	9.80	23.9
1947	32,697	37.8	371	53.0	8.64	8.82	22.8
1948	32,259	41.1	398	55.0	7.85	8.11	22.1
1949	31,701	44.7	424	59.3	7.09	7.47	21.3
1950	34,763	49.2	458	62.2	7.07	7.59	23.0
1951	36,996	51.9	491	64.4	7.13	7.53	24.1
1952	37,794	53.3	514	66.8	7.10	7.36	24.3
1953	37,956	56.3	544	69.9	6.74	6.97	24.0
1954	35,586	58.6	562	72.2	6.07	6.33	22.1
1955	38,426	62.8	606	74.7	6.12	6.34	23.4
1956	39,628	65.2	631	77.9	6.07	6.28	23.7
1957	38,702	67.6	647	79.6	5.73	5.98	22.7
1958	36,981	68.8	665	81.5	5.37	5.56	21.3
1959	37,910	72.1	700	84.5	5.26	5.41	21.5
1960	38,137	74.5	719	87.4	5.12	5.31	21.2
1961	38,091	76.4	738	88.9	4.98	5.16	20.8
1962	40,804	79.7	767	92.0	5.12	5.32	22.0
1963	43,564	83.5	805	93.7	5.22	5.41	23.1
1964	47,700	87.3	847	95.6	5.46	5.63	25.0
1965	49,163	91.8	888	99.0	5.36	5.54	25.4
1966	53,041	95.9	930	101.0	5.53	5.70	27.1
1967	52,924	98.9	962	103.2	5.35	5.50	26.8
1968	54,862	103.1	1,016	105.4	5.32	5.40	27.5
1969	55,791	107.4	1,071	108.3	5.19	5.21	27.7
1970	54,633	111.2	1,120	111.5	4.92	4.88	26.8
1971	54,381	116.3	1,186	114.4	4.68	4.57	26.3
1972	56,278	122.3	1,268	118.4	4.60	4.43	26.9
1973	55,511	129.8	1,309	121.6	4.28	4.24	26.3
1974	46,402	134.9	1,290	125.6	3.44	3.59	21.8
1975	45,853	137.9	1,330	129.8	3.33	3.45	21.3
1976	47,038	143.5	1,412	133.9	3.28	3.33	21.6

See source and footnotes on page 133.

Motor vehicle deaths and rates, United States, 1913-2011 (cont.)

Year	No. of deaths	Estimated no. of vehicles (millions)	Estimated vehicle miles (billions)	Estimated no. of drivers (millions)	Death rates		
					Per 10,000 motor vehicles	Per 100,000,000 vehicle miles	Per 100,000 population
1978	52,411	153.6	1,548	140.8	3.41	3.39	23.6
1979	53,524	159.6	1,529	143.3	3.35	3.50	23.8
1980	53,172	161.6	1,521	145.3	3.29	3.50	23.4
1981	51,385	164.1	1,556	147.1	3.13	3.30	22.4
1982	45,779	165.2	1,592	150.3	2.77	2.88	19.8
1983	44,452	169.4	1,657	154.2	2.62	2.68	19.0
1984	46,263	171.8	1,718	155.4	2.69	2.69	19.6
1985	45,901	177.1	1,774	156.9	2.59	2.59	19.3
1986	47,865	181.4	1,835	159.5	2.63	2.60	19.9
1987	48,290	183.9	1,924	161.8	2.63	2.51	19.9
1988	49,078	189.0	2,026	162.9	2.60	2.42	20.1
1989	47,575	191.7	2,107	165.6	2.48	2.26	19.3
1990	46,814	192.9	2,148	167.0	2.43	2.18	18.8
1991	43,536	192.5	2,172	169.0	2.26	2.00	17.3
1992	40,982	194.4	2,240	173.1	2.11	1.83	16.1
1993	41,893	198.0	2,297	173.1	2.12	1.82	16.3
1994	42,524	201.8	2,360	175.4	2.11	1.80	16.3
1995	43,363	205.3	2,423	176.6	2.11	1.79	16.5
1996	43,649	210.4	2,486	179.5	2.07	1.76	16.5
1997	43,458	211.5	2,562	182.7	2.05	1.70	16.2
1998	43,501	215.0	2,632	185.2	2.02	1.65	16.1
1999	42,401	220.5	2,691	187.2	1.92	1.58	15.5
2000	43,354	225.8	2,747	190.6	1.92	1.58	15.8
2001	43,788	235.3	2,797	191.3	1.86	1.57	15.4
2002	45,380	234.6	2,856	194.3	1.93	1.59	15.8
2003	44,757	236.8	2,890	196.2	1.89	1.55	15.4
2004	44,933	243.0	2,965	199.0	1.85	1.52	15.3
2005	45,343	247.4	2,989	200.5	1.83	1.52	15.3
2006	45,316	250.8	3,014	202.8	1.81	1.50	15.2
2007	43,945	254.4	3,032	205.7	1.73	1.45	14.6
2008	39,790	255.9	2,976	208.3	1.55	1.34	13.1
2009[b]	36,216	254.2	2,957	209.6	1.42	1.22	11.8
2010[b]	35,332	250.3	2,966	210.1	1.41	1.19	11.4
2011[c]	34,600	248.9	2,931	211.6	1.39	1.18	11.1
Changes							
2002 to 2011	-24%	6%	3%	9%	-28%	-26%	-30%
2010 to 2011	-2%	-1%	-1%	1%	-1%	-1%	-3%

Source: Deaths from National Center for Health Statistics except 1964 and 2011, which are National Safety Council estimates based on data from the National Highway Traffic Safety Administration's Fatality Analysis Reporting System. See Technical Appendix for comparability. Motor vehicle registrations, mileage, and drivers estimated by Federal Highway Administration except for 2011 registrations and drivers, which are National Safety Council estimates.
[a]*Mileage data inadequate prior to 1923.*
[b]*Revised.*
[c]*Preliminary.*
[d]*Less than 0.5%.*

Motor vehicle deaths by type of incident, United States, 1913-2011

Year	Total deaths	Pedestrians	Other motor vehicles	Railroad trains	Streetcars	Pedalcycles	Animal-drawn vehicle or animal	Fixed objects	Deaths from noncollision incidents	Nontraffic deaths[a]
				Deaths from collision with...						
1913	4,200	(b)	(b)	(b)	(b)	(b)	(b)	(b)	(b)	(c)
1914	4,700	(b)	(b)	(b)	(b)	(b)	(b)	(b)	(b)	(c)
1915	6,600	(b)	(b)	(b)	(b)	(b)	(b)	(b)	(b)	(c)
1916	8,200	(b)	(b)	(b)	(b)	(b)	(b)	(b)	(b)	(c)
1917	10,200	(b)	(b)	(b)	(b)	(b)	(b)	(b)	(b)	(c)
1918	10,700	(b)	(b)	(b)	(b)	(b)	(b)	(b)	(b)	(c)
1919	11,200	(b)	(b)	(b)	(b)	(b)	(b)	(b)	(b)	(c)
1920	12,500	(b)	(b)	(b)	(b)	(b)	(b)	(b)	(b)	(c)
1921	13,900	(b)	(b)	(b)	(b)	(b)	(b)	(b)	(b)	(c)
1922	15,300	(b)	(b)	(b)	(b)	(b)	(b)	(b)	(b)	(c)
1923	18,400	(b)	(b)	(b)	(b)	(b)	(b)	(b)	(b)	(c)
1924	19,400	(b)	(b)	1,130	410	(b)	(b)	(b)	(b)	(c)
1925	21,900	(b)	(b)	1,410	560	(b)	(b)	(b)	(b)	(c)
1926	23,400	(b)	(b)	1,730	520	(b)	(b)	(b)	(b)	(c)
1927	25,800	10,820	3,430	1,830	520	(b)	(b)	(b)	(b)	(c)
1928	28,000	11,420	4,310	2,140	570	(b)	(b)	540	8,070	(c)
1929	31,200	12,250	5,400	2,050	530	(b)	(b)	620	9,380	(c)
1930	32,900	12,900	5,880	1,830	480	(b)	(b)	720	9,970	(c)
1931	33,700	13,370	6,820	1,710	440	(b)	(b)	870	9,570	(c)
1932	29,500	11,490	6,070	1,520	320	350	400	800	8,500	(c)
1933	31,363	12,840	6,470	1,437	318	400	310	900	8,680	(c)
1934	36,101	14,480	8,110	1,457	332	500	360	1,040	9,820	(c)
1935	36,369	14,350	8,750	1,587	253	450	250	1,010	9,720	(c)
1936	38,089	15,250	9,500	1,697	269	650	250	1,060	9,410	(c)
1937	39,643	15,500	10,320	1,810	264	700	200	1,160	9,690	(c)
1938	32,582	12,850	8,900	1,490	165	720	170	940	7,350	(c)
1939	32,386	12,400	8,700	1,330	150	710	200	1,000	7,900	(c)
1940	34,501	12,700	10,100	1,707	132	750	210	1,100	7,800	(c)
1941	39,969	13,550	12,500	1,840	118	910	250	1,350	9,450	(c)
1942	28,309	10,650	7,300	1,754	124	650	240	850	6,740	(c)
1943	23,823	9,900	5,300	1,448	171	450	160	700	5,690	(c)
1944	24,282	9,900	5,700	1,663	175	400	140	700	5,600	(c)
1945	28,076	11,000	7,150	1,703	163	500	130	800	6,600	(c)
1946	33,411	11,600	9,400	1,703	174	450	130	950	8,900	(c)
1947	32,697	10,450	9,900	1,736	102	550	150	1,000	8,800	(c)
1948	32,259	9,950	10,200	1,474	83	500	100	1,000	8,950	(c)
1949	31,701	8,800	10,500	1,452	56	550	140	1,100	9,100	838
1950	34,763	9,000	11,650	1,541	89	440	120	1,300	10,600	900
1951	36,996	9,150	13,100	1,573	46	390	100	1,400	11,200	966
1952	37,794	8,900	13,500	1,429	32	430	130	1,450	11,900	970
1953	37,956	8,750	13,400	1,506	26	420	120	1,500	12,200	1,026
1954	35,586	8,000	12,800	1,289	28	380	90	1,500	11,500	1,004
1955	38,426	8,200	14,500	1,490	15	410	90	1,600	12,100	989
1956	39,628	7,900	15,200	1,377	11	440	100	1,600	13,000	888
1957	38,702	7,850	15,400	1,376	13	460	80	1,700	11,800	1,016
1958	36,981	7,650	14,200	1,316	9	450	80	1,650	11,600	929
1959	37,910	7,850	14,900	1,202	6	480	70	1,600	11,800	948
1960	38,137	7,850	14,800	1,368	5	460	80	1,700	11,900	995
1961	38,091	7,650	14,700	1,267	5	490	80	1,700	12,200	1,065
1962	40,804	7,900	16,400	1,245	3	500	90	1,750	12,900	1,029
1963	43,564	8,200	17,600	1,385	10	580	80	1,900	13,800	990
1964	47,700	9,000	19,600	1,580	5	710	100	2,100	14,600	1,123
1965	49,163	8,900	20,800	1,556	5	680	120	2,200	14,900	1,113
1966	53,041	9,400	22,200	1,800	2	740	100	2,500	16,300	1,108
1967	52,924	9,400	22,000	1,620	3	750	100	2,350	16,700	1,165
1968	54,862	9,900	22,400	1,570	4	790	100	2,700	17,400	1,061
1969	55,791	10,100	23,700	1,495	2	800	100	3,900[d]	15,700[d]	1,155
1970	54,633	9,900	23,200	1,459	3	780	100	3,800	15,400	1,140
1971	54,381	9,900	23,100	1,378	2	800	100	3,800	15,300	1,015
1972	56,278	10,300	23,900	1,260	2	1,000	100	3,900	15,800	1,064
1973	55,511	10,200	23,600	1,194	2	1,000	100	3,800	15,600	1,164
1974	46,402	8,500	19,700	1,209	1	1,000	100	3,100	12,800	1,088
1975	45,853	8,400	19,550	979	1	1,000	100	3,130	12,700	1,033
1976	47,038	8,600	20,100	1,033	2	1,000	100	3,200	13,000	1,026

See source and footnotes on page 135.

Motor vehicle deaths by type of incident, United States, 1913-2011 (cont.)

| Year | Total deaths | Deaths from collision with... | | | | | | | Deaths from noncollision incidents | Nontraffic deaths[a] |
		Pedestrians	Other motor vehicles	Railroad trains	Streetcars	Pedalcycles	Animal-drawn vehicle or animal	Fixed objects		
1977	49,510	9,100	21,200	902	3	1,100	100	3,400	13,700	1,053
1978	52,411	9,600	22,400	986	1	1,200	100	3,600	14,500	1,074
1979	53,524	9,800	23,100	826	1	1,200	100	3,700	14,800	1,271
1980	53,172	9,700	23,000	739	1	1,200	100	3,700	14,700	1,242
1981	51,385	9,400	22,200	668	1	1,200	100	3,600	14,200	1,189
1982	45,779	8,400	19,800	554	1	1,100	100	3,200	12,600	1,066
1983	44,452	8,200	19,200	520	1	1,100	100	3,100	12,200	1,024
1984	46,263	8,500	20,000	630	0	1,100	100	3,200	12,700	1,055
1985	45,901	8,500	19,900	538	2	1,100	100	3,200	12,600	1,079
1986	47,865	8,900	20,800	574	2	1,100	100	3,300	13,100	998
1987	48,290	7,500[e]	20,700	554	1	1,000[e]	100	13,200[e]	5,200[e]	993
1988	49,078	7,700	20,900	638	2	1,000	100	13,400	5,300	1,054
1989	47,575	7,800	20,300	720	2	900	100	12,900	4,900	989
1990	46,814	7,300	19,900	623	2	900	100	13,100	4,900	987
1991	43,536	6,600	18,200	541	1	800	100	12,600	4,700	915
1992	40,982	6,300	17,600	521	2	700	100	11,700	4,100	997
1993	41,893	6,400	18,300	553	3	800	100	11,500	4,200	994
1994	42,524	6,300	18,900	549	1	800	100	11,500	4,400	1,017
1995	43,363	6,400	19,000	514	(c)	800	100	12,100	4,400	1,032
1996	43,649	6,100	19,600	373	(c)	800	100	12,100	4,600	1,127
1997	43,458	5,900	19,900	371	(c)	800	100	12,000	4,400	1,118
1998	43,501	5,900	19,700	309	(c)	700	100	12,200	4,600	1,310
1999	42,401	6,100	18,600	314	1	800	100	11,800	4,700	1,436
2000	43,354	5,900	19,100	321	(c)	800	100	12,300	4,800	1,360
2001	43,788	6,100	18,800	324	3	800	100	12,800	4,900	1,345
2002	45,380	6,100	19,200	283	(c)	800	100	13,600	5,300	1,315
2003	44,757	6,000	19,300	245	(c)	800	100	13,100	5,200	1,417
2004	44,933	6,000	19,600	253	(c)	900	100	13,000	5,100	1,501
2005	45,343	6,100	19,000	250	(c)	1,000	100	13,600	5,300	1,676
2006	45,316	6,200	18,500	264	(c)	1,000	100	13,900	5,400	1,652
2007	43,945	6,000	17,700	211	(c)	900	100	13,800	5,200	1,914
2008	39,790	5,600	15,500	199	(c)	900	100	12,900	4,600	1,805
2009[f]	36,216	5,300	14,100	154	(c)	800	100	11,700	4,100	1,731
2010[f]	35,332	5,500	13,500	139	(c)	800	100	11,400	3,900	1,645
2011[g]	34,600	5,700	12,800	100	(c)	900	100	11,100	3,900	(c)
Changes in deaths										
2002 to 2011	-24%	-7%	-33%	-65%	–	13%	0%	-18%	-26%	–
2010 to 2011	-2%	4%	-5%	-28%	–	13%	0%	-3%	0%	–

Source: Total deaths from National Center for Health Statistics except 1964 and 2011, which are National Safety Council estimates based on data from the National Highway Traffic Safety Administration's Fatality Analysis Reporting System. Most totals by type are estimated and may not add to the total deaths. See Technical Appendix for comparability.

[a]See definition, page 205. Nontraffic deaths are included in appropriate incident-type totals in the table. In 2009, 34% of the nontraffic deaths were pedestrians, while in 2010 pedestrians accounted for 35% of nontraffic deaths.

[b]Insufficient data for approximations.

[c]Data not available.

[d]1969 through 1986 totals are not comparable to previous years.

[e]Procedures and benchmarks for estimating deaths for certain types of incidents were changed for the 1990 edition. Estimates for 1987 and later years are not comparable to earlier years.

[f]Revised.

[g]Preliminary.

Motor vehicle deaths by age, United States, 1913-2011

Year	All ages	Younger than 5 years	5-14 years	15-24 years	25-44 years	45-64 years	65-74 years	75 and older[a]
1913	4,200	300	1,100	600	1,100	800	300	
1914	4,700	300	1,200	700	1,200	900	400	
1915	6,600	400	1,500	1,000	1,700	1,400	600	
1916	8,200	600	1,800	1,300	2,100	1,700	700	
1917	10,200	700	2,400	1,400	2,700	2,100	900	
1918	10,700	800	2,700	1,400	2,500	2,300	1,000	
1919	11,200	900	3,000	1,400	2,500	2,100	1,300	
1920	12,500	1,000	3,300	1,700	2,800	2,300	1,400	
1921	13,900	1,100	3,400	1,800	3,300	2,700	1,600	
1922	15,300	1,100	3,500	2,100	3,700	3,100	1,800	
1923	18,400	1,200	3,700	2,800	4,600	3,900	2,200	
1924	19,400	1,400	3,800	2,900	4,700	4,100	2,500	
1925	21,900	1,400	3,900	3,600	5,400	4,800	2,800	
1926	23,400	1,400	3,900	3,900	5,900	5,200	3,100	
1927	25,800	1,600	4,000	4,300	6,600	5,800	3,500	
1928	28,000	1,600	3,800	4,900	7,200	6,600	3,900	
1929	31,200	1,600	3,900	5,700	8,000	7,500	4,500	
1930	32,900	1,500	3,600	6,200	8,700	8,000	4,900	
1931	33,700	1,500	3,600	6,300	9,100	8,200	5,000	
1932	29,500	1,200	2,900	5,100	8,100	7,400	4,800	
1933	31,363	1,274	3,121	5,649	8,730	7,947	4,642	
1934	36,101	1,210	3,182	6,561	10,232	9,530	5,386	
1935	36,369	1,253	2,951	6,755	10,474	9,562	5,374	
1936	38,089	1,324	3,026	7,184	10,807	10,089	5,659	
1937	39,643	1,303	2,991	7,800	10,877	10,475	6,197	
1938	32,582	1,122	2,511	6,016	8,772	8,711	5,450	
1939	32,386	1,192	2,339	6,318	8,917	8,292	5,328	
1940	34,501	1,176	2,584	6,846	9,362	8,882	5,651	
1941	39,969	1,378	2,838	8,414	11,069	9,829	6,441	
1942	28,309	1,069	1,991	5,932	7,747	7,254	4,316	
1943	23,823	1,132	1,959	4,522	6,454	5,996	3,760	
1944	24,282	1,203	2,093	4,561	6,514	5,982	3,929	
1945	28,076	1,290	2,386	5,358	7,578	6,794	4,670	
1946	33,411	1,568	2,508	7,445	8,955	7,532	5,403	
1947	32,697	1,502	2,275	7,251	8,775	7,468	5,426	
1948	32,259	1,635	2,337	7,218	8,702	7,190	3,173	2,004
1949	31,701	1,667	2,158	6,772	8,892	7,073	3,116	2,023
1950	34,763	1,767	2,152	7,600	10,214	7,728	3,264	2,038
1951	36,996	1,875	2,300	7,713	11,253	8,276	3,444	2,135
1952	37,794	1,951	2,295	8,115	11,380	8,463	3,472	2,118
1953	37,956	2,019	2,368	8,169	11,302	8,318	3,508	2,271
1954	35,586	1,864	2,332	7,571	10,521	7,848	3,247	2,203
1955	38,426	1,875	2,406	8,656	11,448	8,372	3,455	2,214
1956	39,628	1,770	2,640	9,169	11,551	8,573	3,657	2,268
1957	38,702	1,785	2,604	8,667	11,230	8,545	3,560	2,311
1958	36,981	1,791	2,710	8,388	10,414	7,922	3,535	2,221
1959	37,910	1,842	2,719	8,969	10,358	8,263	3,487	2,272
1960	38,137	1,953	2,814	9,117	10,189	8,294	3,457	2,313
1961	38,091	1,891	2,802	9,088	10,212	8,267	3,467	2,364
1962	40,804	1,903	3,028	10,157	10,701	8,812	3,696	2,507
1963	43,564	1,991	3,063	11,123	11,356	9,506	3,786	2,739
1964	47,700	2,120	3,430	12,400	12,500	10,200	4,150	2,900
1965	49,163	2,059	3,526	13,395	12,595	10,509	4,077	3,002
1966	53,041	2,182	3,869	15,298	13,282	11,051	4,217	3,142
1967	52,924	2,067	3,845	15,646	12,987	10,902	4,285	3,192
1968	54,862	1,987	4,105	16,543	13,602	11,031	4,261	3,333
1969	55,791	2,077	4,045	17,443	13,868	11,012	4,210	3,136
1970	54,633	1,915	4,159	16,720	13,446	11,099	4,084	3,210
1971	54,381	1,885	4,256	17,103	13,307	10,471	4,108	3,251
1972	56,278	1,896	4,258	17,942	13,758	10,836	4,138	3,450
1973	55,511	1,998	4,124	18,032	14,013	10,216	3,892	3,236
1974	46,402	1,546	3,332	15,905	11,834	8,159	3,071	2,555
1975	45,853	1,576	3,286	15,672	11,969	7,663	3,047	2,640
1976	47,038	1,532	3,175	16,650	12,112	7,770	3,082	2,717

See source and footnotes on page 137.

Motor vehicle deaths by age, United States, 1913-2011 (cont.)

Year	All ages	Younger than 5 years	5-14 years	15-24 years	25-44 years	45-64 years	65-74 years	75 and older[a]
1977	49,510	1,472	3,142	18,092	13,031	8,000	3,060	2,713
1978	52,411	1,551	3,130	19,164	14,574	8,048	3,217	2,727
1979	53,524	1,461	2,952	19,369	15,658	8,162	3,171	2,751
1980	53,172	1,426	2,747	19,040	16,133	8,022	2,991	2,813
1981	51,385	1,256	2,575	17,363	16,447	7,818	3,090	2,836
1982	45,779	1,300	2,301	15,324	14,469	6,879	2,825	2,681
1983	44,452	1,233	2,241	14,289	14,323	6,690	2,827	2,849
1984	46,263	1,138	2,263	14,738	15,036	6,954	3,020	3,114
1985	45,901	1,195	2,319	14,277	15,034	6,885	3,014	3,177
1986	47,865	1,188	2,350	15,227	15,844	6,799	3,096	3,361
1987	48,290	1,190	2,397	14,447	16,405	7,021	3,277	3,553
1988	49,078	1,220	2,423	14,406	16,580	7,245	3,429	3,775
1989	47,575	1,221	2,266	12,941	16,571	7,287	3,465	3,824
1990	46,814	1,123	2,059	12,607	16,488	7,282	3,350	3,905
1991	43,536	1,076	2,011	11,664	15,082	6,616	3,193	3,894
1992	40,982	1,020	1,904	10,305	14,071	6,597	3,247	3,838
1993	41,893	1,081	1,963	10,500	14,283	6,711	3,116	4,239
1994	42,524	1,139	2,026	10,660	13,966	7,097	3,385	4,251
1995	43,363	1,004	2,055	10,600	14,618	7,428	3,300	4,358
1996	43,649	1,035	1,980	10,576	14,482	7,749	3,419	4,408
1997	43,458	933	1,967	10,208	14,167	8,134	3,370	4,679
1998	43,501	921	1,868	10,026	14,095	8,416	3,410	4,765
1999	42,401	834	1,771	10,128	13,516	8,342	3,276	4,534
2000	43,354	819	1,772	10,560	13,811	8,867	3,038	4,487
2001	43,788	770	1,686	10,725	14,020	9,029	2,990	4,568
2002	45,380	733	1,614	11,459	14,169	9,701	3,113	4,591
2003	44,757	766	1,642	10,972	13,794	10,032	2,967	4,584
2004	44,933	778	1,653	10,987	13,699	10,369	2,974	4,473
2005	45,343	763	1,447	10,908	13,987	10,851	3,110	4,277
2006	45,316	728	1,339	11,015	14,025	11,133	2,916	4,160
2007	43,945	675	1,285	10,568	13,457	10,889	2,940	4,131
2008	39,790	566	1,027	8,946	12,242	10,457	2,826	3,726
2009[b]	36,216	574	974	7,688	10,953	9,777	2,693	3,557
2010[b]	35,332	528	890	7,250	10,491	9,727	2,676	3,770
2011[c]	34,600	500	900	7,100	10,200	9,600	2,800	3,500
Changes in deaths								
2002 to 2011	-24%	-32%	-44%	-38%	-28%	-1%	-10%	-24%
2010 to 2011	-2%	-5%	1%	-2%	-3%	-1%	5%	-7%

Source: 1913 to 1932 calculated from National Center for Health Statistics (NCHS) data for registration states; 1933 to 1963 and 1965 to 2010 are NCHS totals. All other figures are National Safety Council estimates. See Technical Appendix for comparability.
[a]*Includes "age unknown." In 2009, these deaths numbered 9 and in 2010 they numbered 3.*
[b]*Revised.*
[c]*Preliminary.*

Motor vehicle death rates[a] by age, United States, 1913-2011

Year	All ages	Younger than 5 years	5-14 years	15-24 years	25-44 years	45-64 years	65-74 years	75 and older
1913	4.4	2.3	5.5	3.1	3.8	5.3	8.5	
1914	4.8	2.5	5.7	3.5	4.1	6.2	9.3	
1915	6.6	3.5	7.3	5.0	5.6	8.8	13.5	
1916	8.1	4.7	8.6	6.0	7.0	10.7	15.8	
1917	10.0	5.6	10.6	7.4	8.6	12.6	18.6	
1918	10.3	6.9	12.3	7.7	8.3	13.7	21.2	
1919	10.7	7.5	13.9	7.5	8.1	12.4	24.1	
1920	11.7	8.6	14.6	8.7	8.8	13.5	27.0	
1921	12.9	9.0	14.5	9.2	10.2	15.4	31.0	
1922	13.9	9.2	15.0	10.8	11.1	17.2	34.9	
1923	16.5	9.7	15.6	13.4	13.6	21.0	40.5	
1924	17.1	11.1	16.1	14.3	13.7	21.8	43.7	
1925	19.1	11.0	15.6	17.2	15.8	25.0	48.9	
1926	20.1	11.0	15.9	18.6	17.1	26.3	51.4	
1927	21.8	12.8	16.0	20.0	18.8	28.9	56.9	
1928	23.4	12.7	15.5	21.9	20.2	32.4	62.2	
1929	25.7	13.4	15.6	25.6	22.3	35.6	68.6	
1930	26.7	13.0	14.7	27.4	23.9	37.0	72.5	
1931	27.2	13.3	14.5	27.9	24.8	37.4	70.6	
1932	23.6	11.3	12.0	22.6	22.0	32.9	63.6	
1933	25.0	12.0	12.7	24.8	23.4	34.7	63.1	
1934	28.6	11.7	13.0	28.6	27.2	40.7	71.0	
1935	28.6	12.3	12.2	29.2	27.6	39.9	68.9	
1936	29.7	13.2	12.6	30.8	28.2	41.3	70.5	
1937	30.8	13.0	12.7	33.2	28.2	42.0	75.1	
1938	25.1	11.0	10.8	25.4	22.5	34.3	64.1	
1939	24.7	11.2	10.4	26.5	22.6	32.2	60.2	
1940	26.1	11.1	11.5	28.7	23.5	33.9	62.1	
1941	30.0	12.7	12.6	35.7	27.5	37.0	68.6	
1942	21.1	9.5	8.8	25.8	19.2	26.9	44.5	
1943	17.8	9.4	8.6	20.6	16.1	21.9	37.6	
1944	18.3	9.6	9.1	22.5	16.6	21.6	38.2	
1945	21.2	10.0	10.3	27.8	19.7	24.2	44.1	
1946	23.9	11.9	10.8	34.4	21.1	26.4	49.6	
1947	22.8	10.5	9.7	32.8	20.3	25.7	48.2	
1948	22.1	11.0	9.8	32.5	19.8	24.3	39.6	55.4
1949	21.3	10.7	9.0	30.7	19.9	23.4	37.8	53.9
1950	23.0	10.8	8.8	34.5	22.5	25.1	38.8	52.4
1951	24.1	10.9	9.2	36.0	24.7	26.5	39.5	53.0
1952	24.3	11.3	8.7	38.6	24.7	26.7	38.5	50.8
1953	24.0	11.5	8.5	39.1	24.5	25.8	37.7	52.6
1954	22.1	10.4	8.1	36.2	22.6	24.0	33.9	49.0
1955	23.4	10.2	8.0	40.9	24.5	25.2	35.1	47.1
1956	23.7	9.4	8.4	42.9	24.6	25.3	36.2	46.4
1957	22.7	9.2	8.0	39.7	23.9	24.8	34.4	45.5
1958	21.3	9.1	8.1	37.0	22.3	22.6	33.5	42.3
1959	21.5	9.1	7.9	38.2	22.2	23.2	32.3	41.8
1960	21.2	9.6	7.9	37.7	21.7	22.9	31.3	41.1
1961	20.8	9.2	7.6	36.5	21.8	22.5	30.7	40.5
1962	22.0	9.3	8.1	38.4	22.9	23.7	32.2	41.7
1963	23.1	9.8	8.0	40.0	24.3	25.2	32.6	44.3
1964	25.0	10.5	8.8	42.6	26.8	26.6	35.5	45.2
1965	25.4	10.4	8.9	44.2	27.0	27.0	34.6	45.4
1966	27.1	11.4	9.7	48.7	28.5	27.9	35.4	46.2
1967	26.8	11.2	9.5	48.4	27.8	27.1	35.6	45.4
1968	27.5	11.1	10.1	49.8	28.8	27.0	35.1	46.0
1969	27.7	12.0	9.9	50.7	29.1	26.6	34.3	42.0
1970	26.8	11.2	10.2	46.7	27.9	26.4	32.7	42.2
1971	26.3	10.9	10.5	45.7	27.4	24.7	32.4	41.3
1972	26.9	11.1	10.7	47.1	27.4	25.3	32.0	42.6
1973	26.3	11.9	10.5	46.3	27.2	23.6	29.4	39.1
1974	21.8	9.4	8.6	40.0	22.4	18.8	22.6	30.1
1975	21.3	9.8	8.6	38.7	22.1	17.5	21.9	30.1
1976	21.6	9.8	8.4	40.3	21.8	17.6	21.6	30.1

See source and footnotes on page 139.

Motor vehicle death rates by age, United States, 1913-2011 (cont.)

Year	All ages	Younger than 5 years	5-14 years	15-24 years	25-44 years	45-64 years	65-74 years	75 and older
1977	22.5	9.5	8.5	43.3	22.7	18.1	20.9	29.3
1978	23.6	9.9	8.6	45.4	24.6	18.2	21.5	28.7
1979	23.8	9.1	8.3	45.6	25.6	18.4	20.7	28.1
1980	23.4	8.7	7.9	44.8	25.5	18.0	19.1	28.0
1981	22.4	7.4	7.5	41.1	25.2	17.6	19.4	27.5
1982	19.8	7.5	6.7	36.8	21.5	15.5	17.5	25.2
1983	19.0	7.0	6.6	34.8	20.6	15.0	17.2	26.0
1984	19.6	6.4	6.7	36.4	21.0	15.6	18.2	27.7
1985	19.3	6.7	6.9	35.7	20.5	15.4	17.9	27.5
1986	19.9	6.6	7.0	38.5	21.0	15.2	18.1	28.3
1987	19.9	6.6	7.1	37.1	21.3	15.7	18.8	29.1
1988	20.1	6.7	7.1	37.8	21.2	15.9	19.5	30.2
1989	19.3	6.6	6.5	34.6	20.8	15.9	19.4	29.8
1990	18.8	6.0	5.8	34.2	20.4	15.7	18.5	29.7
1991	17.3	5.6	5.6	32.1	18.3	14.2	17.5	28.9
1992	16.1	5.2	5.2	28.5	17.1	13.6	17.6	27.8
1993	16.3	5.5	5.3	29.1	17.3	13.5	16.7	30.0
1994	16.3	5.8	5.4	29.5	16.8	13.9	18.1	29.4
1995	16.5	5.1	5.4	29.3	17.5	14.2	17.6	29.4
1996	16.5	5.4	5.2	29.2	17.3	14.4	18.3	29.0
1997	16.2	4.9	5.1	27.9	17.0	14.7	18.2	29.9
1998	16.1	4.9	4.8	26.9	16.9	14.7	18.5	29.8
1999	15.5	4.4	4.5	26.8	16.3	14.1	18.0	27.8
2000	15.7	4.3	4.5	27.5	16.8	14.5	16.7	27.0
2001	15.4	4.0	4.1	26.8	16.5	14.0	16.3	26.8
2002	15.8	3.7	3.9	28.2	16.8	14.6	17.0	26.5
2003	15.4	3.9	4.0	26.6	16.4	14.6	16.2	26.0
2004	15.3	3.9	4.1	26.4	16.3	14.7	16.1	25.1
2005	15.3	3.8	3.6	25.9	16.6	14.9	16.7	23.6
2006	15.2	3.6	3.3	26.1	16.8	14.9	15.4	22.7
2007	14.6	3.3	3.2	24.9	16.1	14.2	15.2	22.2
2008	13.1	2.7	2.5	20.8	14.7	13.4	14.0	20.0
2009[b]	11.8	2.7	2.4	17.8	13.2	12.3	13.0	18.9
2010[b]	11.4	2.5	2.2	16.8	12.6	12.0	12.9	19.9
2011[c]	11.1	2.5	2.2	16.2	12.4	11.6	12.5	18.5
Changes in rates								
2002 to 2011	-30%	-32%	-44%	-43%	-26%	-21%	-26%	-30%
2010 to 2011	-3%	0%	0%	-4%	-2%	-3%	-3%	-7%

Source: 1913 to 1932 calculated from National Center for Health Statistics (NCHS) data for registration states; 1933 to 1963 and 1965 to 2010 are NCHS totals. All other figures are National Safety Council estimates. See Technical Appendix for comparability.
[a]Death rates are deaths per 100,000 population in each age group that were calculated using population data from the U.S. Census Bureau.
[b]Revised.
[c]Preliminary.

Home and Community

INJURY FACTS® 2013

141

The home and community venue is the combination of the home class and the public class. Home and community, together with the occupational and transportation venues, make up the totality of unintentional injuries. Home and community includes all unintentional injuries that are not work-related and do not involve motor vehicles on streets and highways.

In 2011, an estimated 86,100 unintentional-injury-related deaths occurred in the home and community venue, or 70% of all unintentional-injury-related deaths that year. The number of deaths was up about 3% from the revised 2010 total of 83,400. An additional 28,500,000 people suffered nonfatal medically consulted injuries. The death rate per 100,000 population was 27.6 – 2% higher than the revised 2010 rate.

About 1 out of 11 people experienced an unintentional injury in the home and community venue, and about 1 out of 3,600 people died from such an injury in 2011. About 40% of the deaths and injuries involved workers while they were away from work (off the job).

The graph on the next page shows the five leading causes

of unintentional-injury-related deaths in the home and community venue and the broad age groups (children, youths and adults, and the elderly) affected by them. This is one way to prioritize issues in this venue. Below is a graph of the trend in deaths and death rates from 1999 to present. Similar graphs for the home and public classes appear on pages 144 and 148.

The National Safety Council adopted the Bureau of Labor Statistics' Census of Fatal Occupational Injuries count for work-related unintentional injuries beginning with 1992 data. Because of the lower work class total resulting from this change, adjustments were made to the home and public classes. Long-term historical comparisons for these three classes should be made with caution. Also, beginning with 1999 data, deaths are now classified according to the 10th revision of the International Classification of Diseases. Caution should be used in comparing data classified under the 10th revision with prior revisions. See the Technical Appendix for more information about both changes.

Deaths...86,100
Medically consulted injuries...28,500,000
Death rate per 100,000 population 27.6
Costs... $322.6 billion

Home and community deaths and death rates, United States, 1999-2011

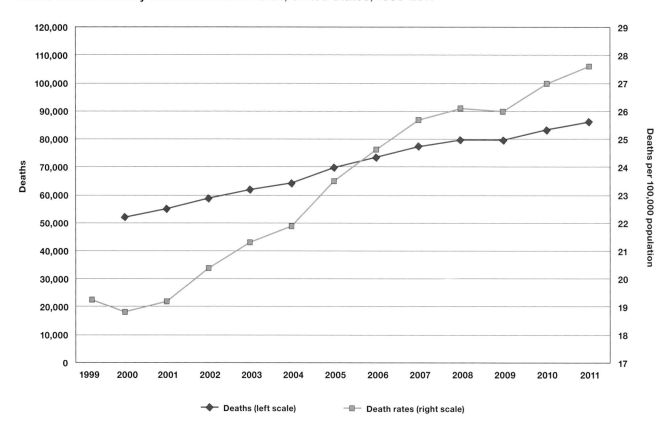

Leading causes of unintentional-injury-related deaths in home and community, United States, 2011

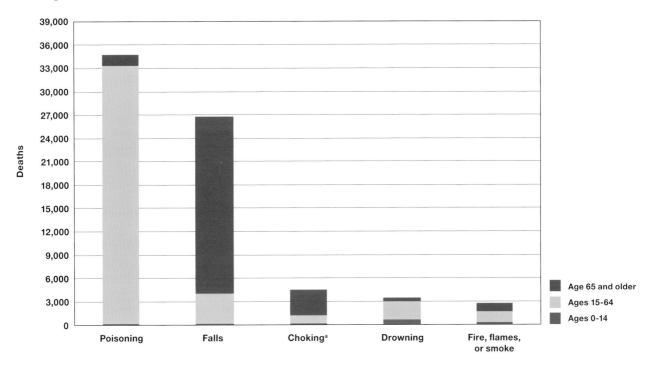

Inhalation and ingestion of food or other object that obstructs breathing.

Causes of unintentional-injury-related deaths in home and community, United States, 2011

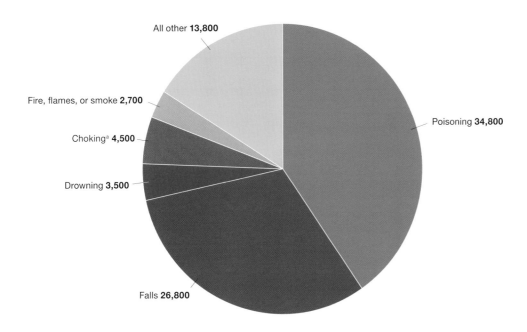

Inhalation and ingestion of food or other object that obstructs breathing.

Between 1912 and 2011, unintentional-home-injury-related deaths per 100,000 population were reduced 31% from 28 to 19.4 (after adjusting for the 1948 classification change). In 1912, when there were 21 million households, an estimated 26,000 to 28,000 people were killed by unintentional-home-related injuries. In 2011, with nearly 119 million households and the population tripled, unintentional-home-related deaths numbered 60,600. However, the number and rate of unintentional-home-injury-related deaths has been steadily increasing since 2000. This increase in deaths is largely driven by increases in both unintentional poisonings and falls.

The injury total of 18,800,000 means that 1 person in 17 in the United States experienced an unintentional injury in the home in 2011 that was serious enough to consult with a medical professional. Medically consulted injuries are more numerous in the home than in public places, the workplace, and motor vehicle crashes combined. The National Health Interview Survey estimates that about 48% of all medically attended injuries occurred at home.

The National Safety Council adopted the Bureau of Labor Statistics' Census of Fatal Occupational Injuries count for work-related unintentional injuries beginning with 1992 data. This affected long-term historical comparisons for the work, home, and public classes. Beginning with 1999 data, deaths are classified according to the 10th revision of the International Classification of Diseases. Caution should be used in comparing current data with data classified under prior revisions. See the Technical Appendix for more information.

Deaths..**60,600**
Medically consulted injuries..**18,800,000**
Death rate per 100,000 population **19.4**
Costs..**$206.7 billion**

Home deaths and death rates, United States, 1999-2011

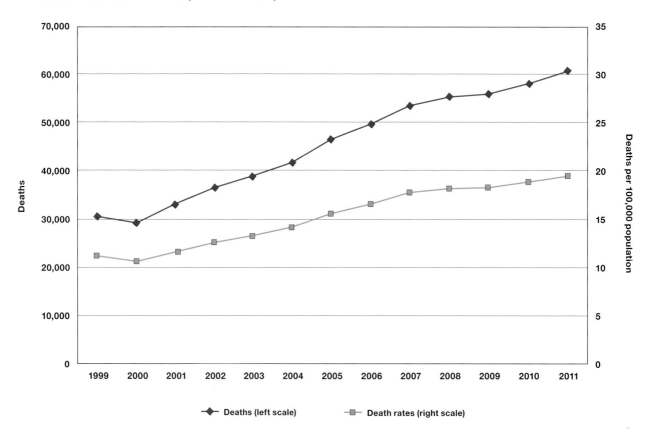

Principal types of unintentional-home-related injury deaths, United States, 1987-2011

Year	Total home	Poisoning	Falls	Fire, flames, or smoke[a]	Choking[b]	Mechanical suffocation	Drowning	Natural heat or cold	Firearms	Other
1987	21,400	4,100	6,300	3,900	2,500	600	700	(c)	800	2,500
1988	22,700	4,800	6,600	4,100	2,600	600	700	(c)	800	2,500
1989	22,500	5,000	6,600	3,900	2,500	600	700	(c)	800	2,400
1990	21,500	4,500	6,700	3,400	2,300	600	900	(c)	800	2,300
1991	22,100	5,000	6,900	3,400	2,200	700	900	(c)	800	2,200
1992	24,000	5,200	7,700	3,700	1,500	700	900	(c)	1,000	3,300
1993	26,100	6,500	7,900	3,700	1,700	700	900	(c)	1,100	3,600
1994	26,300	6,800	8,100	3,700	1,600	800	900	(c)	900	3,500
1995	27,200	7,000	8,400	3,500	1,500	800	900	(c)	900	4,200
1996	27,500	7,300	9,000	3,500	1,500	800	900	(c)	800	3,700
1997	27,700	7,800	9,100	3,200	1,500	800	900	(c)	700	3,500
1998	29,000	8,400	9,500	2,900	1,800	800	1,000	(c)	600	4,000
1999[d]	30,500	9,300	7,600	3,000	1,900	1,100	900	700	600	5,400
2000	29,200	9,800	7,100	2,700	2,100	1,000	1,000	400	500	4,600
2001	33,200	11,300	8,600	3,000	2,000	1,100	900	400	600	5,300
2002	36,400	13,900	9,700	2,800	1,900	1,100	900	400	500	5,200
2003	38,800	15,900	10,300	2,900	2,100	1,000	800	400	500	4,900
2004	41,700	17,500	11,300	2,900	2,200	1,200	900	400	400	4,900
2005	46,400	20,000	12,000	2,900	2,300	1,300	900	500	500	6,000
2006	49,600	23,300	12,800	2,800	2,300	1,400	1,000	600	400	5,000
2007	53,500	25,800	14,200	3,000	2,100	1,400	1,000	500	400	5,100
2008	55,200	26,800	15,100	2,600	2,300	1,500	900	400	400	5,200
2009[e]	55,800	27,500	15,700	2,600	2,300	1,300	1,000	500	400	4,500
2010[e]	58,100	28,800	16,500	2,500	2,200	1,400	1,000	600	400	4,700
2011[f]	60,600	30,200	17,500	2,500	2,300	1,400	1,000	500	400	4,800

Source: National Safety Council estimates based on National Center for Health Statistics (NCHS)–Mortality Data compiled from data provided by the 57 vital statistics jurisdictions through the Vital Statistics Cooperative Program. Rates are National Safety Council estimates based on data from NCHS. The Council adopted the Bureau of Labor Statistics Census of Fatal Occupational Injuries count for work-related unintentional injuries retroactive to 1992 data. Because of the lower work class total resulting from this change, several thousand unintentional-injury-related deaths that had been classified by the Council as work-related had to be reassigned to the home and public classes. For this reason, long-term historical comparisons for these three classes should be made with caution. See the Technical Appendix for an explanation of the methodological changes.
[a]Includes deaths resulting from conflagration, regardless of nature of injury.
[b]Inhalation and ingestion of food or other object that obstructs breathing.
[c]Included in "Other."
[d]In 1999, a revision was made in the International Classification of Diseases. See the Technical Appendix for comparability with earlier years.
[e]Revised.
[f]Preliminary.

Principal types of unintentional-home-related injury deaths, United States, 2011

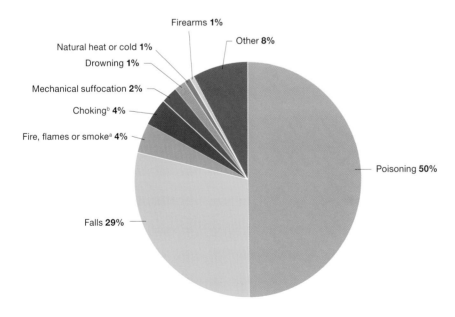

Firearms 1%
Natural heat or cold 1%
Drowning 1%
Mechanical suffocation 2%
Choking[b] 4%
Fire, flames or smoke[a] 4%
Other 8%
Poisoning 50%
Falls 29%

[a]Includes deaths resulting from conflagration, regardless of nature of injury.
[b]Inhalation and ingestion of food or other object that obstructs breathing.

Type of event and age of victim

All home

Includes deaths in the home and on home premises to occupants, guests, and trespassers. Also includes hired household workers but excludes other people working on home premises.

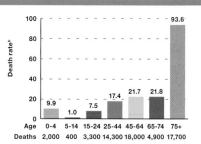

	Total	Change from 2010	Death rate[a]
Deaths	60,600	+4%	19.4

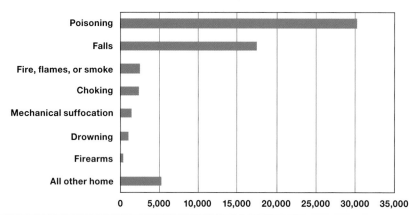

Poisoning

Includes deaths from drugs, medicines, other solid and liquid substances, and gases and vapors. Excludes poisonings from spoiled foods, *Salmonella*, etc., which are classified as disease deaths.

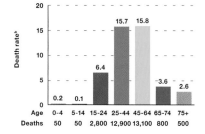

	Total	Change from 2010	Death rate[a]
Deaths	30,200	+5%	9.7

Falls

Includes deaths from falls from one level to another or on the same level in the home or on home premises.

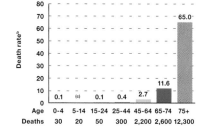

	Total	Change from 2010	Death rate[a]
Deaths	17,500	+6%	5.6

Fire, flames, or smoke

Includes deaths from fire, burns, and injuries in conflagrations in the home – such as asphyxiation, falls, and struck by falling objects. Excludes burns from hot objects or liquids.

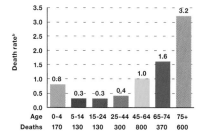

	Total	Change from 2010	Death rate[a]
Deaths	2,500	0%	0.8

See footnotes on page 147.

Type of event and age of victim

Choking

Includes deaths from unintentional ingestion or inhalation of objects or food resulting in the obstruction of respiratory passages.

	Total	Change from 2010	Death rate[a]
Deaths	2,300	+4%	0.7

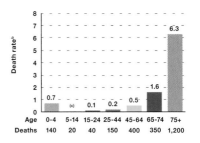

Mechanical suffocation

Includes deaths from smothering by bed clothes, thin plastic materials, etc.; suffocation by cave-ins or confinement in closed spaces; and mechanical strangulation or hanging.

	Total	Change from 2010	Death rate[a]
Deaths	1,400	0%	0.4

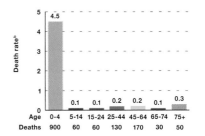

Drowning

Includes drownings of people in or on home premises – such as in swimming pools and bathtubs. Excludes drowning in floods and other cataclysms.

	Total	Change from 2010	Death rate[a]
Deaths	1,000	0%	0.3

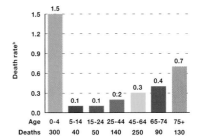

Firearms

Includes firearms injuries in or on home premises – such as while cleaning or playing with guns. Excludes deaths from explosive materials.

	Total	Change from 2010	Death rate[a]
Deaths	400	0%	0.1

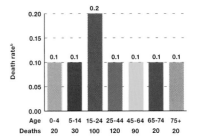

All other home

Most important types included are natural heat and cold, struck by or against objects, machinery, and electric current.

	Total	Change from 2010	Death rate[a]
Deaths	5,300	0%	1.7

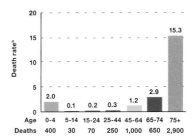

[a]Deaths per 100,000 population.
[b]Deaths per 100,000 population in each age group.
[c]Death rate less than 0.05.

Between 1912 and 2011, public unintentional-injury-related deaths per 100,000 population were reduced 73% from 30 to 8.2 (after adjusting for the 1948 change in classification). In 1912, an estimated 28,000 to 30,000 people died from public non-motor vehicle injuries. In 2011, with the population tripled, and travel and recreational activity greatly increased, 25,500 people died from public unintentional injuries and 9,700,000 suffered injuries serious enough to consult a medical professional. The public class excludes deaths and injuries involving motor vehicles and people at work or at home.

In 2011, the number of public unintentional-injury-related deaths was up 0.8% from the revised 2010 figure of 25,300. The death rate per 100,000 population was unchanged at 8.2.

With an estimated 9,700,000 medically consulted unintentional injuries occurring in public places and a population of more than 311 million people, on average about 1 person in 32 experienced such an injury.

The National Safety Council adopted the Bureau of Labor Statistics Census of Fatal Occupational Injuries count for work-related unintentional injuries beginning with 1992 data. This affected long-term historical comparisons for the work, home, and public classes. Beginning with 1999 data, deaths are classified according to the 10th revision of the International Classification of Diseases. Caution should be used in comparing current data with data classified under prior revisions. See the Technical Appendix for more information.

Deaths..**25,500**
Medically consulted injuries...**9,700,000**
Death rate per 100,000 population **8.2**
Costs...**$115.9 billion**

Public deaths and death rates, United States, 1999-2011

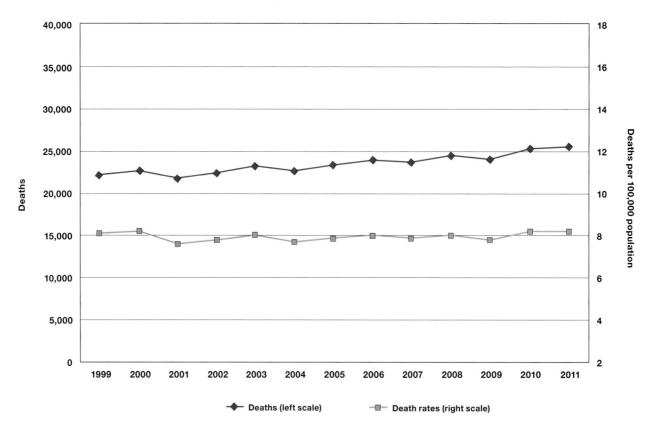

Deaths (left scale)   Death rates (right scale)

Principal types of public unintentional-injury-related deaths, United States, 1987-2011

Year	Total public[a]	Falls	Poisoning	Drowning	Choking[g]	Fire, flames, or smoke	Firearms	Air transport	Water transport	Rail transport[b]	Mechanical suffocation
1987	18,400	4,000	800	3,200	1,100	500	600	900	800	400	(c)
1988	18,400	4,100	900	3,100	1,100	500	600	700	800	400	(c)
1989	18,200	4,200	900	3,000	1,000	500	600	800	700	400	(c)
1990	17,400	4,300	900	2,800	1,000	400	500	700	800	400	(c)
1991	17,600	4,500	1,000	2,800	900	400	600	700	700	500	(c)
1992	19,000	4,400	1,700	2,500	1,600	200	400	700	700	600	(c)
1993	19,700	4,600	1,900	2,800	1,500	200	400	600	700	600	(c)
1994	19,600	4,700	2,100	2,400	1,500	200	400	600	600	600	(c)
1995	20,100	5,000	2,000	2,800	1,600	200	300	600	700	500	(c)
1996	21,000	5,300	2,100	2,500	1,700	200	300	700	600	500	(c)
1997	21,700	5,600	2,300	2,600	1,700	200	300	500	600	400	(c)
1998	22,600	6,000	2,300	2,900	1,700	200	300	500	600	500	(c)
1999[d]	22,200	4,800	2,800	2,600	2,000	200	300	500	600	400	500
2000	22,700	5,500	2,900	2,400	2,200	200	200	500	500	400	300
2001	21,800	5,600	2,700	2,400	2,100	200	200	700	500	400	300
2002	22,500	5,900	3,600	2,500	2,200	300	200	500	500	400	300
2003	23,200	6,300	3,400	2,400	2,200	300	200	600	500	400	300
2004	22,700	6,700	3,400	2,400	2,200	200	200	400	500	400	200
2005	23,400	6,800	3,500	2,600	2,100	(c)	(c)	400	500	400	200
2006	23,900	7,200	4,100	2,500	2,100	(c)	(c)	400	400	400	200
2007	23,700	7,600	3,900	2,400	2,200	(c)	(c)	400	400	400	200
2008	24,500	8,200	4,200	2,500	2,100	(c)	(c)	400	300	400	200
2009[e]	24,000	8,500	4,200	2,400	2,100	(c)	(c)	400	400	300	200
2010[e]	25,300	8,900	4,100	2,700	2,300	(c)	(c)	300	300	400	200
2011[f]	25,500	9,300	4,600	2,500	2,200	(c)	(c)	300	300	400	200

Source: National Safety Council estimates based on data from the National Center for Health Statistics. The Council adopted the Bureau of Labor Statistics' Census of Fatal Occupational Injuries count for work-related unintentional injuries retroactive to 1992 data. Because of the lower work class total resulting from this change, several thousand unintentional-injury-related deaths that had been classified by the Council as work-related had to be reassigned to the home and public classes. For this reason, long-term historical comparisons for these three classes should be made with caution. See the Technical Appendix for an explanation of the methodological changes.

[a]*Includes some deaths not shown separately.*
[b]*Includes subways and elevateds.*
[c]*Estimates not available.*
[d]*In 1999, a revision was made in the International Classification of Diseases. See the Technical Appendix for comparability with earlier years.*
[e]*Revised.*
[f]*Preliminary.*
[g]*Inhalation and ingestion of food or other object that obstructs breathing.*

Principal types of public unintentional-injury-related deaths, United States, 2011

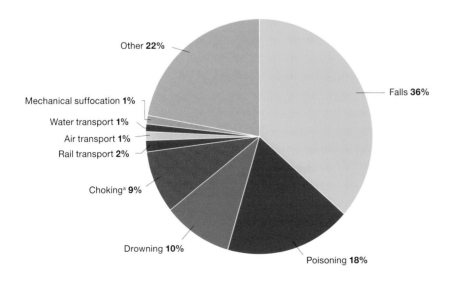

- Other 22%
- Mechanical suffocation 1%
- Water transport 1%
- Air transport 1%
- Rail transport 2%
- Choking[a] 9%
- Drowning 10%
- Poisoning 18%
- Falls 36%

[a]*Inhalation and ingestion of food or other object that obstructs breathing.*

Type of event and age of victim

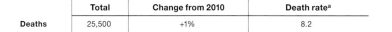

All public

Includes deaths in public places and not involving motor vehicles. Most sports, recreation, and transportation deaths are included. Excludes work deaths.

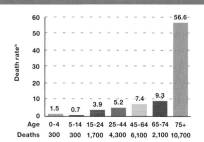

	Total	Change from 2010	Death rate[a]
Deaths	25,500	+1%	8.2

Age	0-4	5-14	15-24	25-44	45-64	65-74	75+
Deaths	300	300	1,700	4,300	6,100	2,100	10,700

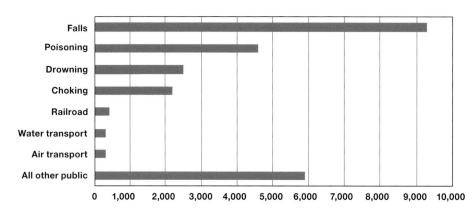

Falls

Includes deaths from falls from one level to another or on the same level in public places. Excludes deaths from falls from moving vehicles.

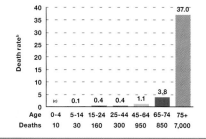

	Total	Change from 2010	Death rate[a]
Deaths	9,300	+4%	3.0

Age	0-4	5-14	15-24	25-44	45-64	65-74	75+
Deaths	10	30	160	300	950	850	7,000

Poisoning

Includes deaths from drugs, medicines, other solid and liquid substances, and gases and vapors. Excludes poisonings from spoiled foods.

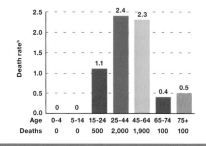

	Total	Change from 2010	Death rate[a]
Deaths	4,600	+12%	1.5

Age	0-4	5-14	15-24	25-44	45-64	65-74	75+
Deaths	0	0	500	2,000	1,900	100	100

Drowning

Includes drownings of people swimming or playing in water, or falling into water, except on home premises or at work. Excludes drownings involving boats, which are included in water transportation.

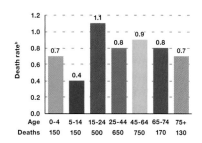

	Total	Change from 2010	Death rate[a]
Deaths	2,500	-7%	0.8

Age	0-4	5-14	15-24	25-44	45-64	65-74	75+
Deaths	150	150	500	650	750	170	130

See footnotes on page 151.

Type of event and age of victim

Choking
Includes deaths from unintentional ingestion or inhalation of food or other objects resulting in the obstruction of respiratory passages.

	Total	Change from 2010	Death rate[a]
Deaths	2,200	-4%	0.7

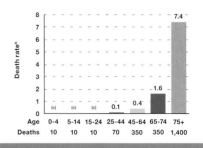

Age	0-4	5-14	15-24	25-44	45-64	65-74	75+
Deaths	10	10	10	70	350	350	1,400

Railroad
Includes deaths arising from railroad vehicles in motion (except involving motor vehicles), subway and elevated trains, and people boarding or alighting from standing trains. Excludes crews and people traveling in the course of employment.

	Total	Change from 2010	Death rate[a]
Deaths	400	0%	0.1

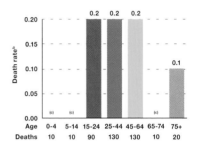

Age	0-4	5-14	15-24	25-44	45-64	65-74	75+
Deaths	10	10	90	130	130	10	20

Water transport
Includes deaths in water transport incidents from falls, burns, etc., as well as drownings. Excludes crews and people traveling in the course of employment.

	Total	Change from 2010	Death rate[a]
Deaths	300	0%	0.1

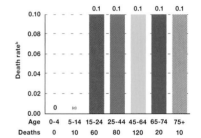

Age	0-4	5-14	15-24	25-44	45-64	65-74	75+
Deaths	0	10	60	80	120	20	10

Air transport
Includes deaths in private flying, passengers in commercial aviation, and deaths of military personnel in the United States. Excludes crews and people traveling in the course of employment.

	Total	Change from 2010	Death rate[a]
Deaths	300	0%	0.1

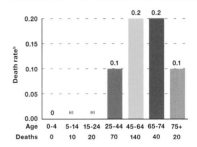

Age	0-4	5-14	15-24	25-44	45-64	65-74	75+
Deaths	0	10	20	70	140	40	20

All other public
Most important types included are mechanical suffocation; excessive natural heat or cold; firearms; fire, flames, or smoke; and machinery.

	Total	Change from 2010	Death rate[a]
Deaths	5,900	-6%	1.9

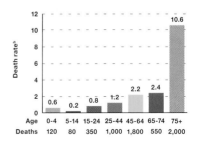

Age	0-4	5-14	15-24	25-44	45-64	65-74	75+
Deaths	120	80	350	1,000	1,800	550	2,000

[a]Deaths per 100,000 population.
[b]Deaths per 100,000 population in each age group.
[c]Death rate less than 0.05.

◆ *In the United States in 2011, bicycle riding and basketball injuries each resulted in more than half a million emergency department visits.*

The table below shows estimates of the number of injuries treated in hospital emergency departments and participants associated with various sports and recreational activities. Differences between the two sources in methods, coverage, classification systems, and definitions can affect comparisons among sports. Because this list of sports is not complete, the frequency and duration of participation is not known, and the number of participants varies greatly, no inference should be made concerning the relative hazard of these sports or rank with respect to risk of injury. In particular, it is *not* appropriate to calculate injury rates from these data.

Sports participation and injuries, United States, 2011

Sport or activity	Participants	Injuries	Percent of injuries by age				
			Younger than 5	5-14	15-24	25-64	65 and older
Archery	6,300,000	4,933	5.4	7.7	17.5	58.9	10.9
Baseball	12,300,000	155,100	2.7	48.2	28.1	20.3	0.7
Softball	10,400,000	107,033	0.2	29.0	30.0	39.8	0.9
Basketball	26,100,000	536,840	0.3	32.9	48.3	18.2	0.2
Bicycle riding[a]	39,100,000	540,339	5.4	36.8	19.3	34.1	4.3
Billiards/pool	20,000,000	3,266	8.7	23.7	17.4	47.0	3.3
Bowling	34,900,000	19,281	6.5	14.5	16.2	51.6	11.3
Boxing	[b]	19,698	0.3	10.2	49.6	39.1	0.8
Cheerleading	[b]	38,108	0.2	51.7	47.1	1.0	0.0
Exercise	[b]	317,215[c]	2.0	12.1	19.9	55.3	10.7
Fishing	37,700,000[d]	66,893	4.0	18.9	13.0	54.1	10.0
Football	9,000,000[e]	467,731	0.2	50.0	40.1	9.6	0.1
Golf	20,900,000	32,677[f]	5.8	14.9	7.0	44.7	27.6
Gymnastics	5,100,000	26,371[g]	3.8	67.5	23.5	5.2	0.0
Hockey (street, roller, and field)	[b]	9,351	0.1	35.2	55.6	9.1	0.0
Horseback riding	[b]	69,906	1.3	15.2	24.6	55.5	3.4
Horseshoe pitching	[b]	1,637	1.0	24.4	11.5	53.8	9.3
Ice hockey	3,000,000	19,703	0.3	28.7	52.0	18.9	0.1
Ice skating	[b]	20,578[h]	2.0	45.9	19.4	31.3	1.3
Martial arts	[b]	35,037	0.5	23.8	29.6	45.7	0.5
Mountain biking	6,000,000	8,859	1.1	4.7	20.0	73.4	0.9
Mountain climbing	[b]	5,433	0.3	10.3	39.0	49.0	1.4
Racquetball, squash, and paddleball	[b]	5,532	0.0	1.4	31.3	61.6	5.7
Roller skating	[b]	67,274[i]	1.4	54.7	13.7	29.6	0.7
Rugby	[b]	15,186	0.0	5.2	77.7	17.1	0.0
Scuba diving	[b]	1,331[j]	1.2	6.2	34.0	52.3	6.3
Skateboarding	6,600,000	108,510	1.5	40.6	44.0	13.7	0.2
Snowboarding	5,100,000	42,537	0.2	24.5	49.3	25.5	0.4
Snowmobiling	[b]	10,305	0.7	8.5	21.9	68.1	0.8
Soccer	13,900,000	214,053	0.9	41.8	38.8	18.3	0.1
Swimming	46,000,000	205,662[k]	9.8	43.1	17.5	25.7	3.9
Tennis	13,100,000	18,920	2.2	15.6	20.4	42.4	19.4
Track and field	[b]	27,992	0.0	41.5	46.7	11.6	0.2
Volleyball	10,100,000	58,803	0.2	30.9	44.2	23.8	0.8
Water skiing	4,300,000	6,539	1.1	15.2	35.3	47.4	1.0
Weight lifting	29,100,000	95,486	3.7	9.3	35.0	49.0	3.0
Wrestling	3,200,000	44,850	0.0	40.5	55.2	4.3	0.0

Source: Participants: National Sporting Goods Association; figures include those age 7 or older who participated more than once per year except for bicycle riding, swimming, and weight lifting, which include those who participated six or more times per year.
Injuries: Consumer Product Safety Commission; figures include only injuries treated in hospital emergency departments.
[a]*Excludes mountain biking.*
[b]*Data not available.*
[c]*Includes exercise equipment (61,721 injuries) and exercise activity (255,494 injuries).*
[d]*Includes participation in fresh and salt water fishing.*
[e]*Includes participation in tackle football only.*
[f]*Excludes golf carts (14,053 injuries).*
[g]*Excludes trampolines (83,292 injuries).*
[h]*Excludes 6,393 injuries in skating, unspecified.*
[i]*Includes roller skating (53,835 injuries) and in-line skating (13,439 injuries).*
[j]*Data for 2009.*
[k]*Includes injuries associated with swimming, swimming pools, pool slides, diving or diving boards, and swimming pool equipment.*

Overall, drowning was the fifth leading cause of unintentional-injury-related death in 2009, according to data from the National Center for Health Statistics. Among children, it was the leading cause of unintentional-injury-related death for 1- and 2-year-olds and the second leading cause for children ages 3, 5-8, and 12-14. The table on this page shows the drowning deaths by location among children 14 and younger for 2009.

Of the 617 drowning fatalities among children younger than 15 where the location was specified, 338 (55%) occurred in swimming pools; 171 (28%) occurred in natural bodies of water such as rivers, lakes, ponds, streams, and oceans; 89 (14%) occurred in bathtubs; and 19 (3%) occurred in other specified places. Drowning in a swimming pool was the most common location for children younger than 10, while drowning in a natural body of water was the most common location for those 10-14 years old.

Nine out of 10 bathtub drowning fatalities among children occurred at home, with 74% occurring to those younger than 5. Sixty-one percent of drownings in a swimming pool occurred at home, while 86% of pool drownings following a fall into a pool occurred at home. Overall, about 26% of all drownings occurred at home.

A recent study examined trends in pediatric drowning hospitalizations and found that the overall incidence rate of such hospitalizations declined 57% from 4.9 to 2.1 per 100,000 from 1993 to 2008. Significant declines were observed for all ages and both genders, although the rate for males remained greater at each point in time. Significant declines in pediatric drowning hospitalizations also were observed by circumstance and age group, including those ages 10-14 who were engaged in swimming or diving, those younger than 5 in bathtubs, and those younger than 5 and 10-14 from other drowning episodes.

Source: Bowman, S.M., Aitken, M.E., Robbins, J.M., & Baker, S.P. (February 2012). Trends in U.S. Pediatric Drowning Hospitalizations, 1993-2008. Pediatrics, Vol. 129, No. 2, pp. 275-281.

Drowning deaths among children by location and age group, United States, 2009

Location	Total	Younger than 5	5-9 years	10-14 years
Total	704	495	119	90
Bathtub	89	75	6	8
While in bathtub	82	68	6	8
Following fall into bathtub	7	7	0	0
Swimming pool	338	263	52	23
While in swimming pool	281	212	47	22
Following fall into swimming pool	57	51	5	1
Natural body of water	171	82	43	46
While in natural water	137	61	36	40
Following fall into natural water	34	21	7	6
Other specified drowning	19	12	3	4
Unspecified drowning	87	63	15	9

Source: National Safety Council analysis of National Center for Health Statistics – Mortality Data for 2009, as compiled from data provided by the 57 vital statistics jurisdictions through the Vital Statistics Cooperative Program.

Unintentional drowning deaths and death rates, ages 14 and younger, United States, 1999-2009

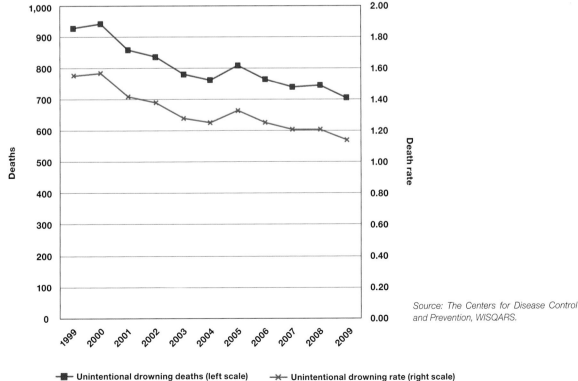

Source: The Centers for Disease Control and Prevention, WISQARS.

— ■ — Unintentional drowning deaths (left scale)   — ✕ — Unintentional drowning rate (right scale)

◆ *Tornadoes drove weather-related deaths up 164% in 2011.*

A variety of weather events resulted in 1,012 deaths in the United States and District of Columbia in 2011, compared with 384 deaths in 2010. Tornadoes accounted for 58% of the deaths, while floods and temperature extremes each accounted for an additional 13%. 2011 was an unusually active and deadly year for tornadoes across the United States, with a total of 1,691 tornadoes reported across the country – the second highest count on record after 2004. Several tornado records were broken in 2011, including number of tornadoes in a single month (758 in April) and the greatest daily total (200 on April 27).

Data on weather-related deaths were compiled by the National Climatic Data Center (NCDC), which is part of the National Oceanic and Atmospheric Administration. NCDC data may differ from data based on death certificates that appear elsewhere in *Injury Facts*.

Weather-related deaths, United States, 2011

Event	Total	Jan.	Feb.	March	April	May	June	July	Aug.	Sept.	Oct.	Nov.	Dec.
Total	1,012	20	24	14	445	209	42	83	98	42	4	21	10
Tornado	587	0	1	1	394	178	6	0	2	0	0	5	0
Flood	127	0	6	4	18	15	5	7	37	26	0	9	0
Temperature extremes	127	11	10	2	1	3	12	55	29	1	0	0	3
Thunderstorm/high winds	75	1	3	1	21	7	11	8	14	2	1	4	2
Ocean/lake surf/rip current	42	5	2	3	6	5	3	4	5	4	2	2	1
Lightning	26	0	0	0	0	1	5	9	6	4	1	0	0
Avalanche	11	0	1	3	4	0	0	0	0	0	0	1	2
Wild/forest fire	6	0	0	0	1	0	0	0	0	5	0	0	0
Hurricane/tropical storm	4	0	0	0	0	0	0	0	4	0	0	0	0
Snow/ice	4	3	1	0	0	0	0	0	0	0	0	0	0
Fog	2	0	0	0	0	0	0	0	0	0	0	0	2
Precipitation	1	0	0	0	0	0	0	0	1	0	0	0	0
Drought	0	0	0	0	0	0	0	0	0	0	0	0	0
Dust storm	0	0	0	0	0	0	0	0	0	0	0	0	0
Funnel cloud	0	0	0	0	0	0	0	0	0	0	0	0	0
Hail	0	0	0	0	0	0	0	0	0	0	0	0	0
Waterspout	0	0	0	0	0	0	0	0	0	0	0	0	0

Source: National Safety Council analysis of National Climatic Data Center data.

Weather-related fatalities by month, United States, 2011

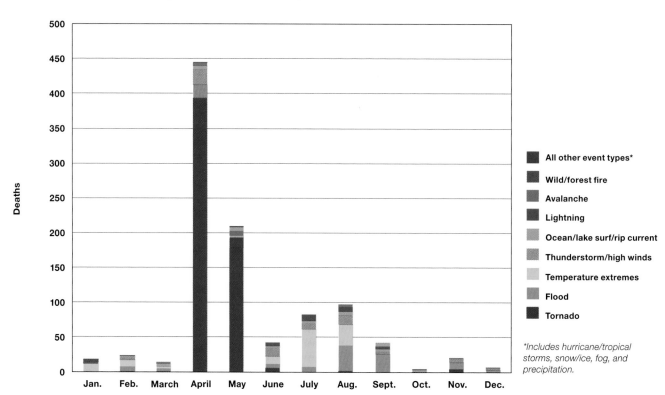

Legend:
- All other event types*
- Wild/forest fire
- Avalanche
- Lightning
- Ocean/lake surf/rip current
- Thunderstorm/high winds
- Temperature extremes
- Flood
- Tornado

Includes hurricane/tropical storms, snow/ice, fog, and precipitation.

❖ Unintentional firearms-related deaths were down more than 6% to a record low in 2009.

Firearms-related deaths from unintentional, intentional, and undetermined causes totaled 31,347 in 2009, a decrease of nearly 1% from 2008. Suicides accounted for 59.8% of deaths related to firearms – 36.7% were homicides and 1.8% were unintentional deaths. Males dominated all categories of deaths related to firearms and accounted for 86% of the total.

The number of homicide deaths related to firearms decreased by 5.6% from 2008 to 2009. Unintentional deaths related to firearms also declined in 2009 for the fourth year in a row, falling to a new record low. However, suicide deaths related to firearms increased by 2.8% from 2008 to 2009, marking the third consecutive annual increase.

Hospital emergency department surveillance data[a] indicate an estimated 18,610 nonfatal unintentional firearms-related injuries occurred in 2009. Assault was related to an estimated 44,466 nonfatal injuries, while the estimated total for intentionally self-inflicted nonfatal injuries was 3,013.[b]

[a]Source: National Center for Injury Prevention and Control injury surveillance data using WISQARS from www.cdc.gov/injury/wisqars/nonfatal.html.
[b]Estimate for self-inflicted nonfatal injuries does not meet standard of reliability or precision and should be used with caution.

Deaths involving firearms by age and sex, United States, 2009

Type and sex	All ages	Younger than 5	5-14 years	15-19 years	20-24 years	25-44 years	45-64 years	65-74 years	75 and older
Total firearms deaths	**31,347**	**86**	**269**	**2,456**	**3,840**	**10,838**	**9,127**	**2,320**	**2,411**
Male	26,921	50	207	2,194	3,451	9,226	7,572	2,029	2,192
Female	4,426	36	62	262	389	1,612	1,555	291	219
Unintentional	**554**	**16**	**32**	**66**	**66**	**175**	**121**	**46**	**32**
Male	497	11	31	64	59	159	102	40	31
Female	57	5	1	2	7	16	19	6	1
Suicide	**18,735**	**–**	**64**	**736**	**1,266**	**5,253**	**7,166**	**2,035**	**2,215**
Male	16,307	–	53	655	1,142	4,461	6,075	1,834	2,087
Female	2,428	–	11	81	124	792	1,091	201	128
Homicide	**11,493**	**66**	**168**	**1,621**	**2,430**	**5,169**	**1,672**	**215**	**152**
Male	9,615	36	119	1,446	2,175	4,391	1,252	134	62
Female	1,878	30	49	175	255	778	420	81	90
Legal intervention	**333**	**1**	**0**	**17**	**52**	**163**	**87**	**11**	**2**
Male	311	1	0	16	52	154	77	9	2
Female	22	0	0	1	0	9	10	2	0
Undetermined[a]	**232**	**3**	**5**	**16**	**26**	**78**	**81**	**13**	**10**
Male	191	2	4	13	23	61	66	12	10
Female	41	1	1	3	3	17	15	1	0

Source: National Safety Council tabulation of National Center for Health Statistics–Mortality Data for 2009, as compiled from data provided by the 57 vital statistics jurisdictions through the Vital Statistics Cooperative Program.
Note: Dashes (–) indicate category not applicable.
[a]Undetermined means the intentionality of the deaths (unintentional, homicide, suicide) was not determined.

Firearms deaths by intentionality, United States, 1999-2009

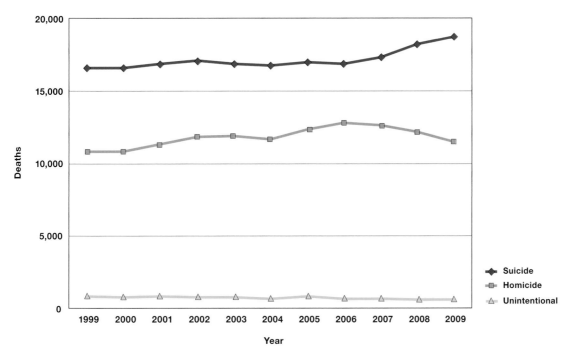

Overall, passenger transportation incidents account for about 4 out of 10 unintentional-injury-related deaths. But the risk of death for the passenger, expressed on a per-mile basis, varies greatly by transportation mode. Highway travel by personal vehicle presents the greatest risk; air, rail, and bus travel have much lower death rates. The tables below show the latest information on passenger transportation deaths and death rates.

In recognition of the current use of vans, sport utility vehicles (SUVs), pickups, and other light trucks as passenger vehicles, the Federal Highway Administration (FHWA) reclassified these vehicles and passenger automobiles as "light duty vehicles" beginning in 2009. Because the data for 2007 and 2008 also meet the requirements of the new FHWA methodology, they are presented with the data for later years in the table below. The statistics for light duty vehicles shown in the tables below represent all use of such vehicles, both intercity and local. The bus data also include intercity and local (transit) bus travel. Railroad includes both intercity (Amtrak) and local commuting travel. Scheduled airlines includes both large airlines and commuter airlines, but excludes on-demand air taxis and charter operations. In comparing the four modes, drivers of light duty vehicles (except taxis) are considered passengers. Bus drivers and airline or railroad crews are not considered passengers.

Other comparisons are possibly based on passenger trips, vehicle miles, or vehicle trips, but passenger miles is the most commonly used basis for comparing the safety of various modes of travel.

Transportation incident death rates, 2008-2010

Mode of transportation	2010			2008-2010 average death rate
	Passenger deaths	Passenger miles (billions)	Deaths per 100,000,000 passenger miles	
Light duty vehicles[a]	22,185	4,421.6	0.50	0.54
Buses[b]	28	57.7	0.05	0.06
Transit buses	3	21.2	0.01	0.04
Intercity buses	14	36.5	0.04	0.03
Railroad passenger trains[c]	3	19.8	0.02	0.05
Scheduled airlines[d]	0	552.9	0.00	0.003

Source: Highway passenger deaths – Fatality Analysis Reporting System data. Railroad passenger deaths and miles – Federal Railroad Administration. Airline passenger deaths – National Transportation Safety Board. Airline passenger miles – Bureau of Transportation Statistics. Passenger miles for transit buses – American Public Transit Association. All other figures – National Safety Council estimates.
[a]Includes passenger cars, light trucks, vans, and SUVs regardless of wheelbase. Includes taxi passengers. Drivers of light duty vehicles are considered passengers.
[b]Figures exclude school buses but include "other" and "unknown" bus types.
[c]Includes Amtrak and commuter rail service.
[d]Includes large airlines and scheduled commuter airlines; excludes charter, cargo, on-demand service, and suicide/sabotage.

Passenger deaths and death rates, United States, 2007-2010

Year	Light duty vehicles[a]		Buses		Railroad passenger trains		Scheduled airlines	
	Deaths	Rate[b]	Deaths	Rate[b]	Deaths	Rate[b]	Deaths	Rate[b]
2007	29,075	0.66	18	0.03	5	0.03	0	0.00
2008	25,344	0.59	50	0.08	24	0.13	0	0.00
2009	23,376	0.53	21	0.04	3	0.02	49	0.01
2010	22,185	0.50	28	0.05	3	0.02	0	0.00

Source: See table above.
[a]Includes passenger cars, light trucks, vans, and SUVs regardless of wheelbase. Includes taxi passengers. Drivers of light duty vehicles are considered passengers.
[b]Deaths per 100,000,000 passenger miles.

Passenger death rates, United States, 2008-2010

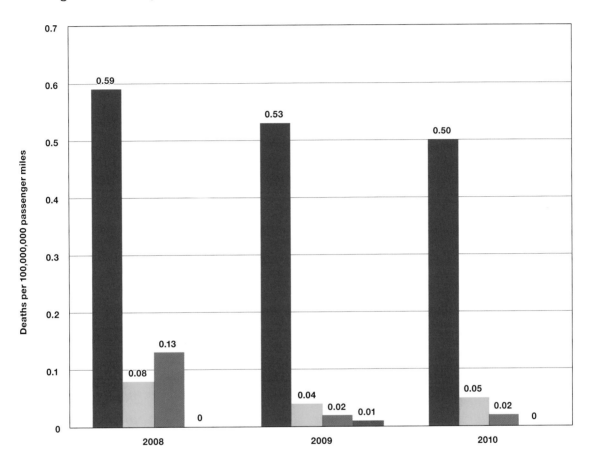

- ■ Light duty vehicles[a]
- ■ Buses
- ■ Railroad passenger trains
- ■ Scheduled airlines

[a]*With the exception of taxi drivers, drivers of these vehicles are considered passengers.*

In the United States, the rate of civil aviation incidents per 100,000 flight hours has decreased since 1991 for general aviation, on-demand air taxis, and large airlines.

U.S. civil aviation incidents, deaths, and death rates, 2006-2011

| | | | | Incident rates | | | |
| | Incidents | | | Per 100,000 flight hours | | Per million miles flown | |
Year	Total	Fatal	Total deaths[a]	Total	Fatal	Total	Fatal
Large airlines[b]							
2006	26	2	50	0.139	0.011	0.0033	0.0003
2007	26	0	0	0.137	0	0.0032	0
2008	20	0	0	0.108	0	0.0026	0
2009	26	1	50	0.152	0.006	0.0036	0.0001
2010	27	0	0	0.157	0	0.0037	0
2011	28	0	0	0.162	0	0.0038	0
Commuter airlines[b]							
2006	3	1	2	0.995	0.332	0.0645	0.0215
2007	3	0	0	1.028	0	0.0651	0
2008	7	0	0	2.385	0	0.1508	0
2009	2	0	0	0.685	0	0.0444	0
2010	6	0	0	1.947	0	0.1264	0
2011	4	0	0	1.303	0	0.0843	0
On-demand air taxis[b]							
2006	52	10	16	1.39	0.27	–	–
2007	62	14	43	1.54	0.35	–	–
2008	58	20	69	1.81	0.62	–	–
2009	47	2	17	1.62	0.07	–	–
2010	31	6	17	1.00	0.19	–	–
2011	50	16	41	1.50	0.48	–	–
General aviation[b]							
2006[c]	1,523	308	706	6.35	1.28	–	–
2007[c]	1,651	288	496	6.92	1.20	–	–
2008[c]	1,569	275	494	6.87	1.21	–	–
2009[c]	1,480	275	478	7.08	1.32	–	–
2010[c]	1,439	268	454	6.63	1.23	–	–
2011[c]	1,466	263	444	6.51	1.17	–	–

Source: National Transportation Safety Board: 2011 preliminary, 2006-2010 revised; exposure data for rates from the Federal Aviation Administration.

Note: Dash (–) indicates data not available.

[a]Includes passengers, crew members, and others such as people on the ground.

[b]Civil aviation incident statistics collected by the National Transportation Safety Board are classified according to federal air regulations under which the flights were made. The classifications are (1) large airlines operating scheduled service under Title 14, Code of Federal Regulations, part 121 (14 CFR 121); (2) commuter carriers operating scheduled service under 14 CFR 135; (3) unscheduled, "on-demand" air taxis under 14 CFR 135; and (4) "general aviation," which includes incidents involving aircraft flown under rules other than 14 CFR 121 and 14 CFR 135. Not shown in the table is nonscheduled air carrier operations under 14 CFR 121 that experienced (6 incidents/0 fatalities) in 2005, (7/0) in 2006, (2/1) in 2007, (8/3) in 2008, (4/2) in 2009, and (3/2) in 2010. Since 1997, "large airlines" includes aircraft with 10 or more seats, formerly operated as commuter carriers under 14 CFR 135.

[c]Suicide/sabotage/terrorism and stolen/unauthorized cases are included in incident and fatality totals but excluded from rates – General Aviation, 2006 (2/1), 2007 (2/2), 2008 (2/0), 2009 (3/0), 2010 (2/1), and 2011 (0/0).

Civil aviation incident rates, United States, 1991-2011

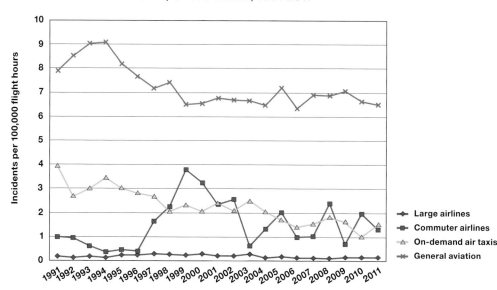

Railroad deaths totaled 689 in 2011, a 5% decrease from the 2010 revised total of 726 and 19% lower than the 2001-2010 average of 854. From 2010 to 2011, there was a 5% decrease in fatalities at highway-rail crossings, as well as fatalities involving other types of incidents. The latter included 410 deaths, or 92%, to trespassers. Twenty-one employees were killed while on duty, a 5% increase compared to the 2010 death toll and equal to the 2001-2010 average. Deaths to passengers on trains totaled six, doubling the 2010 total of three deaths but still down from the 10-year average of seven deaths a year.

The ratio of railroad-related deaths to nonfatal injuries and illnesses is approximately 1:12. In 2011, railroad incidents resulted in 8,149 cases of nonfatal conditions, compared to 8,348 in 2010 and the 2001-2010 average of 9,398. Twelve percent of the total was attributed to highway-rail crossing incidents, which increased by 13% from the 2010 total of 868 but was still slightly lower than the 2001-2010 average of 1,007. Of the 4,152 nonfatal occupational railroad injuries and illnesses reported in 2011, less than 2% were attributed to highway-rail crossing incidents.

Deaths and nonfatal cases in railroad incidents, United States, 2001-2011

Year	Total	Highway-rail crossing incident?		Occurring in other than highway-rail crossing incident		Employees on duty At highway-rail crossing?		Passengers on trains[a] At highway-rail crossing?	
		Yes	No	Trespassers	Others	Yes	No	Yes	No
Deaths									
2001	971	421	550	511	39	1	21	0	3
2002	951	357	594	540	54	1	19	0	7
2003	865	334	531	498	33	1	18	1	2
2004	891	371	520	472	48	2	23	0	3
2005	884	359	525	458	67	2	23	0	16
2006	903	369	534	511	23	4	12	0	2
2007	851	339	512	470	42	1	16	0	5
2008	803	290	513	457	56	3	22	0	24
2009	696	249	447	416	31	0	16	0	3
2010	726	257	469	434	35	0	20	0	3
2011	689	245	444	410	34	6	15	4	2
Nonfatal conditions									
2001	10,985	1,157	9,828	404	9,424	97	7,718	20	726
2002	11,103	999	10,104	395	9,709	110	6,534	26	851
2003	9,264	1,035	8,229	398	7,831	76	6,182	74	653
2004	9,194	1,094	8,100	406	7,694	116	5,906	28	675
2005	9,550	1,053	8,497	420	8,077	111	5,711	33	924
2006	8,797	1,070	7,727	481	7,246	96	5,179	95	841
2007	9,667	1,059	8,608	407	8,201	105	5,357	72	1,442
2008	9,059	990	8,069	433	7,636	75	4,924	101	1,228
2009	8,014	742	7,272	344	6,928	72	4,415	61	1,140
2010	8,348	868	7,480	390	7,090	81	4,322	106	1,259
2011	8,149	986	7,163	346	6,817	70	4,082	230	1,259

Source: Federal Railroad Administration.
[a]Passenger cases include all circumstances, including getting on/off standing trains, stumbling aboard trains, assaults, train incidents, crossing incidents, etc.

Casualties at public and private highway-rail crossings, United States, 2001-20011

Year	Deaths				Nonfatal conditions			
	Total	Motor vehicle-related	Pedestrians	Others	Total	Motor vehicle-related	Pedestrians	Others
2001	421	345	67	9	1,157	1,110	31	16
2002	357	310	35	12	999	939	29	31
2003	334	281	50	3	1,035	1,000	28	7
2004	371	289	73	9	1,095	1,059	30	6
2005	359	284	58	17	1,053	1,006	37	10
2006	369	305	53	11	1,070	1,035	29	6
2007	339	265	59	15	1,059	1,018	32	9
2008	290	221	64	5	990	923	55	12
2009	249	182	59	8	742	696	38	8
2010	257	166	79	12	868	800	49	19
2011	245	164	70	11	986	930	40	16

Source: Federal Railroad Administration.

* *Poisoning deaths were up 2% from 2008 to 2009.*

Deaths from unintentional poisoning numbered 31,758 in 2009, the latest year for which data are available. The death rate per 100,000 population was 10.3. Males are at greatest risk, with a death rate of 13.6 compared with 7.2 for females. Total poisoning deaths increased 2% from 31,116 in 2008 and are more than 2.5 times the 1999 total. See pages 52-55 for long-term trends.

Thirty-nine percent of the poisoning deaths were classified in the "narcotics and psychodysleptics (hallucinogens), not else-where classified," category, which includes prescription narcotic analgesics and illegal drugs such as cocaine, heroin, cannabinol, and LSD. A recent report from the Centers for Disease Control and Prevention[a] indicates that prescription opioid analgesics were involved in 14,800 overdose deaths in 2008, more than cocaine and heroin combined. States in the Appalachian region and the Southwest have the highest death rates from drug overdoses (see map on the following page). A large part of the problem is nonmedical use of prescription painkillers – in 2010, about 12 million Americans 12 or older reported nonmedical use of such drugs in the past year.

Deaths due to alcohol poisoning decreased less than 0.5% from 2008 and totaled 2,014 in 2009. Alcohol poisoning deaths for males outnumbered those for females by more than 3 to 1. However, alcohol poisoning deaths among males decreased 3% from 2008 to 2009, while such deaths for females increased 8% over the same period. It should be noted that alcohol also may be present in combination with other drugs.

Carbon monoxide poisoning is included in the category of "other gases and vapors." Additional information on human poisoning exposure cases may be found on pages 162 and 191.

[a]*Policy Impact: Prescription Painkiller Overdoses. Accessed July 10, 2012, at www.cdc.gov/homeandrecreationalsafety/rxbrief.*

Unintentional poisoning deaths by type, age, and sex, United States, 2009

Type of poison	All ages	Younger than 5	5-14 years	15-19 years	20-24 years	25-44 years	45-64 years	65 and older
Both sexes								
Total poisoning deaths	**31,758**	**59**	**50**	**715**	**2,329**	**13,597**	**13,588**	**1,420**
Deaths per 100,000 population	*10.3*	*0.3*	*0.1*	*3.3*	*10.8*	*16.4*	*17.1*	*3.6*
Total drug-related poisoning deaths	28,754	35	25	636	2,181	12,601	12,209	1,067
Nonopioid analgesics, antipyretics and antirheumatics (X40)[a]	*252*	*2*	*0*	*4*	*8*	*91*	*110*	*37*
Antiepileptic, sedative-hypnotic, antiparkinsonism, and psychotropic drugs, n.e.c. (X41)	*1,681*	*4*	*2*	*29*	*69*	*662*	*854*	*61*
Narcotics and psychodysleptics (hallucinogens), n.e.c. (X42)	*12,458*	*12*	*14*	*313*	*1,073*	*5,581*	*5,193*	*272*
Other drugs acting on the autonomic nervous system (X43)	*15*	*0*	*1*	*0*	*1*	*3*	*8*	*2*
Other and unspecified drugs, medicaments, and biological substances (X44)	*14,348*	*17*	*8*	*290*	*1,030*	*6,264*	*6,044*	*695*
Alcohol (X45)	2,014	0	2	44	93	675	1,072	128
Organic solvents and halogenated hydrocarbons and their vapors (X46)	54	4	1	3	1	29	11	5
Other gases and vapors (X47)	730	15	22	27	39	221	225	181
Pesticides (X48)	4	2	0	0	0	0	1	1
Other and unspecified chemical and noxious substances (X49)	202	3	0	5	15	71	70	38
Males								
Total poisoning deaths	**20,577**	**33**	**25**	**545**	**1,784**	**9,276**	**8,217**	**697**
Deaths per 100,000 population	*13.6*	*0.3*	*0.1*	*4.9*	*16.1*	*22.0*	*21.2*	*4.1*
Total drug-related poisoning deaths	18,377	15	13	493	1,675	8,507	7,193	481
Nonopioid analgesics, antipyretics and antirheumatics (X40)	*112*	*1*	*0*	*3*	*5*	*36*	*53*	*14*
Antiepileptic, sedative-hypnotic, antiparkinsonism, and psychotropic drugs, n.e.c. (X41)	*1,025*	*0*	*1*	*19*	*51*	*429*	*493*	*32*
Narcotics and psychodysleptics (hallucinogens), n.e.c. (X42)	*8,866*	*5*	*10*	*250*	*850*	*4,142*	*3,453*	*156*
Other drugs acting on the autonomic nervous system (X43)	*10*	*0*	*1*	*0*	*1*	*3*	*5*	*0*
Other and unspecified drugs, medicaments, and biological substances (X44)	*8,364*	*9*	*1*	*221*	*768*	*3,897*	*3,189*	*279*
Alcohol (X45)	1,545	0	2	35	71	536	805	96
Organic solvents and halogenated hydrocarbons and their vapors (X46)	37	2	0	1	1	18	10	5
Other gases and vapors (X47)	506	11	10	15	28	171	172	99
Pesticides (X48)	3	2	0	0	0	0	1	0
Other and unspecified chemical and noxious substances (X49)	109	3	0	1	9	44	36	16
Females								
Total poisoning deaths	**11,181**	**26**	**25**	**170**	**545**	**4,321**	**5,371**	**723**
Deaths per 100,000 population	*7.2*	*0.2*	*0.1*	*1.6*	*5.2*	*10.5*	*13.2*	*3.2*
Total drug-related poisoning deaths	10,377	20	12	143	506	4,094	5,016	586
Nonopioid analgesics, antipyretics and antirheumatics (X40)	*140*	*1*	*0*	*1*	*3*	*55*	*57*	*23*
Antiepileptic, sedative-hypnotic, antiparkinsonism, and psychotropic drugs, n.e.c. (X41)	*656*	*4*	*1*	*10*	*18*	*233*	*361*	*29*
Narcotics and psychodysleptics (hallucinogens), n.e.c. (X42)	*3,592*	*7*	*4*	*63*	*223*	*1,439*	*1,740*	*116*
Other drugs acting on the autonomic nervous system (X43)	*5*	*0*	*0*	*0*	*0*	*0*	*3*	*2*
Other and unspecified drugs, medicaments, and biological substances (X44)	*5,984*	*8*	*7*	*69*	*262*	*2,367*	*2,855*	*416*
Alcohol (X45)	469	0	0	9	22	139	267	32
Organic solvents and halogenated hydrocarbons and their vapors (X46)	17	2	1	2	0	11	1	0
Other gases and vapors (X47)	224	4	12	12	11	50	53	82
Pesticides (X48)	1	0	0	0	0	0	0	1
Other and unspecified chemical and noxious substances (X49)	93	0	0	4	6	27	34	22

Source: National Safety Council tabulations of National Center for Health Statistics–Mortality Data for 2009, as compiled from data provided by the 57 vital statistics jurisdictions through the Vital Statistics Cooperative Program.
Note: n.e.c. means not elsewhere classified.
[a]Numbers following titles refer to external cause of injury and poisoning classifications in 10th revision of the International Classification of Diseases.

Unintentional poisoning deaths, United States, 1996-2009

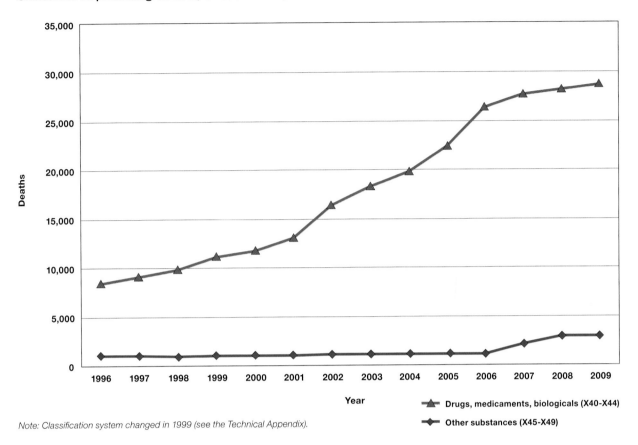

Note: Classification system changed in 1999 (see the Technical Appendix).

— Drugs, medicaments, biologicals (X40-X44)

— Other substances (X45-X49)

Overall drug overdose death rates[a] by state, United States, 2008

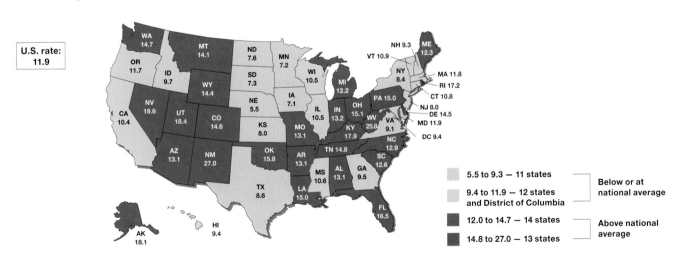

U.S. rate: 11.9

5.5 to 9.3 — 11 states } Below or at national average
9.4 to 11.9 — 12 states and District of Columbia
12.0 to 14.7 — 14 states } Above national average
14.8 to 27.0 — 13 states

[a]Age-adjusted death rates per 100,000 population.
Source: Policy Impact: Prescription Drug Overdose State Rates, accessed July 10, 2012
from www.cdc.gov/HomeandRecreationalSafety/rxbrief/states.html.

Most people think of poisoning as a childhood issue. That is true for poisonings exposures, but not for nonfatal and fatal poisonings.

The pie charts below show the distribution of poisoning exposures, nonfatal poisonings, and fatal poisonings by age groups. The poisoning exposure data are from the American Association of Poison Control Centers and represent the calls received by poison control centers. The nonfatal data represent emergency department visits, while the fatality data are from death certificates.

Nonfatal exposures occur predominantly among young children, whereas nonfatal and fatal poisonings are overwhelmingly among adults. While about half of the poisoning exposures involve children 5 or younger, nearly 85% of the nonfatal poisonings and 97% of the fatalities occur among adults 19 and older.

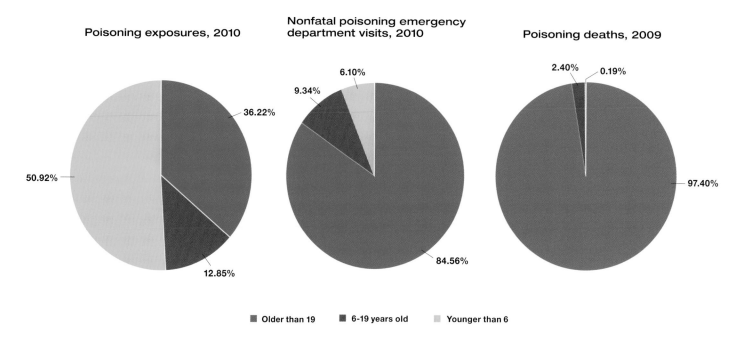

For the first time since 2006, nonfatal poisonings increased substantially in 2010, while the increase in fatal poisonings appears to have slowed. The charts below illustrate the trends for both categories of poisonings starting in 2002.

Nonfatal unintentional poisoning trend

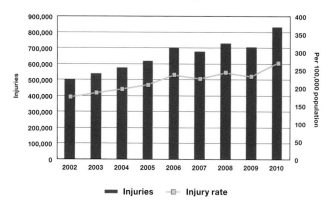

Source: Centers for Disease Control and Prevention, NEISS-AIP

Fatal unintentional poisoning trend[a]

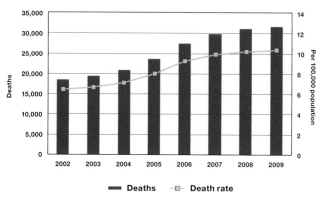

Source: Centers for Disease Control and Prevention, WISQARS

[a]2009 is the latest official data available. National Safety Council estimates for 2010 and 2011 are available on page 53.

The 65-and-older age group has seen a 99% increase in unintentional fall fatalities between 2000 and 2009.

The impact of unintentional falls on the older adult population has been highlighted in numerous editions of *Injury Facts* (2012, 2011, 2010, 2008, 2007, etc.). In 2010 alone, 2,350,009 individuals age 65 and older were treated in hospital emergency departments for nonfatal unintentional fall injuries. This compares sharply with the 55-to-64 age group that accounted for only 860,611 fall-related emergency department visits. The prevalence of fall-related fatalities also is strongly associated with age.

As shown in the chart below, the number of fall-related deaths among the 65 and older age group is 4 times as much as the number of fall-related deaths among all other age groups.

The number and rate of fall-related deaths among older individuals also is increasing, while other ages have shown little to no increase since 1999. From 2000 to 2009, the number of unintentional fall-related fatalities among the 65-and-older age group has increased 99%, while the fatality rate per 100,000 population has increased 76% over this same period.

Source: National Safety Council analysis of National Center for Health Statistics (NCHS)–Mortality Data for 2009, as compiled from data provided by the 57 vital statistics jurisdictions through the Vital Statistics Cooperative Program. Rates are National Safety Council estimates based on data from NCHS and the U.S. Census Bureau.

Fall deaths and death rates, United States, 1999-2009

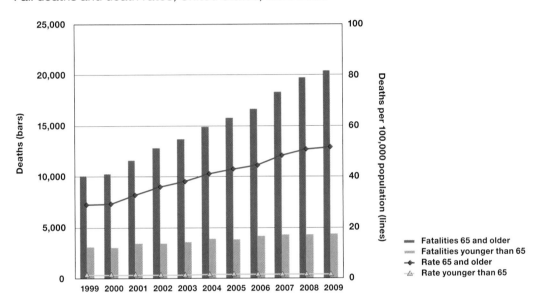

A recent study found that, on average, an estimated 52,482 adults 65 and older are treated in emergency departments each year for nonfatal pedestrian injuries. Falling was the leading type of injury, resulting in more than 75% of older adult pedestrian injuries, followed by being hit by a motor vehicle

representing only 15% of injuries. The study also found that nearly one-quarter of these pedestrian fall-related injuries involved a curb. As shown in the bottom graph, the prevalence of fall-related pedestrian injuries peaks for adults age 80 and older, while the prevalence of being hit by a motor vehicle steadily decreases with age.

Older adult pedestrian injuries by mechanism of injury

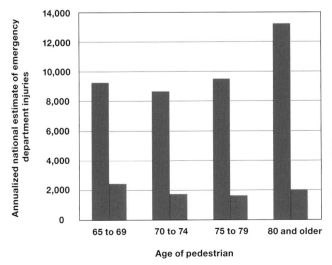

Source: Naumann, R.B., Dellinger, A.M., et al. (2011). Older adult pedestrian injuries in the United States: Causes and contributing circumstances. International Journal of Injury Control and Safety Promotion, Vol. 18, No. 1, pp. 65-73.

According to the National Fire Protection Association, in 2010 an estimated 15,500 reported fires and 8,600 nonfatal injuries involved fireworks. One-quarter of these injuries occurred among children younger than 10, and half occurred among individuals younger than 20. Males accounted for about two-thirds (65%) of fireworks-related injuries. In the past 10 years, fireworks-related fires have decreased by 56%, while injuries resulting in emergency department visits have decreased 9%.

Fireworks-related injuries by age, United States, 2010

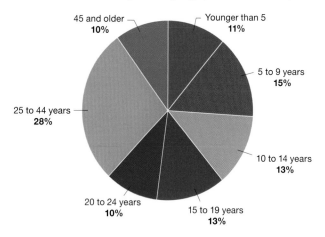

Fireworks-related fires and emergency department injuries, United States, 2001-2010

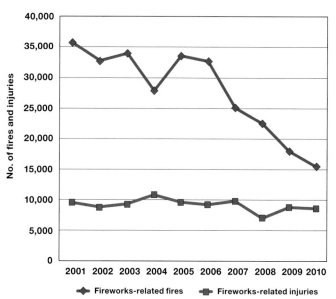

More than half (57%) of all reported fireworks-related fires occur during the 15-day period of June 27 to July 11, centered on the July 4th holiday, and two-thirds (64%) occur in the 31-day month centered on July 4 (June 18 to July 19). An additional 9% occur during the period from Dec. 30 through Jan. 3, with the peak on New Year's Day.

In 2010, 5 out of 6 (83%) emergency department fireworks-related injuries involved fireworks that federal regulations permit consumers to use. The other 17% were large/illegal firecrackers (8%) and public display fireworks (9%). As shown in the graph below, sparklers, fountains, and novelties alone accounted for more than 2 out of 5 (43%) emergency department fireworks-related injuries, including more than half of all fireworks-related injuries among preschool children (age 4 and younger).

Fireworks-related injuries by type of firework, United States, 2010

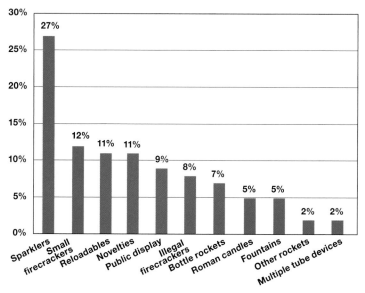

Source: Hall, J.R. (June 2012). Fireworks. Quincy, MA: National Fire Protection Association.

The estimated number of deaths from collisions between pedalcycles and motor vehicles increased from about 750 in 1940 to 1,200 in 1980, and then declined to about 900 in 2011.

In 2009, 552 pedalcyclists died in motor vehicle crashes and 233 in other incidents, according to National Center for Health Statistics mortality data. Males accounted for 88% of all pedalcycle deaths, more than 7 times the female fatalities.

Emergency department-treated injuries associated with bicycles and bicycle accessories were estimated to total 541,746 in 2010 and 549,182 in 2011, according to the Consumer Product Safety Commission (also see page 168).

A meta-analysis of bicycle helmet efficacy by Attewell, Glase,

and McFadden (2001) estimated that bicycle helmets reduce the risk of head injury by 60% and brain injury by 58%. As of June 2012, 21 states, the District of Columbia, and at least 201 localities had bicycle helmet-use laws, according to the Bicycle Helmet Safety Institute.

Source: National Safety Council estimates and tabulations of National Center for Health Statistics mortality data obtained via WISQARS at www.cdc.gov/injury/wisqars/index.html. Population data for rates are from the U.S. Census Bureau. Data from Bicycle Helmet Safety Institute was retrieved Sept. 5, 2012, from www.bhsi.org.
Attewell, R.G., Glase, K., & McFadden, M. (2001). Bicycle helmet efficacy: A meta-analysis. Accident Analysis & Prevention, Vol. 33, No. 3, pp. 345-352.

Pedalcycle deaths and death rates by sex and age group, United States, 2009

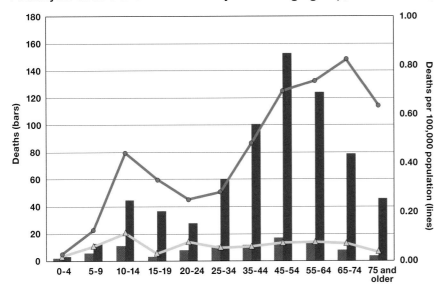

Source: National Safety Council tabulations based on U.S. Census Bureau and National Center for Health Statistics data.

Pedalcycle fatalities by month, United States, 2009

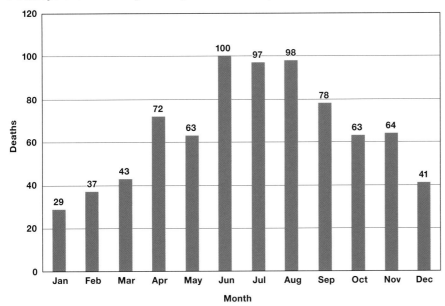

Source: National Safety Council tabulations of National Center for Health Statistics data.

The leading risks for unintentional injury vary with age and are different for deaths and nonfatal injuries. The tables here and on the next page list, for eight age groups, the five leading causes of unintentional-injury-related deaths and the five leading causes of hospital emergency department visits, which is one measure of nonfatal injuries.

For all ages, the five leading causes account for 85% of all unintentional-injury-related deaths and 76% of unintentional-injury-related emergency department visits. Only motor vehicle crashes and falls are common to both lists. Motor vehicle crashes rank first for unintentional-injury-related deaths and fourth for unintentional-injury-related emergency department visits. Falls rank third for unintentional-injury-related deaths and first for emergency department unintentional-injury-related visits.

The five leading causes of unintentional-injury-related deaths account for between 82% and 93% of such deaths depending on the age group. The leading causes of unintentional-injury-related emergency department visits account for between 74% and 89% of such hospital visits.

For deaths, motor vehicle crashes; poisoning; falls; fire, flames, or smoke; and drowning are most often among the top five, with choking, firearms, and mechanical suffocation sometimes included. For emergency department visits, falls, struck by or against, overexertion, motor vehicle occupant injuries, and cut or pierce injuries are most often in the top five. In the younger age groups, bites and stings (except dog bites), foreign body injuries, and struck by or against are among the leading risks.

Leading unintentional-injury risks, all ages, United States, 2009

Rank	Unintentional-injury-related deaths				Emergency department unintentional-injury-related visits			
	Event	Number	Percent	Rate[a]	Event	Number	Percent	Rate[a]
–	Total	118,021	100.0%	38.4	Total	27,632,781	100.0%	9,001
1	Motor vehicle crashes	36,216	30.7%	11.8	Falls	8,765,597	31.7%	2,855
2	Poisoning	31,758	26.9%	10.3	Struck by or against	4,435,906	16.1%	1,445
3	Falls	24,792	21.0%	8.1	Overexertion	3,207,877	11.6%	1,045
4	Choking[b]	4,370	3.7%	1.4	Motor vehicle occupant	2,643,652	9.6%	861
5	Drowning	3,517	3.0%	1.1	Cut or pierce	1,997,752	7.2%	651

Leading unintentional-injury risks, young children (ages 0-4), United States, 2009

Rank	Unintentional-injury-related deaths				Emergency department unintentional-injury-related visits			
	Event	Number	Percent	Rate[a]	Event	Number	Percent	Rate[a]
–	Total	2,647	100.0%	12.4	Total	2,355,302	100.0%	11,058
1	Mechanical suffocation	914	34.5%	4.3	Falls	1,102,661	46.8%	5,177
2	Motor vehicle crashes	574	21.7%	2.7	Struck by or against	403,762	17.1%	1,896
3	Drowning	495	18.7%	2.3	Bite or sting (except dog)	148,274	6.3%	696
4	Fire, flames, or smoke	191	7.2%	0.9	Foreign body	134,920	5.7%	633
5	Choking[b]	118	4.5%	0.6	Cut or pierce	90,144	3.8%	423

Leading unintentional-injury risks, children and young adolescents (ages 5-14), United States, 2009

Rank	Unintentional-injury-related deaths				Emergency department unintentional-injury-related visits			
	Event	Number	Percent	Rate[a]	Event	Number	Percent	Rate[a]
–	Total	1,689	100.0%	4.2	Total	3,823,419	100.0%	9,421
1	Motor vehicle crashes	974	57.7%	2.4	Falls	1,246,526	32.6%	3,072
2	Drowning	209	12.4%	0.5	Struck by or against	980,312	25.6%	2,416
3	Fire, flames, or smoke	141	8.3%	0.3	Overexertion	353,817	9.3%	872
4	Poisoning	50	3.0%	0.1	Cut or pierce	223,380	5.8%	550
4	Mechanical suffocation	50	3.0%	0.1	Pedalcyclist	202,685	5.3%	499

Leading unintentional-injury risks, teens (ages 15-19), United States, 2009

Rank	Unintentional-injury-related deaths				Emergency department unintentional-injury-related visits			
	Event	Number	Percent	Rate[a]	Event	Number	Percent	Rate[a]
–	Total	4,807	100.0%	22.3	Total	2,612,130	100.0%	12,128
1	Motor vehicle crashes	3,365	70.0%	15.6	Struck by or against	617,631	23.6%	2,868
2	Poisoning	715	14.9%	3.3	Falls	468,967	18.0%	2,177
3	Drowning	279	5.8%	1.3	Overexertion	372,035	14.2%	1,727
4	Firearms	66	1.4%	0.3	Motor vehicle occupant	341,257	13.1%	1,584
5	Falls	58	1.2%	0.3	Cut or pierce	184,972	7.1%	859

See footnotes on page 167.

Leading unintentional-injury risks, young adults (ages 20-24), United States, 2009

Rank	Unintentional-injury-related deaths				Emergency department unintentional-injury-related visits			
	Event	Number	Percent	Rate[a]	Event	Number	Percent	Rate[a]
–	Total	7,651	100.0%	35.5	Total	2,454,744	100.0%	11,396
1	Motor vehicle crashes	4,323	56.5%	20.1	Falls	448,200	18.3%	2,081
2	Poisoning	2,329	30.4%	10.8	Struck by or against	410,015	16.7%	1,904
3	Drowning	269	3.5%	1.2	Motor vehicle occupant	399,903	16.3%	1,857
4	Falls	134	1.8%	0.6	Overexertion	331,774	13.5%	1,540
5	Fire, flames, or smoke	86	1.1%	0.4	Cut or pierce	237,210	9.7%	1,101

Leading unintentional-injury risks, adults (ages 25-44), United States, 2009

Rank	Unintentional-injury-related deaths				Emergency department unintentional-injury-related visits			
	Event	Number	Percent	Rate[a]	Event	Number	Percent	Rate[a]
–	Total	29,164	100.0%	35.1	Total	7,508,037	100.0%	9,035
1	Poisoning	13,597	46.6%	16.4	Falls	1,586,536	21.1%	1,909
2	Motor vehicle crashes	10,953	37.6%	13.2	Overexertion	1,218,673	16.2%	1,467
3	Falls	853	2.9%	1.0	Struck by or against	1,138,554	15.2%	1,370
4	Drowning	788	2.7%	0.9	Motor vehicle occupant	973,245	13.0%	1,171
5	Fire, flames, or smoke	433	1.5%	0.5	Cut or pierce	690,989	9.2%	832

Leading unintentional-injury risks, adults (ages 45-64), United States, 2009

Rank	Unintentional-injury-related deaths				Emergency department unintentional-injury-related visits			
	Event	Number	Percent	Rate[a]	Event	Number	Percent	Rate[a]
–	Total	32,907	100.0%	41.5	Total	5,475,637	100.0%	6,898
1	Poisoning	13,588	41.3%	17.1	Falls	1,710,141	31.2%	2,154
2	Motor vehicle crashes	9,777	29.7%	12.3	Overexertion	662,120	12.1%	834
3	Falls	3,229	9.8%	4.1	Struck by or against	643,408	11.8%	811
4	Drowning	925	2.8%	1.2	Motor vehicle occupant	580,515	10.6%	731
5	Fire, flames, or smoke	861	2.6%	1.1	Cut or pierce	443,202	8.1%	558

Leading unintentional-injury risks, older adults (ages 65-74), United States, 2009

Rank	Unintentional-injury-related deaths				Emergency department unintentional-injury-related visits			
	Event	Number	Percent	Rate[a]	Event	Number	Percent	Rate[a]
–	Total	8,940	100.0%	43.0	Total	1,318,528	100.0%	6,341
1	Falls	2,850	31.9%	13.7	Falls	666,697	50.6%	3,206
2	Motor vehicle crashes	2,693	30.1%	13.0	Struck by or against	116,855	8.9%	562
3	Poisoning	764	8.5%	3.7	Motor vehicle occupant	103,409	7.8%	497
4	Choking[b]	635	7.1%	3.1	Overexertion	101,069	7.7%	486
5	Fire, flames, or smoke	386	4.3%	1.9	Cut or pierce	80,748	6.1%	388

Leading unintentional-injury risks, elderly (age 75 and older), United States, 2009

Rank	Unintentional-injury-related deaths				Emergency department unintentional-injury-related visits			
	Event	Number	Percent	Rate[a]	Event	Number	Percent	Rate[a]
–	Total	30,171	100.0%	160.7	Total	2,082,328	100.0%	11,089
1	Falls	17,572	58.2%	93.6	Falls	1,535,327	73.7%	8,176
2	Motor vehicle crashes	3,548	11.8%	18.9	Struck by or against	125,159	6.0%	667
3	Choking[b]	2,522	8.4%	13.4	Overexertion	79,083	3.8%	421
4	Poisoning	650	2.2%	3.5	Motor vehicle occupant	71,590	3.4%	381
5	Fire, flames, or smoke	602	2.0%	3.2	Cut or pierce	46,987	2.3%	250

Source: National Safety Council analysis of National Center for Health Statistics (NCHS)–Mortality Data for 2009, as compiled from data provided by the 57 vital statistics jurisdictions through the Vital Statistics Cooperative Program. Rates are National Safety Council estimates based on data from NCHS and the U.S. Census Bureau. Emergency department data are from NEISS-AIP.
[a]Deaths or emergency department visits per 100,000 population.
[b]Inhalation and ingestion of food or other object obstructing breathing.

More than 2 million injury-related emergency department visits each year are associated with stairs, steps, floors, and flooring materials.

The following list of items found in and around the home was selected from the U.S. Consumer Product Safety Commission's National Electronic Injury Surveillance System (NEISS) for 2011. NEISS estimates are calculated from a statistically representative sample of hospitals in the United States. Injury totals represent estimates of the number of hospital emergency department-treated cases nationwide associated with various products. However, product involvement may or may not be the cause of the injury.

Consumer product-related injuries treated in hospital emergency departments, 2011
(excluding most sports and sports equipment; also see page 152)

Description	Injuries	Description	Injuries
Home workshop equipment		**Home communication or entertainment equipment**	
Saws (hand or power)	78,972	Televisions	59,431
Hammers	31,461	Computers (equipment or electronic games)	37,082
Workshop grinders, buffers, or polishers	24,404	**Personal use items**	
Tools, not specified	22,531	Footwear	193,108
Packaging or containers, household		Jewelry	101,783
Household containers and packaging	237,301	Daywear	65,792
Bottles and jars	75,888	Razors or shavers	43,898
Bags	50,852	Other clothing[d]	40,649
Paper products	25,012	Coins	39,703
Housewares		Desk supplies	35,139
Knives	396,621	Luggage	27,674
Tableware and flatware (excludes knives)	101,528	Hair grooming equipment and accessories	26,136
Drinking glasses	77,310	**Yard and garden equipment**	
Waste containers, trash baskets, etc.	40,821	Lawn mowers	83,291
Cookware, bowls, and canisters	36,113	Pruning, trimming, and edging equipment	46,247
Manual cleaning equipment (excluding buckets)	29,216	Manual snow or ice removal tools	36,162
Scissors	26,212	Chain saws	30,212
Other kitchen gadgets	25,877	Other unpowered garden tools[e]	26,399
Home furnishing, fixtures, or accessories		**Sports and recreation**	
Beds	678,415	Bicycles	549,182
Chairs	378,414	Skateboards	108,510
Tables, n.e.c.[a]	342,120	Swimming pools	97,484
Bathtubs and showers	300,809	Trampolines	83,292
Household cabinets, racks, and shelves	297,414	Monkey bars or other playground climbing equipment	83,118
Sofas, couches, davenports, divans, etc.	192,364	Minibikes or trailbikes	61,826
Ladders	186,183	Swings or swing sets	59,841
Rugs and carpets	149,185	Dancing	58,024
Other furniture[b]	126,329	Aquariums and other pet supplies	58,008
Toilets	101,504	Scooters (unpowered)	57,447
Stools	55,386	Slides or sliding boards	51,046
Miscellaneous decorating items	41,252	Other playground equipment[f]	42,704
Benches	36,034	Amusement attractions (including rides)	23,785
Sinks	29,467	Sleds	22,555
Mirrors and mirror glass	28,156	**Miscellaneous products**	
Electric lighting equipment	22,538	Carts	53,434
Home structures or construction materials		Hot water	44,227
Floors or flooring materials	1,406,545	Elevators, escalators, or moving walkways	23,633
Stairs or steps	1,293,080	**Household chemicals**	
Ceilings and walls	368,981	Bleaches (noncosmetic)	21,620
Other doors[c]	325,664		
Porches, balconies, or open-side floors	146,236		
Nails, screws, tacks, or bolts	137,513		
Windows	117,131		
Fences or fence posts	116,722		
Door sills or frames	60,133		
Counters or countertops	57,635		
Handrails, railings, or banisters	53,052		
Poles	48,754		
Glass doors	29,309		
General household appliances			
Refrigerators	41,793		
Ranges or ovens, not specified	32,900		
Heating, cooling, or ventilating equipment			
Pipes (excluding smoking pipes)	31,692		

Source: U.S. Consumer Product Safety Commission, National Electronic Injury Surveillance System, Product Summary Report, All Products, CY2011.
Note: Products are listed above if the estimate was greater than 20,000 cases.
"n.e.c." = not elsewhere classified.
[a]*Excludes baby changing tables (4,012 injuries) and television tables or stands (12,872 injuries).*
[b]*Excludes household cabinets, racks, shelves, desks, bureaus, chests, buffets, etc. (297,414 injuries).*
[c]*Excludes glass doors (29,309 injuries) and garage doors (19,252 injuries).*
[d]*Excludes costumes, masks, daywear (65,792 injuries); footwear (193,108 injuries); nightwear (5,223 injuries); and outerwear (5,123 injuries).*
[e]*Includes cultivators, hoes, pitchforks, rakes, shovels, spades, and trowels.*
[f]*Excludes monkey bars (83,118 injuries), seesaws (4,699 injuries), slides (51,046 injuries), and swings (59,841 injuries).*

Principal types of home and community unintentional-injury-related deaths, United States, 1987-2011

Year	Total home and community[a]	Falls	Drowning	Poisoning	Choking[b]	Fire, flames, or burns	Firearms	Mechanical suffocation	Air transport	Water transport	Rail transport[c]	Other
1987	39,800	10,300	3,900	4,900	3,600	4,400	1,400	[(d)]	900	800	400	9,200
1988	41,100	10,700	3,800	5,700	3,700	4,600	1,400	[(d)]	700	800	400	9,300
1989	40,700	10,800	3,700	5,900	3,500	4,400	1,400	[(d)]	800	700	400	9,100
1990	38,900	11,000	3,700	5,400	3,300	3,800	1,300	[(d)]	700	800	400	8,500
1991	39,700	11,400	3,700	6,000	3,100	3,800	1,400	[(d)]	700	700	500	8,400
1992	43,000	12,100	3,400	6,900	3,100	3,900	1,400	[(d)]	700	700	600	10,200
1993	45,800	12,500	3,700	8,400	3,200	3,900	1,500	[(d)]	600	700	600	10,700
1994	45,900	12,800	3,300	8,900	3,100	3,900	1,300	[(d)]	600	600	600	10,800
1995	47,300	13,400	3,700	9,000	3,100	3,700	1,200	[(d)]	600	700	500	11,400
1996	48,500	14,300	3,400	9,400	3,200	3,700	1,100	[(d)]	700	600	500	11,600
1997	49,400	14,700	3,500	10,100	3,200	3,400	1,000	[(d)]	500	600	400	12,000
1998	51,600	15,500	3,900	10,700	3,500	3,100	900	[(d)]	500	600	500	12,400
1999[e]	52,700	12,400	3,500	12,100	3,900	3,200	900	1,600	500	600	400	13,600
2000	51,900	12,600	3,400	12,700	4,300	2,900	800	1,300	500	500	400	12,500
2001	55,000	14,200	3,300	14,000	4,100	3,200	800	1,400	700	500	400	12,400
2002	58,700	15,600	3,400	17,500	4,100	3,100	700	1,400	500	500	400	11,500
2003	61,800	16,600	3,200	19,300	4,300	3,200	700	1,300	600	500	400	11,700
2004	64,200	18,000	3,300	20,900	4,400	3,100	600	1,400	400	500	400	11,200
2005	69,600	18,800	3,500	23,500	4,400	3,100	[(d)]	1,500	400	500	400	13,500
2006	73,300	20,000	3,500	27,400	4,400	3,000	[(d)]	1,600	400	400	400	12,200
2007	77,200	21,800	3,400	29,700	4,300	3,200	[(d)]	1,600	400	400	400	12,000
2008	79,700	23,300	3,400	31,000	4,400	2,800	[(d)]	1,700	400	300	400	12,000
2009[f]	79,800	24,200	3,400	31,700	4,400	2,700	[(d)]	1,500	400	400	300	10,800
2010[f]	83,400	25,400	3,700	32,900	4,500	2,700	[(d)]	1,600	300	300	400	11,600
2011[g]	86,100	26,800	3,500	34,800	4,500	2,700	[(d)]	1,600	300	300	400	11,200

Source: National Safety Council estimates based on data from National Center for Health Statistics and state vital statistics departments. The Council adopted the Bureau of Labor Statistics Census of Fatal Occupational Injuries count for work-related unintentional injuries retroactive to 1992 data. Because of the lower work class total resulting from this change, several thousand unintentional-injury-related deaths that had been classified by the Council as work-related had to be reassigned to the home and public classes. For this reason, long-term historical comparisons for these three classes should be made with caution. See the Technical Appendix for an explanation of the methodological changes.
[a]Includes some deaths not shown separately.
[b]Inhalation and ingestion of food or other object that obstructs breathing.
[c]Includes subways and elevateds.
[d]Estimates for both home and public are not available.
[e]In 1999, a revision was made in the International Classification of Diseases. See the Technical Appendix for comparability with earlier years.
[f]Revised.
[g]Preliminary.

Leading types of home and community unintentional-injury-related deaths, United States, 2001-2011

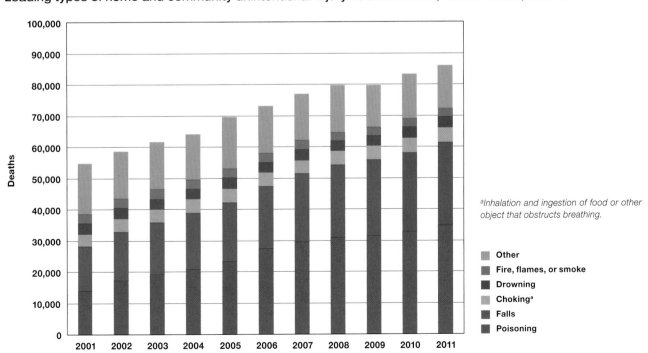

[a]Inhalation and ingestion of food or other object that obstructs breathing.

Legend:
- Other
- Fire, flames, or smoke
- Drowning
- Choking[a]
- Falls
- Poisoning

State Data

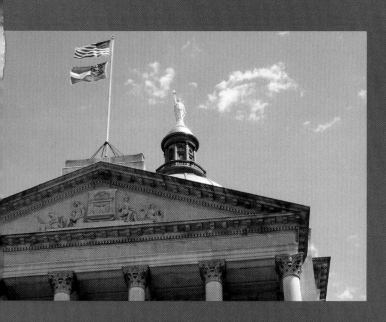

⬩ *Motor vehicle crashes are the leading cause of unintentional-injury-related deaths in 25 states and the District of Columbia.*

This section on state-level data includes data for occupational and motor vehicle injuries, as well as general injury mortality.

Death rates by state of residence for unintentional injuries can vary greatly from one type of injury to the next and from state to state. The graph on the next page shows for each state the death rates (per 100,000 population) for total unintentional-injury-related deaths and the four leading types of unintentional-injury-related deaths nationally – motor vehicle crashes, poisonings, falls, and choking (inhalation or ingestion of food or other object that obstructs breathing).

The map on page 174 shows graphically the overall unintentional-injury-related death rates by state of residence. Rates by region were lowest in Middle Atlantic and highest in East South Central states.

The charts on pages 175-177 show the total unintentional-injury-related deaths by state of residence and where unintentional injuries rank as a cause of death in each state, as well as the five leading causes of unintentional-injury-related deaths in each state.

Unintentional injuries as a whole are the fifth leading cause of death in the United States and in 26 states. Unintentional injuries are the third leading cause of death in 11 states, the fourth leading cause in nine states and the District of Columbia, and the sixth leading cause in four states.

In 2009, motor vehicle crashes were the leading cause of unintentional-injury-related deaths in 25 states and the District of Columbia. Poisoning was the leading cause in 19 states. Falls were the leading cause in six states.

The second leading cause of unintentional-injury-related deaths was poisoning in 19 states, while motor vehicle crashes were the second leading cause in 17 states. Falls were second in 14 states and the District of Columbia.

The most common third leading cause of unintentional-injury-related deaths was falls, in 30 states, while poisoning was the third leading cause in 12 states and the District of

Columbia. Motor vehicle crashes ranked third in eight states.

Choking was the fourth leading cause of unintentional-injury-related deaths in 31 states, while the fourth ranking cause was drowning in 15 states, and fire, flames, or smoke in nine states and the District of Columbia. Natural heat and cold was the fourth ranked cause in Alaska, while mechanical suffocation was the fourth ranked cause in South Dakota. (States with ties for fourth leading causes were included in multiple counts.)

Drowning was the fifth leading unintentional-injury-related cause of death in 18 states. Choking ranked fifth in 15 states and the District of Columbia, and fire, flames, or smoke was fifth in 12 states. The fifth ranking cause in Rhode Island was natural heat and cold. (States with ties for fifth leading causes were included in multiple counts.)

The table on pages 178-179 shows the number of unintentional-injury-related deaths by state of occurrence for the 15 most common types of injury events. State populations also are shown to facilitate computation of detailed death rates.

The table on page 180 consists of a four-year state-by-state comparison of unintentional-injury-related deaths by state of residence and death rates for 2006 through 2009.

Page 181 shows fatal occupational injuries by state and counts of deaths for some of the principal types of events – transportation incidents, assaults or violent acts, contact with objects or equipment, falls, exposure to harmful substances or environments, and fires or explosions.

Nonfatal occupational injury and illness incidence rates for most states are shown in the table on page 182 and graphically in the map on page 183. States not shown do not have state occupational safety and health plans.

Pages 184 and 185 show motor vehicle-related deaths and death rates by state both in tables and maps. The maps show death rates based on population, vehicle miles traveled, and registered vehicles.

Unintentional-injury-related death rates by state of residence, United States, 2009

Deaths per 100,000 population

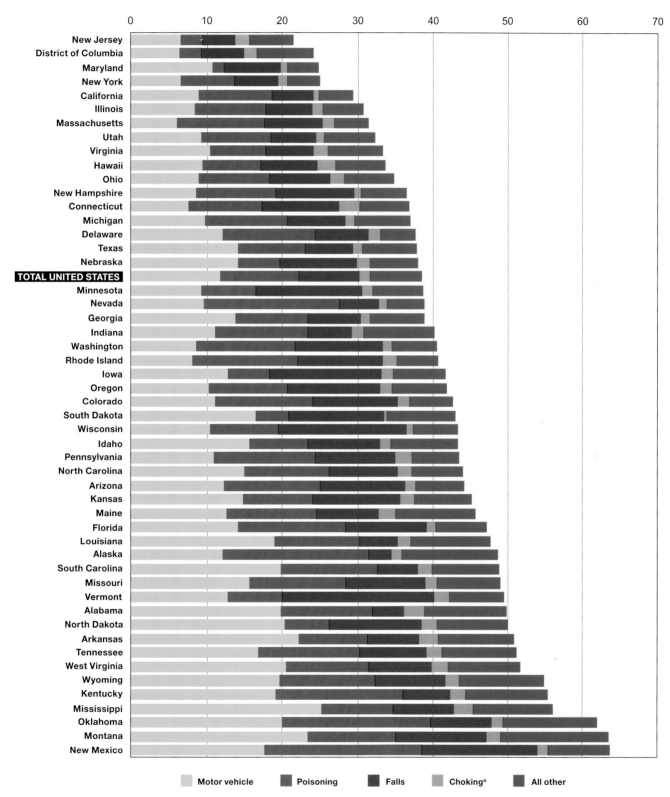

Legend: Motor vehicle | Poisoning | Falls | Choking[a] | All other

[a]Suffocation by ingestion or inhalation of food or other object.

Unintentional-Injury-Related Death Rates by State

Unintentional-injury-related deaths per 100,000 population by state, United States, 2009

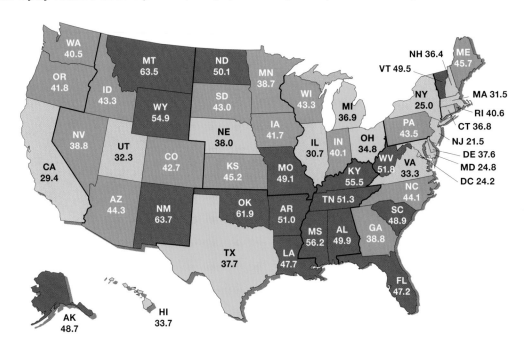

U.S. rate: 38.4

WA 40.5
OR 41.8
ID 43.3
MT 63.5
ND 50.1
MN 38.7
WI 43.3
MI 36.9
NH 36.4
VT 49.5
ME 45.7
NY 25.0
MA 31.5
RI 40.6
CT 36.8
NJ 21.5
DE 37.6
MD 24.8
DC 24.2
NV 38.8
UT 32.3
WY 54.9
SD 43.0
IA 41.7
IL 30.7
IN 40.1
OH 34.8
PA 43.5
WV 51.8
VA 33.3
CA 29.4
CO 42.7
KS 45.2
MO 49.1
KY 55.5
NC 44.1
AZ 44.3
NM 63.7
OK 61.9
AR 51.0
TN 51.3
SC 48.9
MS 56.2
AL 49.9
GA 38.8
TX 37.7
LA 47.7
FL 47.2
AK 48.7
HI 33.7

REGIONAL RATES

NEW ENGLAND (CT, ME, MA, NH, RI, VT)	36.0
MIDDLE ATLANTIC (NJ, NY, PA)	30.0
EAST NORTH CENTRAL (IL, IN, MI, OH, WI)	35.9
WEST NORTH CENTRAL (IA, KS, MN, MO, NE, ND, SD)	43.6
SOUTH ATLANTIC (DE, DC, FL, GA, MD, NC, SC, VA, WV)	41.2
EAST SOUTH CENTRAL (AL, KY, MS, TN)	52.7
WEST SOUTH CENTRAL (AR, LA, OK, TX)	42.5
MOUNTAIN (AZ, CO, ID, MT, NV, NM, UT, WY)	44.6
PACIFIC (AK, CA, HI, OR, WA)	32.2

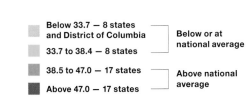

Below 33.7 — 8 states and District of Columbia ⎤
33.7 to 38.4 — 8 states ⎦ Below or at national average
38.5 to 47.0 — 17 states ⎤
Above 47.0 — 17 states ⎦ Above national average

Source: National Safety Council analysis of National Center for Health Statistics (NCHS)–Mortality Data for 2009, as compiled from data provided by the 57 vital statistics jurisdictions through the Vital Statistics Cooperative Program. Rates are National Safety Council estimates based on data from NCHS and the U.S. Census Bureau.

Unintentional-Injury-Related Deaths by State

STATE DATA

The following series of tables is a state-by-state ranking of the five leading causes of deaths due to unintentional injuries based on 2009 data. The data are classified by state of residence. The first line of each section gives the rank of unintentional-injury-related deaths among all causes of death, the total number of unintentional-injury-related deaths, and the rate of unintentional-injury-related deaths per 100,000 population in the state. The following lines list the five leading types of unintentional-injury-related deaths in the state, along with the number and rate for each type.

2009

UNITED STATES

Rank	Cause	Deaths	Rate
5	All unintentional injuries	118,021	38.4
1	Motor vehicle	36,216	11.8
2	Poisoning[a]	31,758	10.3
3	Falls	24,792	8.1
4	Choking[b]	4,370	1.4
5	Drowning[c]	3,517	1.1

ALABAMA

Rank	Cause	Deaths	Rate
5	All unintentional injuries	2,351	49.9
1	Motor vehicle	933	19.8
2	Poisoning[a]	573	12.2
3	Falls	198	4.2
4	Choking[b]	126	2.7
5	Drowning[c]	88	1.9

ALASKA

Rank	Cause	Deaths	Rate
3	All unintentional injuries	340	48.7
1	Poisoning[a]	135	19.3
2	Motor vehicle	84	12.0
3	Falls	22	3.1
4	Natural heat or cold	21	3.0
5	Drowning[c]	17	2.4

ARIZONA

Rank	Cause	Deaths	Rate
3	All unintentional injuries	2,919	44.3
1	Poisoning[a]	844	12.8
2	Motor vehicle	807	12.2
3	Falls	741	11.2
4	Drowning	105	1.6
5	Choking[b]	92	1.4

ARKANSAS

Rank	Cause	Deaths	Rate
5	All unintentional injuries	1,473	51.0
1	Motor vehicle	643	22.3
2	Poisoning[a]	262	9.1
3	Falls	197	6.8
4	Fire, flames, or smoke	73	2.5
4	Choking[b]	73	2.5

CALIFORNIA

Rank	Cause	Deaths	Rate
5	All unintentional injuries	10,860	29.4
1	Poisoning[a]	3,600	9.7
2	Motor vehicle	3,293	8.9
3	Falls	2,055	5.6
4	Drowning[c]	447	1.2
5	Choking[b]	234	0.6

COLORADO

Rank	Cause	Deaths	Rate
3	All unintentional injuries	2,144	42.7
1	Poisoning[a]	649	12.9
2	Falls	565	11.2
3	Motor vehicle	557	11.1
4	Choking[b]	78	1.6
5	Drowning[c]	52	1.0

CONNECTICUT

Rank	Cause	Deaths	Rate
5	All unintentional injuries	1,293	36.8
1	Falls	364	10.3
2	Poisoning[a]	345	9.8
3	Motor vehicle	263	7.5
4	Choking[b]	90	2.6
5	Drowning[c]	33	0.9

DELAWARE

Rank	Cause	Deaths	Rate
5	All unintentional injuries	333	37.6
1	Poisoning[a]	108	12.2
2	Motor vehicle	107	12.1
3	Falls	63	7.1
4	Choking[b]	14	1.6
5	Fire, flames, or smoke	–	–

DISTRICT OF COLUMBIA

Rank	Cause	Deaths	Rate
4	All unintentional injuries	145	24.2
1	Motor vehicle	38	6.3
2	Falls	35	5.8
3	Poisoning[a]	17	2.8
4	Fire, flames, or smoke	16	2.7
5	Choking[b]	10	1.7

FLORIDA

Rank	Cause	Deaths	Rate
4	All unintentional injuries	8,746	47.2
1	Poisoning[a]	2,651	14.3
2	Motor vehicle	2,610	14.1
3	Falls	1,983	10.7
4	Drowning[c]	377	2.0
5	Choking[b]	233	1.3

GEORGIA

Rank	Cause	Deaths	Rate
3	All unintentional injuries	3,812	38.8
1	Motor vehicle	1,356	13.8
2	Poisoning[a]	944	9.6
3	Falls	686	7.0
4	Fire, flames, or smoke	121	1.2
5	Drowning[c]	120	1.2

HAWAII

Rank	Cause	Deaths	Rate
4	All unintentional injuries	436	33.7
1	Motor vehicle	121	9.3
2	Poisoning[a]	101	7.8
3	Falls	98	7.6
4	Drowning[c]	42	3.2
5	Choking[b]	30	2.3

IDAHO

Rank	Cause	Deaths	Rate
4	All unintentional injuries	670	43.3
1	Motor vehicle	242	15.7
2	Falls	146	9.4
3	Poisoning[a]	120	7.8
4	Drowning[c]	23	1.5
4	Choking[b]	23	1.5

ILLINOIS

Rank	Cause	Deaths	Rate
5	All unintentional injuries	3,961	30.7
1	Poisoning[a]	1,229	9.5
2	Motor vehicle	1,074	8.3
3	Falls	802	6.2
4	Choking[b]	176	1.4
5	Drowning[c]	93	0.7

INDIANA

Rank	Cause	Deaths	Rate
5	All unintentional injuries	2,577	40.1
1	Poisoning[a]	790	12.3
2	Motor vehicle	714	11.1
3	Falls	374	5.8
4	Choking[b]	99	1.5
5	Drowning[c]	71	1.1

IOWA

Rank	Cause	Deaths	Rate
6	All unintentional injuries	1,255	41.7
1	Falls	444	14.8
2	Motor vehicle	383	12.7
3	Poisoning[a]	169	5.6
4	Choking[b]	45	1.5
5	Fire, flames, or smoke	30	1.0

KANSAS

Rank	Cause	Deaths	Rate
5	All unintentional injuries	1,273	45.2
1	Motor vehicle	416	14.8
2	Falls	329	11.7
3	Poisoning[a]	260	9.2
4	Choking[b]	50	1.8
5	Drowning[c]	32	1.1

See source and footnotes on page 177.

2009

KENTUCKY

Rank	Cause	Deaths	Rate
4	All unintentional injuries	2,394	55.5
1	Motor vehicle	823	19.1
2	Poisoning[a]	731	16.9
3	Falls	273	6.3
4	Choking[b]	90	2.1
5	Fire, flames, or smoke	84	1.9

LOUISIANA

Rank	Cause	Deaths	Rate
3	All unintentional injuries	2,142	47.7
1	Motor vehicle	853	19.0
2	Poisoning[a]	504	11.2
3	Falls	226	5.0
4	Drowning[c]	98	2.2
5	Choking[b]	76	1.7

MAINE

Rank	Cause	Deaths	Rate
5	All unintentional injuries	602	45.7
1	Motor vehicle	166	12.6
2	Poisoning[a]	157	11.9
3	Falls	109	8.3
4	Choking[b]	29	2.2
5	Drowning[c]	21	1.6

MARYLAND

Rank	Cause	Deaths	Rate
5	All unintentional injuries	1,415	24.8
1	Motor vehicle	614	10.8
2	Falls	423	7.4
3	Poisoning[a]	88	1.5
4	Choking[b]	51	0.9
5	Fire, flames, or smoke	47	0.8

MASSACHUSETTS

Rank	Cause	Deaths	Rate
5	All unintentional injuries	2,076	31.5
1	Poisoning[a]	766	11.6
2	Falls	505	7.7
3	Motor vehicle	397	6.0
4	Choking[b]	102	1.5
5	Drowning[c]	40	0.6

MICHIGAN

Rank	Cause	Deaths	Rate
5	All unintentional injuries	3,682	36.9
1	Poisoning[a]	1,091	10.9
2	Motor vehicle	962	9.6
3	Falls	773	7.8
4	Fire, flames, or smoke	130	1.3
5	Choking[b]	122	1.2

See source and footnotes on page 177.

MINNESOTA

Rank	Cause	Deaths	Rate
3	All unintentional injuries	2,037	38.7
1	Falls	739	14.0
2	Motor vehicle	490	9.3
3	Poisoning[a]	379	7.2
4	Choking[b]	71	1.3
5	Drowning[c]	52	1.0

MISSISSIPPI

Rank	Cause	Deaths	Rate
3	All unintentional injuries	1,658	56.2
1	Motor vehicle	745	25.2
2	Poisoning[a]	279	9.5
3	Falls	240	8.1
4	Fire, flames, or smoke	80	2.7
5	Choking[b]	73	2.5

MISSOURI

Rank	Cause	Deaths	Rate
5	All unintentional injuries	2,939	49.1
1	Motor vehicle	939	15.7
2	Poisoning[a]	762	12.7
3	Falls	635	10.6
4	Fire, flames, or smoke	101	1.7
5	Choking[b]	84	1.4

MONTANA

Rank	Cause	Deaths	Rate
3	All unintentional injuries	619	63.5
1	Motor vehicle	227	23.3
2	Falls	121	12.4
3	Poisoning[a]	113	11.6
4	Drowning[c]	20	2.1
5	Choking[b]	18	1.8

NEBRASKA

Rank	Cause	Deaths	Rate
5	All unintentional injuries	683	38.0
1	Motor vehicle	253	14.1
2	Falls	186	10.4
3	Poisoning[a]	99	5.5
4	Choking[b]	29	1.6
5	Fire, flames, or smoke	14	0.8

NEVADA

Rank	Cause	Deaths	Rate
4	All unintentional injuries	1,025	38.8
1	Poisoning[a]	472	17.9
2	Motor vehicle	254	9.6
3	Falls	142	5.4
4	Drowning[c]	28	1.1
5	Choking[b]	26	1.0

NEW HAMPSHIRE

Rank	Cause	Deaths	Rate
5	All unintentional injuries	482	36.4
1	Poisoning[a]	140	10.6
2	Falls	137	10.3
3	Motor vehicle	114	8.6
4	Choking[b]	12	0.9
4	Drowning[c]	12	0.9
4	Fire, flames, or smoke	12	0.9

NEW JERSEY

Rank	Cause	Deaths	Rate
6	All unintentional injuries	1,875	21.5
1	Motor vehicle	566	6.5
2	Falls	382	4.4
3	Poisoning[a]	253	2.9
4	Choking[b]	155	1.8
5	Drowning[c]	55	0.6

NEW MEXICO

Rank	Cause	Deaths	Rate
3	All unintentional injuries	1,281	63.7
1	Poisoning[a]	419	20.8
2	Motor vehicle	354	17.6
3	Falls	314	15.6
4	Drowning[c]	36	1.8
5	Choking[b]	26	1.3

NEW YORK

Rank	Cause	Deaths	Rate
5	All unintentional injuries	4,891	25.0
1	Poisoning[a]	1,385	7.1
2	Motor vehicle	1,265	6.5
3	Falls	1,163	6.0
4	Choking[b]	218	1.1
5	Fire, flames, or smoke	169	0.9

NORTH CAROLINA

Rank	Cause	Deaths	Rate
5	All unintentional injuries	4,136	44.1
1	Motor vehicle	1,404	15.0
2	Poisoning[a]	1,060	11.3
3	Falls	845	9.0
4	Choking[b]	173	1.8
5	Drowning[c]	106	1.1

NORTH DAKOTA

Rank	Cause	Deaths	Rate
6	All unintentional injuries	324	50.1
1	Motor vehicle	131	20.3
2	Falls	80	12.4
3	Poisoning[a]	38	5.9
4	Choking[b]	13	2.0
5	Drowning[c]	–	–
5	Fire, flames, or smoke	–	–

2009

OHIO

Rank	Cause	Deaths	Rate
5	All unintentional injuries	4,012	34.8
1	Poisoning[a]	1,094	9.5
2	Motor vehicle	1,021	8.8
3	Falls	936	8.1
4	Choking[b]	210	1.8
5	Fire, flames, or smoke	95	0.8

OKLAHOMA

Rank	Cause	Deaths	Rate
4	All unintentional injuries	2,284	61.9
1	Motor vehicle	736	20.0
2	Poisoning[a]	724	19.6
3	Falls	307	8.3
4	Drowning[c]	70	1.9
4	Fire, flames, or smoke	70	1.9

OREGON

Rank	Cause	Deaths	Rate
5	All unintentional injuries	1,598	41.8
1	Falls	472	12.3
2	Poisoning[a]	400	10.5
3	Motor vehicle	391	10.2
4	Drowning[c]	61	1.6
5	Choking[b]	56	1.5

PENNSYLVANIA

Rank	Cause	Deaths	Rate
5	All unintentional injuries	5,477	43.5
1	Poisoning[a]	1,686	13.4
2	Motor vehicle	1,378	10.9
3	Falls	1,346	10.7
4	Choking[b]	278	2.2
5	Fire, flames, or smoke	124	1.0

RHODE ISLAND

Rank	Cause	Deaths	Rate
5	All unintentional injuries	428	40.6
1	Poisoning[a]	147	14.0
2	Falls	120	11.4
3	Motor vehicle	84	8.0
4	Choking[b]	19	1.8
5	Drowning[c]	–	–
5	Natural heat or cold	–	–

SOUTH CAROLINA

Rank	Cause	Deaths	Rate
5	All unintentional injuries	2,229	48.9
1	Motor vehicle	906	19.9
2	Poisoning[a]	579	12.7
3	Falls	248	5.4
4	Drowning[c]	90	2.0
5	Choking[b]	84	1.8

SOUTH DAKOTA

Rank	Cause	Deaths	Rate
6	All unintentional injuries	349	43.0
1	Motor vehicle	134	16.5
2	Falls	102	12.6
3	Poisoning[a]	35	4.3
4	Fire, flames, or smoke	11	1.4
4	Mechanical suffocation	11	1.4

TENNESSEE

Rank	Cause	Deaths	Rate
4	All unintentional injuries	3,231	51.3
1	Motor vehicle	1,056	16.8
2	Poisoning[a]	851	13.5
3	Falls	553	8.8
4	Choking[b]	127	2.0
5	Fire, flames, or smoke	89	1.4

TEXAS

Rank	Cause	Deaths	Rate
3	All unintentional injuries	9,349	37.7
1	Motor vehicle	3,508	14.2
2	Poisoning[a]	2,182	8.8
3	Falls	1,579	6.4
4	Choking[b]	308	1.2
5	Drowning[c]	304	1.2

UTAH

Rank	Cause	Deaths	Rate
3	All unintentional injuries	899	32.3
1	Poisoning[a]	257	9.2
2	Motor vehicle	256	9.2
3	Falls	172	6.2
4	Drowning[c]	27	1.0
5	Choking[b]	24	0.9

VERMONT

Rank	Cause	Deaths	Rate
4	All unintentional injuries	308	49.5
1	Falls	126	20.3
2	Motor vehicle	79	12.7
3	Poisoning[a]	45	7.2
4	Choking[b]	12	1.9
5	Fire, flames, or smoke	–	–

VIRGINIA

Rank	Cause	Deaths	Rate
5	All unintentional injuries	2,622	33.3
1	Motor vehicle	826	10.5
2	Poisoning[a]	575	7.3
3	Falls	504	6.4
4	Choking[b]	142	1.8
5	Fire, flames, or smoke	73	0.9

WASHINGTON

Rank	Cause	Deaths	Rate
5	All unintentional injuries	2,696	40.5
1	Poisoning[a]	867	13.0
2	Falls	775	11.6
3	Motor vehicle	574	8.6
4	Drowning[c]	91	1.4
5	Choking[b]	81	1.2

WEST VIRGINIA

Rank	Cause	Deaths	Rate
5	All unintentional injuries	942	51.8
1	Motor vehicle	373	20.5
2	Poisoning[a]	198	10.9
3	Falls	154	8.5
4	Choking[b]	40	2.2
5	Fire, flames, or smoke	23	1.3

WISCONSIN

Rank	Cause	Deaths	Rate
5	All unintentional injuries	2,449	43.3
1	Falls	952	16.8
2	Motor vehicle	589	10.4
3	Poisoning[a]	516	9.1
4	Choking[b]	52	0.9
5	Drowning[c]	51	0.9

WYOMING

Rank	Cause	Deaths	Rate
4	All unintentional injuries	299	54.9
1	Motor vehicle	107	19.7
2	Poisoning[a]	69	12.7
3	Falls	51	9.4
4	Choking[b]	10	1.8
5	Drowning[c]	–	–

Source: National Safety Council analysis of National Center for Health Statistics (NCHS)–Mortality Data for 2009, as compiled from data provided by the 57 vital statistics jurisdictions through the Vital Statistics Cooperative Program. Rates are National Safety Council estimates based on data from NCHS and the U.S. Census Bureau. Dashes (–) indicate data values less than 10 as per NCHS publication guidelines.
[a]*Solid, liquid, gas, and vapor poisoning.*
[b]*Inhalation or ingestion of food or other objects.*
[c]*Excludes transport drownings.*

Unintentional-Injury-Related Deaths by State and Event

Unintentional-injury-related deaths by state of occurrence and type of event, United States, 2009

State	Population (000)	Total[a]	Motor vehicle[b]	Poisoning	Falls	Choking[c]	Drowning[d]	Fire, flames, or smoke	Mechanical suffocation
Total U.S.	307,007	118,021	36,216	31,758	24,792	4,370	3,517	2,756	1,569
Alabama	4,709	2,301	907	567	177	127	86	87	28
Alaska	698	355	83	139	22	–	20	–	–
Arizona	6,596	2,965	820	850	747	93	109	33	22
Arkansas	2,889	1,432	632	260	174	75	64	70	14
California	36,962	10,781	3,255	3,612	2,038	230	437	143	88
Colorado	5,025	2,146	534	660	577	78	46	22	39
Connecticut	3,518	1,268	247	339	360	92	32	31	–
Delaware	885	328	119	113	50	15	–	–	–
District of Columbia	600	197	48	20	59	12	–	17	–
Florida	18,538	8,929	2,681	2,715	2,006	236	416	129	136
Georgia	9,829	3,786	1,345	925	685	115	115	142	52
Hawaii	1,295	471	119	102	103	31	69	–	–
Idaho	1,546	657	235	121	145	23	22	–	–
Illinois	12,910	3,753	973	1,223	737	166	79	81	71
Indiana	6,423	2,573	723	787	374	100	65	69	66
Iowa	3,008	1,254	386	168	441	45	20	30	21
Kansas	2,819	1,234	401	255	318	50	26	28	19
Kentucky	4,314	2,305	785	716	247	92	56	77	38
Louisiana	4,492	2,189	871	509	220	77	97	59	33
Maine	1,318	621	180	159	113	30	25	11	–
Maryland	5,699	1,365	594	68	413	45	45	50	18
Massachusetts	6,594	2,040	367	758	508	104	31	26	11
Michigan	9,970	3,611	938	1,080	743	121	90	132	88
Minnesota	5,266	2,016	459	383	739	68	48	35	32
Mississippi	2,952	1,618	740	279	235	72	50	74	23
Missouri	5,988	3,038	974	764	683	86	64	106	71
Montana	975	645	235	112	124	19	21	–	–
Nebraska	1,797	694	259	101	190	30	–	14	10
Nevada	2,643	1,100	285	486	164	29	35	10	25
New Hampshire	1,325	491	124	138	141	14	13	10	–
New Jersey	8,708	1,768	550	212	359	153	56	41	–
New Mexico	2,010	1,258	370	414	304	25	32	13	–
New York	19,541	4,778	1,175	1,383	1,149	215	87	167	52
North Carolina	9,381	4,160	1,420	1,062	845	177	103	113	31
North Dakota	647	376	155	40	97	17	10	–	–
Ohio	11,543	3,930	999	1,085	916	206	62	93	67
Oklahoma	3,687	2,261	749	715	295	52	77	69	22
Oregon	3,826	1,603	415	397	466	55	61	21	23
Pennsylvania	12,605	5,512	1,363	1,717	1,367	280	82	133	39
Rhode Island	1,053	457	96	149	133	19	–	–	–
South Carolina	4,561	2,211	915	582	232	79	95	50	30
South Dakota	812	363	148	32	111	–	–	–	–
Tennessee	6,296	3,494	1,182	843	630	141	75	98	51
Texas	24,782	9,380	3,483	2,187	1,599	310	307	209	104
Utah	2,785	966	284	260	183	28	30	11	23
Vermont	622	307	79	50	121	12	–	–	–
Virginia	7,883	2,606	820	569	506	138	69	69	31
Washington	6,664	2,654	545	865	783	82	78	48	36
West Virginia	1,820	1,005	422	194	164	39	19	27	–
Wisconsin	5,655	2,465	606	521	959	48	55	43	46
Wyoming	544	304	121	72	40	–	14	–	–

See source and footnotes on page 179.

Unintentional-injury-related deaths by state of occurrence and type of event, United States, 2009

State	Natural heat or cold	Struck by or against	Machinery	Firearms	Electric current	Water transportation	Air transportation	Rail transportation	All other incidents
Total U.S.	968	755	608	554	303	462	541	367	8,485
Alabama	15	12	11	27	–	–	–	–	233
Alaska	20	–	–	–	–	–	–	–	25
Arizona	90	11	–	–	–	–	25	–	134
Arkansas	15	16	14	11	–	–	–	–	72
California	73	61	26	31	24	32	74	50	607
Colorado	14	12	–	–	–	11	11	–	124
Connecticut	–	10	–	–	–	–	–	–	130
Delaware	–	–	–	–	–	–	–	–	17
District of Columbia	–	–	–	–	–	–	–	12	17
Florida	31	34	14	22	43	53	46	18	349
Georgia	26	16	14	26	13	–	19	–	280
Hawaii	–	–	–	–	–	–	–	–	21
Idaho	–	–	12	–	–	13	–	–	41
Illinois	35	20	24	17	–	–	–	22	284
Indiana	–	18	34	21	–	–	–	–	283
Iowa	–	–	20	–	–	–	–	–	90
Kansas	11	13	19	–	–	–	–	–	81
Kentucky	20	14	11	15	–	11	–	–	211
Louisiana	12	14	23	25	17	30	19	–	176
Maine	–	–	–	–	–	–	–	–	79
Maryland	17	13	–	–	–	–	–	–	69
Massachusetts	10	14	–	–	–	–	–	–	187
Michigan	45	29	13	12	–	17	10	–	278
Minnesota	20	14	17	–	–	–	–	–	184
Mississippi	14	13	–	16	–	18	–	–	68
Missouri	26	20	29	18	–	10	–	–	166
Montana	10	–	–	–	–	–	19	–	63
Nebraska	–	–	–	–	–	–	–	–	52
Nevada	–	–	–	–	–	–	12	–	31
New Hampshire	–	–	–	–	–	–	–	–	25
New Jersey	12	11	–	–	–	–	–	14	330
New Mexico	16	–	–	–	–	–	–	10	45
New York	36	23	21	12	–	20	58	34	342
North Carolina	23	24	15	20	–	14	17	14	278
North Dakota	–	–	–	–	–	–	–	–	29
Ohio	21	25	10	19	13	–	–	13	388
Oklahoma	30	10	12	16	–	–	13	–	190
Oregon	26	10	–	–	–	–	11	–	92
Pennsylvania	21	30	24	24	–	–	–	14	401
Rhode Island	–	–	–	–	–	–	–	–	33
South Carolina	20	16	–	16	11	–	16	–	132
South Dakota	–	–	–	–	–	–	–	–	24
Tennessee	22	30	26	32	11	–	11	–	330
Texas	71	78	51	56	43	30	38	24	790
Utah	17	–	–	–	–	–	11	–	99
Vermont	–	–	–	–	–	–	–	–	19
Virginia	26	24	21	11	–	17	–	–	285
Washington	23	12	20	–	–	17	–	10	121
West Virginia	–	12	–	15	–	–	10	–	63
Wisconsin	17	22	28	–	–	–	–	–	94
Wyoming	–	–	–	–	–	–	–	–	23

Source: National Safety Council analysis of National Center for Heatlh Statistics (NCHS)–Mortality Data for 2009, as compiled from data provided by the 57 vital statistics jurisdictions through the Vital Statistics Cooperative Program. Dashes (–) indicate data values less than 10 as per NCHS publication guidelines.
[a]Deaths are by place of occurrence and exclude nonresident aliens.
[b]See page 184 for motor vehicle deaths by place of residence.
[c]Suffocation by inhalation or ingestion of food or object obstructing breathing.
[d]Excludes water transport drownings.

Unintentional-Injury Trends by State

Nationwide, from 2006 to 2009, unintentional-injury-related deaths decreased 3% and the death rate decreased nearly 6%. By state, the greatest decrease in the number of unintentional-injury-related deaths and death rates occurred in the District of Columbia (-35% and -37%, respectively). The greatest increase in unintentional-injury-related deaths and death rates occurred in Utah (+26% and +17%, respectively).

The table below shows the trend in unintentional-injury-related deaths and death rates by state over the most recent four years for which data are available.

Unintentional-injury-related deaths by state of residence, United States, 2006-2009

State	Deaths[a]				Deaths per 100,000 population			
	2009[b]	2008	2007	2006	2009[b]	2008	2007	2006
Total U.S.	118,021	121,902	123,706	121,599	38.4	40.0	41.1	40.8
Alabama	2,351	2,509	2,542	2,506	49.9	53.7	54.9	54.6
Alaska	340	332	354	316	48.7	48.4	52.0	46.7
Arizona	2,919	2,956	3,161	3,352	44.3	45.5	49.8	54.3
Arkansas	1,473	1,477	1,391	1,415	51.0	51.5	49.1	50.5
California	10,860	10,761	11,614	11,375	29.4	29.5	31.9	31.5
Colorado	2,144	2,172	2,056	1,917	42.7	44.1	42.5	40.3
Connecticut	1,293	1,386	1,343	1,302	36.8	39.6	38.5	37.3
Delaware	333	352	309	329	37.6	40.1	35.8	38.7
District of Columbia	145	160	193	224	24.2	27.1	32.8	38.3
Florida	8,746	8,939	9,113	8,917	47.2	48.6	50.1	49.5
Georgia	3,812	3,774	4,012	3,879	38.8	38.9	42.1	41.6
Hawaii	436	406	470	441	33.7	31.7	36.8	34.6
Idaho	670	649	641	682	43.3	42.5	42.8	46.7
Illinois	3,961	4,218	4,367	4,451	30.7	32.9	34.0	34.9
Indiana	2,577	2,558	2,499	2,480	40.1	40.1	39.4	39.4
Iowa	1,255	1,266	1,252	1,188	41.7	42.3	42.0	40.0
Kansas	1,273	1,174	1,205	1,198	45.2	42.0	43.4	43.5
Kentucky	2,394	2,379	2,372	2,446	55.5	55.5	56.0	58.2
Louisiana	2,142	2,409	2,466	2,422	47.7	54.1	56.4	57.1
Maine	602	628	584	572	45.7	47.6	44.4	43.6
Maryland	1,415	1,465	1,480	1,456	24.8	25.9	26.3	26.0
Massachusetts	2,076	2,040	2,139	2,214	31.5	31.2	33.1	34.4
Michigan	3,682	3,685	3,764	3,590	36.9	36.9	37.5	35.6
Minnesota	2,037	2,010	2,066	1,919	38.7	38.4	39.9	37.3
Mississippi	1,658	1,693	1,808	1,856	56.2	57.6	61.9	64.1
Missouri	2,939	2,997	2,975	3,009	49.1	50.4	50.6	51.6
Montana	619	592	614	558	63.5	61.2	64.2	59.0
Nebraska	683	714	674	683	38.0	40.1	38.1	38.8
Nevada	1,025	1,134	1,212	1,091	38.8	43.4	47.4	43.9
New Hampshire	482	488	527	460	36.4	36.9	40.2	35.1
New Jersey	1,875	2,436	2,425	2,590	21.5	28.1	28.0	30.0
New Mexico	1,281	1,366	1,329	1,297	63.7	68.8	67.7	66.9
New York	4,891	5,042	5,160	5,235	25.0	25.9	26.6	27.0
North Carolina	4,136	4,313	4,389	4,156	44.1	46.7	48.5	47.0
North Dakota	324	342	279	275	50.1	53.4	43.7	43.2
Ohio	4,012	5,093	4,922	4,821	34.8	44.2	42.9	42.1
Oklahoma	2,284	2,119	2,149	2,039	61.9	58.2	59.6	57.1
Oregon	1,598	1,674	1,646	1,586	41.8	44.3	44.1	43.1
Pennsylvania	5,477	5,787	5,568	5,299	43.5	46.1	44.8	42.8
Rhode Island	428	480	416	434	40.6	45.4	39.5	41.0
South Carolina	2,229	2,285	2,364	2,315	48.9	50.8	53.7	53.5
South Dakota	349	381	366	452	43.0	47.4	46.0	57.4
Tennessee	3,231	3,250	3,257	3,307	51.3	52.1	53.0	54.5
Texas	9,349	9,189	9,392	9,140	37.7	37.8	39.4	39.1
Utah	899	881	811	715	32.3	32.3	30.4	27.7
Vermont	308	306	303	301	49.5	49.3	48.8	48.5
Virginia	2,622	2,820	2,931	2,703	33.3	36.2	38.1	35.4
Washington	2,696	2,727	2,637	2,679	40.5	41.5	40.9	42.1
West Virginia	942	1,253	1,241	1,177	51.8	69.0	68.6	65.1
Wisconsin	2,449	2,484	2,619	2,524	43.3	44.1	46.8	45.3
Wyoming	299	351	299	306	54.9	65.9	57.1	59.7

Source: Deaths are from the National Center for Health Statistics (NCHS)–Mortality Data for 2009, as compiled from data provided by the 57 vital statistics jurisdictions through the Vital Statistics Cooperative Program. Rates are National Safety Council estimates based on data from NCHS and the U.S. Census Bureau. See Technical Appendix for comparability.
[a]Deaths for each state are by state of residence and exclude nonresident aliens.
[b]Latest official figures.

In general, states with the largest number of people employed have the largest number of work-related fatalities. The four largest states – California, Florida, New York, and Texas – accounted for 26% of the total 2011 work-related fatalities in the United States. Each state's industry mix, geographic features, age of population, and other characteristics of the workforce must be considered when evaluating state fatality profiles. Overall, the six leading events or exposures accounted for all but 13 of the 4,609 total occupational fatalities in all states in 2011.

Fatal occupational injuries by state and event or exposure, United States, 2010-2011

State	Total fatal injuries[a]		Event or exposure[d] 2011					
	2010[b]	2011[c]	Violence and other injuries by persons or animals[e]	Transportation incidents[f]	Fires and explosions	Slips, trips, and falls	Exposure to harmful substances or environments	Contact with objects and equipment
Total	4,690	4,609	780	1,898	143	666	401	708
Alabama	92	74	6	36	1	10	4	17
Alaska	39	38	8	18	1	4	5	–
Arizona	77	65	14	25	3	13	5	–
Arkansas	88	93	11	50	1	6	14	11
California	326	360	85	118	9	60	36	50
Colorado	85	87	16	34	–	15	5	16
Connecticut	49	36	12	13	–	7	1	3
Delaware	8	10	5	3	–	–	1	–
District of Columbia	16	9	3	–	–	–	–	3
Florida	225	227	44	90	4	36	27	26
Georgia	108	107	17	45	5	16	9	15
Hawaii	19	26	–	10	5	6	2	–
Idaho	33	37	–	26	–	3	–	5
Illinois	206	177	44	54	4	29	25	20
Indiana	118	122	17	61	3	16	7	18
Iowa	77	93	11	55	2	7	2	16
Kansas	85	77	7	38	8	8	7	9
Kentucky	69	86	10	39	6	6	7	17
Louisiana	111	109	10	54	6	14	13	12
Maine	20	26	4	16	–	–	3	–
Maryland	71	71	17	29	3	8	4	9
Massachusetts	54	63	19	17	3	16	3	5
Michigan	146	139	33	46	3	24	12	21
Minnesota	70	60	5	16	–	14	5	19
Mississippi	68	63	9	31	–	5	7	9
Missouri	106	133	14	60	–	16	10	28
Montana	36	49	5	25	–	5	3	8
Nebraska	54	39	2	25	–	3	–	5
Nevada	38	38	9	22	–	4	–	–
New Hampshire	6	9	–	4	–	–	–	–
New Jersey	81	98	24	37	–	15	7	15
New Mexico	38	51	4	21	–	3	6	15
New York	182	205	48	69	–	39	14	34
North Carolina	139	148	29	51	4	28	12	24
North Dakota	30	44	5	23	–	3	–	9
Ohio	161	153	22	61	3	22	20	25
Oklahoma	94	77	6	38	–	9	10	12
Oregon	47	57	10	20	3	9	–	12
Pennsylvania	221	186	28	69	6	34	17	32
Rhode Island	9	7	–	–	–	5	–	–
South Carolina	69	81	12	46	–	12	5	5
South Dakota	36	31	5	14	3	–	–	7
Tennessee	138	120	26	39	10	15	5	24
Texas	461	433	70	168	18	67	43	66
Utah	41	39	3	24	–	5	–	5
Vermont	12	8	–	–	–	–	2	4
Virginia	107	127	23	60	1	10	12	21
Washington	104	58	6	29	–	9	5	9
West Virginia	95	43	3	18	–	6	5	11
Wisconsin	91	89	13	33	–	12	9	22
Wyoming	33	29	–	17	–	3	–	–

Source: Bureau of Labor Statistics. National Census of Fatal Occupational Injuries in 2011 (preliminary results) accessed Sept. 26, 2012, from www.bls.gov/news.release/cfoi.nr0.htm.
Note: Dashes (–) indicate no data or data that do not meet publication criteria.
[a]State totals include other events and exposures, such as bodily reaction, in addition to those shown separately.
[b]Data for 2010 are revised and final. The totals include one fatal injury for which a state of occurrence could not be determined.
[c]Data for 2011 are preliminary. The totals include two fatal injuries for which a state of occurrence could not be determined.
[d]Based on the BLS Occupational Injury and Illness Classification System (OIICS) 2.01, implemented for 2011 data forward.
[e]Includes violence by persons, self-inflicted injuries, and attacks by animals.
[f]Includes highway, nonhighway, air, water, and rail fatal injuries, and fatal injuries resulting from being struck by a motor vehicle.

Nonfatal occupational injury and illness incidence rates[a] by state, private industry, 2010

State	Total recordable cases	Cases with days away from work[b]	Cases with job transfer or restriction	Other recordable cases
Private industry[c]	**3.5**	**1.1**	**0.8**	**1.7**
Alabama	3.5	0.9	0.8	1.7
Alaska	4.5	1.6	0.5	2.3
Arizona	3.3	0.9	0.7	1.6
Arkansas	3.3	0.8	0.8	1.7
California	3.7	1.1	1.1	1.6
Colorado	–	–	–	–
Connecticut	4.0	1.4	0.8	1.8
Delaware	3.2	1.0	0.5	1.6
District of Columbia	1.9	0.8	0.1	1.0
Florida	3.4	0.9	0.8	1.7
Georgia	3.1	0.9	0.7	1.5
Hawaii	3.9	2.0	0.3	1.6
Idaho	–	–	–	–
Illinois	3.3	1.0	0.7	1.5
Indiana	4.1	1.0	1.1	2.1
Iowa	4.4	1.3	1.0	2.1
Kansas	3.7	0.9	0.9	2.0
Kentucky	4.2	1.3	0.9	2.0
Louisiana	2.7	0.9	0.4	1.4
Maine	5.6	1.4	1.6	2.6
Maryland	3.6	1.4	0.5	1.7
Massachusetts	3.2	1.3	0.4	1.5
Michigan	4.2	1.1	1.0	2.2
Minnesota	3.8	1.1	0.8	2.0
Mississippi	–	–	–	–
Missouri	3.4	0.8	0.8	1.8
Montana	5.0	1.7	0.6	2.7
Nebraska	4.2	1.2	0.8	2.1
Nevada	3.8	1.1	0.9	1.8
New Hampshire	–	–	–	–
New Jersey	3.2	1.2	0.5	1.5
New Mexico	3.7	1.2	0.7	1.9
New York	2.7	1.3	0.2	1.3
North Carolina	3.1	0.8	0.8	1.5
North Dakota	–	–	–	–
Ohio	–	–	–	–
Oklahoma	4.0	1.2	0.9	1.9
Oregon	3.9	1.5	0.8	1.7
Pennsylvania	–	–	–	–
Rhode Island	–	–	–	–
South Carolina	3.1	0.9	0.7	1.5
South Dakota	–	–	–	–
Tennessee	3.7	1.0	0.9	1.8
Texas	2.7	0.8	0.7	1.1
Utah	3.4	0.8	0.7	1.9
Vermont	5.2	1.8	0.8	2.6
Virginia	3.1	1.0	0.6	1.5
Washington	4.8	1.6	0.8	2.4
West Virginia	4.4	2.0	0.4	2.0
Wisconsin	4.3	1.2	1.0	2.1
Wyoming	4.0	1.4	0.5	2.1

Source: Bureau of Labor Statistics, U.S. Department of Labor.
Note: Because of rounding, components may not add to totals. Dashes (–) indicate data not available.
[a]Incidence rates represent the number of injuries and illnesses per 100 full-time workers using 200,000 hours as the equivalent.
[b]Days-away-from-work cases include those that result in days away from work with or without job transfer or restriction.
[c]Data cover all 50 states.

Nonfatal occupational injury and illness incidence rates per 100 full-time workers
for total recordable cases by state, private industry, 2010

U.S. private
industry: 3.5

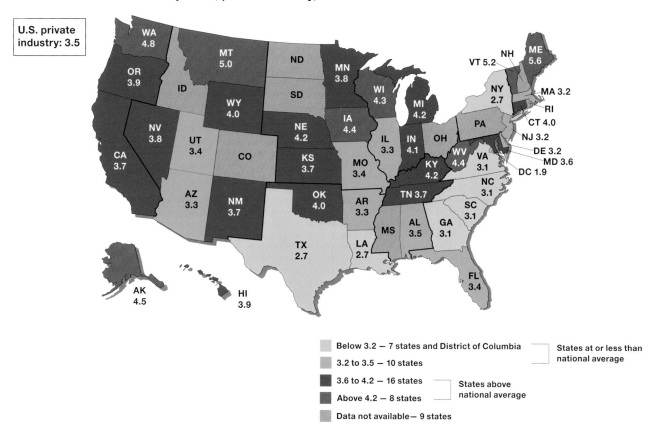

	Below 3.2 — 7 states and District of Columbia	States at or less than national average
	3.2 to 3.5 — 10 states	
	3.6 to 4.2 — 16 states	States above national average
	Above 4.2 — 8 states	
	Data not available— 9 states	

Motor vehicle deaths by state, United States, 2008-2011

State	Motor vehicle traffic deaths (Place of incident)				Total motor vehicle deaths[a] (Place of residence)			
	Number		Mileage rate[b]		Number		Population rate[b]	
	2011	2010	2011	2010	2009[c]	2008	2009	2008
Total U.S.[a]	34,600	35,332	1.2	1.2	36,216	39,790	11.8	13.1
Alabama	894	862	1.4	1.5	933	1,085	19.8	23.2
Alaska	72	56	1.5	1.1	84	73	12.0	10.6
Arizona	826	765	1.4	1.2	807	965	12.2	14.8
Arkansas	549	571	1.7	1.7	643	641	22.3	22.4
California	2,769	2,718	0.9	0.8	3,293	3,619	8.9	9.9
Colorado	447	448	1.0	1.0	557	588	11.1	11.9
Connecticut	221	318	0.7	1.0	263	330	7.5	9.4
Delaware	103	103	1.2	1.1	107	127	12.1	14.5
District of Columbia	32	25	0.9	0.7	38	48	6.3	8.1
Florida	2,382	2,446	1.2	1.2	2,610	3,040	14.1	16.5
Georgia	1,232	1,250	1.1	1.1	1,356	1,510	13.8	15.6
Hawaii	101	112	1.0	1.1	121	108	9.3	8.4
Idaho	167	209	1.1	1.3	242	250	15.7	16.4
Illinois	918	927	0.9	0.9	1,074	1,159	8.3	9.0
Indiana	750	754	1.0	1.0	714	870	11.1	13.6
Iowa	360	390	1.2	1.2	383	440	12.7	14.7
Kansas	386	431	1.3	1.4	416	421	14.8	15.1
Kentucky	721	760	1.5	1.6	823	871	19.1	20.3
Louisiana	677	720	1.5	1.6	853	926	19.0	20.8
Maine	137	162	1.0	1.1	166	175	12.6	13.3
Maryland	473	492	0.9	0.9	614	646	10.8	11.4
Massachusetts	339	333	0.6	0.6	397	383	6.0	5.9
Michigan	889	937	0.9	1.0	962	1,100	9.6	11.0
Minnesota	368	408	0.7	0.7	490	528	9.3	10.1
Mississippi	630	641	1.6	1.6	745	780	25.2	26.5
Missouri	784	821	1.1	1.2	939	992	15.7	16.7
Montana	209	189	1.9	1.7	227	220	23.3	22.7
Nebraska	181	186	0.9	0.9	253	244	14.1	13.7
Nevada	246	257	1.2	1.2	254	341	9.6	13.1
New Hampshire	90	128	0.7	1.0	114	149	8.6	11.3
New Jersey	627	556	0.9	0.7	566	585	6.5	6.8
New Mexico	353	346	1.4	1.3	354	373	17.6	18.8
New York	1,153	1,192	0.9	0.9	1,265	1,284	6.5	6.6
North Carolina	1,230	1,320	1.2	1.2	1,404	1,563	15.0	16.9
North Dakota	148	105	1.8	1.3	131	121	20.3	18.9
Ohio	1,021	1,080	0.9	1.0	1,021	1,301	8.8	11.3
Oklahoma	696	668	1.5	1.4	736	766	20.0	21.0
Oregon	331	317	1.0	0.9	391	443	10.2	11.7
Pennsylvania	1,286	1,324	1.3	1.3	1,378	1,584	10.9	12.6
Rhode Island	66	67	0.8	0.8	84	72	8.0	6.8
South Carolina	828	811	1.7	1.6	906	957	19.9	21.3
South Dakota	111	140	1.3	1.4	134	131	16.5	16.3
Tennessee	946	1,031	1.4	1.4	1,056	1,164	16.8	18.7
Texas	3,013	3,026	1.3	1.3	3,508	3,780	14.2	15.6
Utah	243	236	0.9	0.9	256	302	9.2	11.1
Vermont	55	71	0.8	0.9	79	76	12.7	12.2
Virginia	764	740	0.9	0.9	826	884	10.5	11.4
Washington	454	459	0.8	0.8	574	620	8.6	9.4
West Virginia	338	315	1.8	1.6	373	372	20.5	20.5
Wisconsin	565	562	1.0	1.0	589	642	10.4	11.4
Wyoming	135	153	1.4	1.6	107	141	19.7	26.5

Source: Motor vehicle traffic deaths are provisional counts from state traffic authorities; total motor vehicle deaths are from the National Center for Health Statistics (also see page 178).

[a]Includes both traffic and nontraffic motor vehicle deaths. See definitions of motor vehicle traffic and nontraffic incidents on page 205. The total U.S. figure for 2010 is from NCHS.

[b]The mileage death rate is deaths per 100,000,000 vehicle miles; the population death rate is deaths per 100,000 population. Death rates are National Safety Council estimates.

[c]Latest year available. See Technical Appendix for comparability.

Mileage death rates, 2011
Motor vehicle traffic deaths per 100,000,000 vehicle miles

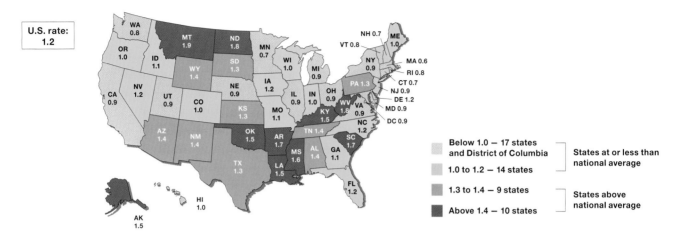

U.S. rate: 1.2

Below 1.0 — 17 states and District of Columbia
1.0 to 1.2 — 14 states
} States at or less than national average

1.3 to 1.4 — 9 states
Above 1.4 — 10 states
} States above national average

Registration death rates, 2011
Motor vehicle traffic deaths per 10,000 motor vehicles

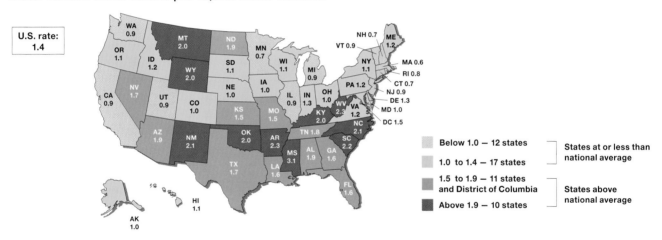

U.S. rate: 1.4

Below 1.0 — 12 states
1.0 to 1.4 — 17 states
} States at or less than national average

1.5 to 1.9 — 11 states and District of Columbia
Above 1.9 — 10 states
} States above national average

Population death rates, 2011
Motor vehicle traffic deaths per 100,000 population

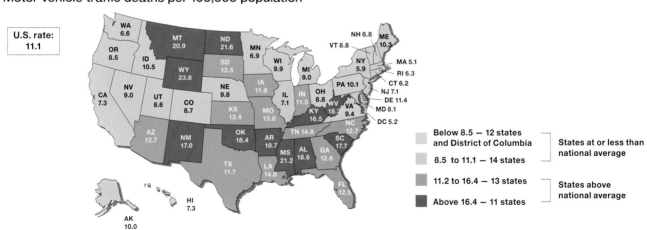

U.S. rate: 11.1

Below 8.5 — 12 states and District of Columbia
8.5 to 11.1 — 14 states
} States at or less than national average

11.2 to 16.4 — 13 states
Above 16.4 — 11 states
} States above national average

International Data

INJURY FACTS® 2013

♦ *Unintentional injuries account for more than 6% of total fatalities across the world.*

This section on international injury and fatalities includes data for occupational and motor vehicle injuries, as well as general unintentional injury and mortality. The two primary data sources used in this section are the World Health Organization (WHO) and the International Labour Organization.

Looking at specific causes, road traffic incidents are the leading cause of unintentional fatalities for each region in the world. To address the growing road traffic safety issue, "A Decade of Action for Road Safety 2011-2020 – Saving Millions of Lives" was officially proclaimed by the United Nations General Assembly in March 2010. This proclamation has been drawn to guide efforts at global, regional, national, and local levels with the goal to stabilize and then reduce the forecasted level of road traffic fatalities around the world.

According to WHO:
- Road traffic crashes take the lives of nearly 1.3 million people every year, and injure 20-50 million more.
- Road traffic injuries are the leading cause of death for people 15-29 years old.
- More than 90% of road traffic deaths and injuries occur in low-income and middle-income countries, which have only 48% of the world's registered vehicles.
- Nearly half (46%) of road traffic deaths occur among "vulnerable road users": pedestrians, cyclists, and motorcyclists.
- Without action, road traffic crashes are predicted to result in 1.9 million deaths annually by 2020.

In addition, WHO's Global Health Observatory reports that the success of interventions to reduce road traffic injuries has been limited by the failure of countries to implement policies or standards in five key risk areas:
- Urban speed limit range – efforts to reduce urban speed limits are still needed in most countries.
- Blood-alcohol concentration limit for drivers – less than 50% of countries have drunk-driving laws based on international recommendations.
- Existence of a national safety belt law – only 57% of countries require all vehicle occupants to wear safety belts.
- Motorcycle helmet laws and helmet standard – helmet laws in many countries are ineffective due to a lack of helmet standards.
- Existence of child restraint legislation – just less than half of countries have a law requiring the use of child restraints for young children in vehicles.

Overall, only 15% of countries have comprehensive laws relating to these five key risk areas.

If the goal of "A Decade of Action for Road Safety 2011-2020 – Saving Millions of Lives" is achieved, WHO estimates that a cumulative total of 5 million lives, 50 million serious injuries, and $5 trillion dollars could be saved over the 10-year period.

The charts on pages 189-193 provide the unintentional-injury-related deaths and death rates for 52 countries. The most current year of mortality data available is reported for motor vehicle, poisonings, falls, drowning, and overall unintentional-injury-related deaths. Looking at overall age trends across the world, the 65-and-older age group has the highest rate of unintentional-injury-related deaths per 100,000 population, while the 5- to 14-year-old age group has the lowest. Death rates for all causes except poisonings peak for those 65 and older. The poisoning death rate peaks for the 45-to-64 age group. Because of differences in recordkeeping, comparisons among countries are not recommended.

The charts on pages 194 and 195 detail the occupational deaths and death rates by country for the past five years. Because of the wide range of recordkeeping standards used in the world, countries with similar recordkeeping practices are grouped together. Although comparison among countries is not recommended even within these recordkeeping groupings, trends over the years are evident. Of the 45 countries listed on page 195, fully 29 show improvement in the occupational death rate. Thirteen of these improving countries have decreased work-related deaths by at least one worker per units measured. Four of the 13 countries that show an increased death rate are up by at least one worker per units measured over the years reported.

Source: World Health Organization. (2011). A Decade of Action for Road Safety 2011-2020 – Saving Millions of Lives. Geneva: Author. Downloaded from www.who.int/violence_injury_prevention/publications/road_traffic/decade_booklet/en/index.html on Nov. 7, 2012. Information from WHO Global Health Observatory downloaded from www.who.int/gho/road_safety/legislation/en/index.html on Nov. 8, 2012.

The term "Accidents and Adverse Effects" used in the International Classification of Diseases (ICD) system refers to all causes of unintentional-injury-related deaths, including transportation incidents; unintentional poisonings; falls; fires; burns; natural and environmental factors; drowning; suffocation; medical and surgical complications and misadventures; and other causes, such as those involving machinery, firearms, or electric current.

The data presented in the table below are identified by codes V01-X59 and Y85-Y86 of the 10th revision of ICD (except where noted).

The table below and those on pages 190 through 193 show the number of injury-related deaths and the unadjusted death rates for 52 countries for which mortality data and population estimates were obtained.

Unintentional-injury-related deaths and death rates by age group, latest year available

| Name | Year | Deaths | | Deaths per 100,000 population[a] | | | | | | |
		Total	% male	All ages	0 to 4	5 to 14	15 to 24	25 to 44	45 to 64	65 and older
Argentina	2010	10,187	73%	24.6	15.8	6.6	25.7	24.3	27.7	53.3
Austria	2010	2,523	60%	30.1	3.6	1.4	16.0	10.3	20.0	110.5
Belarus[b]	2009	13,896	78%	143.7	17.7	13.9	67.3	148.1	234.1	179.4
Brazil	2010	70,002	78%	35.7	13.1	7.9	36.1	38.1	41.6	107.1
Canada	2009	10,168	59%	30.4	4.8	2.5	18.3	18.1	23.5	104.3
Chile	2009	4,968	75%	29.9	12.4	5.3	18.6	25.8	39.5	100.2
Colombia	2009	10,805	79%	24.7	16.5	7.1	23.0	26.8	28.2	78.6
Costa Rica	2009	1,155	74%	25.9	5.3	5.9	21.0	21.7	31.5	131.9
Croatia	2010	2,086	57%	46.5	3.7	4.2	18.3	23.1	31.4	168.7
Cuba	2010	4,830	53%	43.5	7.9	5.4	12.3	15.7	26.5	256.3
Cyprus	2010	232	71%	21.0	5.1	0.8	14.8	15.0	12.8	100.7
Czech Republic	2010	4,018	65%	39.4	5.5	2.4	20.2	21.6	39.2	119.4
Egypt	2010	11,010	79%	14.0	13.0	8.6	14.9	14.1	17.8	25.8
El Salvador	2009	2,275	77%	37.7	10.9	9.2	24.1	43.5	57.9	158.8
Estonia	2010	755	76%	56.3	16.9	6.3	29.9	55.5	84.1	77.9
Finland	2010	2,856	65%	54.3	4.0	2.1	18.0	29.1	59.5	157.0
France	2009	25,319	55%	39.2	5.0	2.2	17.8	15.8	24.8	155.4
Germany	2010	18,530	55%	22.7	3.6	1.8	11.0	8.3	12.9	74.0
Guatemala	2009	5,893	82%	44.4	15.7	10.1	38.2	65.3	78.3	185.4
Hong Kong SAR	2009	766	61%	10.9	2.2	0.8	2.6	6.8	8.1	46.1
Hungary	2009	4,395	62%	43.9	3.5	3.8	13.8	21.6	46.2	139.2
Iraq	2008	10,923	83%	38.7	20.0	15.4	43.1	58.7	54.6	55.8
Ireland	2010	910	65%	19.7	3.1	1.0	14.9	15.9	24.7	59.2
Israel	2009	1,136	59%	15.7	3.0	2.1	9.3	7.5	13.6	90.8
Italy	2009	19,730	54%	32.6	3.0	2.3	18.1	13.9	14.0	112.8
Japan	2010	42,568	59%	33.4	4.7	2.1	7.7	7.5	17.9	111.2
Kazakhstan[b]	2009	17,258	77%	108.4	41.2	18.1	81.2	154.3	155.9	131.9
Kyrgyzstan	2009	2,363	77%	45.4	42.5	10.5	23.4	60.9	91.3	63.9
Latvia	2010	1,349	76%	60.8	12.3	12.6	31.8	43.3	100.7	91.1
Lithuania	2010	2,384	76%	67.2	14.6	6.2	28.2	49.4	118.8	102.0
Mexico	2010	36,372	77%	32.3	18.7	7.7	30.8	34.2	39.0	105.2
Netherlands	2010	3,912	50%	23.5	3.2	1.5	7.7	6.2	10.9	113.6
New Zealand	2008	1,309	61%	30.8	21.9	4.9	30.3	20.2	22.3	105.1
Norway	2010	1,941	55%	41.5	1.1	1.7	17.8	21.8	28.0	165.0
Panama	2009	865	81%	25.7	22.7	7.7	25.2	28.5	26.5	68.8
Paraguay	2009	1,973	81%	31.4	21.0	7.5	40.2	33.9	37.8	74.1
Philippines	2008	16,186	75%	16.8	9.0	8.5	14.5	18.8	26.4	55.4
Poland	2010	14,332	73%	37.3	4.5	3.9	23.7	25.9	48.4	90.0
Portugal	2010	1,981	70%	18.5	3.4	2.2	10.1	13.9	18.0	46.7
Republic of Korea (South)	2010	13,552	70%	27.9	7.1	3.5	10.5	14.6	32.8	110.0
Romania	2010	8,769	76%	40.9	17.6	10.1	23.0	30.0	60.5	76.7
Russian Federation[b]	2010	216,867	77%	152.2	26.5	17.3	96.8	183.4	205.5	177.5
Serbia	2010	1,716	73%	23.4	6.4	3.5	15.5	15.5	25.1	56.8
Slovakia	2010	1,738	78%	31.8	8.3	5.8	19.0	22.9	49.6	61.8
Slovenia	2010	923	61%	46.1	3.3	1.7	14.6	20.4	36.7	165.3
South Africa	2009	36,851	76%	75.1	48.8	19.1	63.2	113.0	90.4	133.6
Spain	2010	10,100	63%	21.7	4.4	1.8	10.3	12.4	15.7	72.3
Sweden	2010	2,970	58%	31.7	0.9	1.4	10.1	10.1	18.9	123.9
Switzerland[b]	2007	3,782	61%	50.1	4.6	3.2	28.7	28.8	41.2	163.4
Ukraine[b]	2010	43,955	78%	96.8	26.5	12.9	58.2	107.7	136.5	111.2
United Kingdom	2010	14,143	56%	22.7	3.5	1.7	12.3	14.7	15.4	77.7
United States	2008	121,902	64%	40.1	13.7	4.6	32.5	37.2	42.1	101.6

Source: National Safety Council tabulations of World Health Organization (WHO) data.
[a]Population estimates based on data from WHO and the U.S. Census Bureau (International Data Base).
[b]Data include deaths due to all external causes, including self-harm and assault.

International Motor Vehicle Injury-Related Deaths and Death Rates

The International Classification of Diseases (ICD) system identifies motor vehicle traffic incidents by codes V02-V04, V09, V12-V14, V19-V79, and V86-V89 of the 10th revision of ICD. A motor vehicle is a mechanically or electrically powered device used in the transportation of people or property on a land highway. A motor vehicle traffic incident involves a motor vehicle in transport (i.e., in motion or on a roadway) on a public highway.

Motor vehicle injury-related deaths and death rates by age group, latest year available

Name	Year	Deaths Total	% male	Deaths per 100,000 population[a] All ages	0 to 4	5 to 14	15 to 24	25 to 44	45 to 64	65 and older
Argentina	2010	4,432	78%	10.7	2.6	2.7	14.1	13.3	13.5	13.1
Austria	2010	328	77%	3.9	0.8	0.0	7.9	3.2	3.7	5.8
Belarus[b]	2009	1,588	77%	16.4	2.0	4.2	17.2	20.1	19.6	15.4
Brazil	2010	34,220	82%	17.5	2.6	2.9	24.0	23.0	19.6	24.8
Canada	2009	2,377	72%	7.1	1.2	1.3	12.2	7.3	7.0	8.6
Chile	2009	1,171	80%	7.1	1.8	1.3	8.2	8.7	8.6	9.8
Colombia	2009	5,633	80%	12.9	2.9	2.5	14.3	17.2	14.5	30.6
Costa Rica	2009	460	84%	10.3	1.4	1.5	13.7	12.3	13.4	17.6
Croatia	2010	407	79%	9.1	2.3	1.5	11.4	10.2	9.0	12.3
Cuba	2010	852	77%	7.7	1.6	2.4	6.3	7.7	9.9	13.2
Cyprus	2010	80	81%	7.3	3.4	0.8	10.9	7.2	4.1	17.8
Czech Republic	2010	591	78%	5.8	0.9	0.8	9.6	6.5	4.8	7.4
Egypt	2010	7,028	81%	8.9	5.6	4.7	8.6	9.8	13.7	18.8
El Salvador	2009	1,247	81%	20.7	2.2	4.4	14.0	25.8	35.6	75.2
Estonia	2010	74	72%	5.5	1.3	0.0	7.1	4.5	7.5	7.4
Finland	2010	264	74%	5.0	0.7	1.0	8.3	5.0	4.4	7.6
France	2009	4,135	76%	6.4	1.2	1.0	12.6	7.6	5.4	7.5
Germany	2010	3,231	73%	4.0	0.9	0.8	7.7	3.7	3.6	4.8
Guatemala	2009	6	67%	0.0	0.0	0.0	0.0	0.1	0.1	0.0
Hong Kong SAR	2009	156	62%	2.2	0.4	0.5	1.5	1.3	2.4	6.6
Hungary	2009	931	75%	9.3	1.4	1.5	8.2	11.2	10.1	12.3
Iraq	2008	1,473	76%	5.2	3.9	3.1	4.0	6.1	10.3	13.1
Ireland	2010	169	75%	3.7	1.4	0.5	9.6	3.5	3.4	3.2
Israel	2009	240	80%	3.3	0.4	0.7	5.7	3.6	3.7	5.6
Italy	2009	4,416	79%	7.3	0.8	1.1	13.0	7.9	5.8	10.0
Japan	2010	6,530	67%	5.1	0.9	0.7	4.6	2.8	4.2	11.8
Kazakhstan[b]	2009	3,275	73%	20.6	5.9	5.4	20.0	30.0	25.0	21.2
Kyrgyzstan	2009	679	77%	13.0	4.1	3.6	9.6	21.0	21.5	14.4
Latvia	2010	216	70%	9.7	1.9	3.7	13.2	8.4	13.3	8.7
Lithuania	2010	305	75%	8.6	1.3	1.8	11.4	7.6	9.9	11.8
Mexico	2010	10,699	79%	9.5	3.3	2.2	12.4	12.3	11.4	14.4
Netherlands	2010	545	73%	3.3	0.8	0.7	5.2	2.8	2.6	6.7
New Zealand	2008	398	66%	9.4	4.0	2.7	20.4	8.9	7.7	11.3
Norway	2010	199	74%	4.3	0.8	0.2	7.3	3.9	4.7	6.0
Panama	2009	364	87%	10.8	2.7	2.5	11.6	16.0	12.4	18.3
Paraguay	2009	974	84%	15.5	4.6	2.8	25.9	19.6	17.0	18.7
Philippines	2008	6,938	79%	7.2	1.4	2.3	7.8	9.8	12.2	17.0
Poland	2010	3,609	78%	9.4	1.3	1.8	13.2	9.2	10.3	12.5
Portugal	2010	879	77%	8.2	0.9	1.0	7.8	8.9	8.4	13.5
Republic of Korea (South)	2010	6,621	73%	13.6	3.0	2.2	8.3	8.8	16.6	43.5
Romania	2010	2,051	76%	9.6	2.6	2.6	10.1	9.1	11.6	13.9
Russian Federation[b]	2010	28,558	73%	20.0	3.3	4.3	25.5	26.5	19.9	18.5
Serbia	2010	608	78%	8.3	2.6	1.3	9.2	7.7	9.4	12.6
Slovakia	2010	396	75%	7.2	1.0	2.8	10.1	7.1	7.9	9.4
Slovenia	2010	152	80%	7.6	1.1	0.6	8.4	8.1	7.6	11.7
South Africa	2009	5,655	75%	11.5	5.0	4.3	9.7	17.5	15.5	14.8
Spain	2010	2,407	79%	5.2	1.5	0.9	6.5	5.3	5.0	8.0
Sweden	2010	252	73%	2.7	0.4	0.8	4.2	2.4	2.9	3.6
Switzerland[b]	2007	415	78%	5.5	1.6	1.2	8.7	4.4	4.9	10.1
Ukraine[b]	2010	5,916	76%	13.0	1.4	2.9	15.7	16.8	13.8	11.5
United Kingdom	2010	1,967	74%	3.2	0.4	0.7	5.9	3.6	2.7	3.7
United States	2008	39,790	71%	13.1	2.8	2.5	20.6	14.9	13.3	16.9

Source: National Safety Council tabulations of World Health Organization (WHO) data.
[a]Population estimates based on data from WHO and the U.S. Census Bureau (International Data Base).
[b]Data include deaths due to all transportation-related causes, ICD codes V01-V99.

The International Classification of Diseases (ICD) system identifies unintentional poisonings by codes X40-X49, which include cases of unintentional poisoning by drugs, medicaments, biological substances, alcohol, solvents, gases, vapors, and pesticides. Other unintentional poisonings by unspecified chemicals and noxious substances also are included.

Unintentional poisoning injury-related deaths and death rates by age group, latest year available

Name	Year	Deaths		Deaths per 100,000 population[a]						
		Total	% male	All ages	0 to 4	5 to 14	15 to 24	25 to 44	45 to 64	65 and older
Argentina	2010	276	62%	0.7	1.3	0.2	0.2	0.5	1.0	1.5
Austria	2010	29	72%	0.3	0.0	0.1	0.3	0.3	0.3	0.7
Belarus	2009	896	81%	9.3	2.4	1.6	1.4	9.2	16.1	12.6
Brazil	2010	706	76%	0.4	0.1	0.0	0.3	0.5	0.6	0.5
Canada	2009	1,510	68%	4.5	0.1	0.1	2.8	6.7	6.8	2.6
Chile	2009	324	81%	2.0	0.2	0.1	1.0	2.0	4.0	3.3
Colombia	2009	100	80%	0.2	0.2	0.1	0.2	0.3	0.2	0.5
Costa Rica	2009	42	90%	0.9	0.0	0.0	0.2	1.2	2.1	2.2
Croatia	2010	130	72%	2.9	0.0	0.2	1.8	6.2	2.1	2.1
Cuba	2010	88	88%	0.8	0.2	0.0	0.1	0.6	1.9	1.1
Cyprus	2010	10	90%	0.9	0.0	0.0	0.5	1.9	0.4	0.9
Czech Republic	2010	325	79%	3.2	0.0	0.1	1.2	3.3	5.6	3.0
Egypt	2010	104	51%	0.1	0.2	0.0	0.2	0.1	0.1	0.2
El Salvador	2009	187	95%	3.1	0.2	0.0	0.7	5.0	7.9	7.6
Estonia	2010	220	76%	16.4	1.3	0.8	10.9	29.0	20.5	7.9
Finland	2010	704	74%	13.4	0.0	0.0	6.8	14.9	23.9	10.7
France	2009	1,596	53%	2.5	0.0	0.1	0.7	1.9	2.3	7.7
Germany	2010	678	74%	0.8	0.0	0.0	0.4	1.5	0.9	0.7
Guatemala	2009	818	85%	6.2	0.7	0.6	3.8	9.9	17.2	20.6
Hong Kong SAR	2009	125	75%	1.8	0.0	0.0	0.3	3.1	2.1	1.0
Hungary	2009	139	78%	1.4	0.0	0.2	0.7	1.5	1.8	2.0
Iraq	2008	12	42%	0.0	0.1	0.0	0.0	0.0	0.1	0.0
Ireland	2010	277	72%	6.0	0.0	0.0	2.7	9.4	9.1	4.8
Israel	2009	1	100%	0.0	0.0	0.0	0.0	0.0	0.0	0.1
Italy	2009	509	78%	0.8	0.0	0.0	0.7	1.5	0.7	0.8
Japan	2010	862	65%	0.7	0.0	0.0	0.4	1.0	0.8	0.7
Kazakhstan	2009	2,350	77%	14.8	3.7	0.9	5.1	22.6	27.0	17.0
Kyrgyzstan	2009	492	77%	9.5	2.2	0.6	2.5	13.8	25.8	17.2
Latvia	2010	184	78%	8.3	0.0	0.5	1.3	8.1	16.0	8.7
Lithuania	2010	543	78%	15.3	0.6	0.0	4.8	14.1	30.8	15.2
Mexico	2010	1,051	80%	0.9	0.5	0.2	0.7	1.1	1.6	2.1
Netherlands	2010	113	69%	0.7	0.0	0.0	0.5	1.1	0.8	0.7
New Zealand	2008	106	68%	2.5	0.0	0.3	1.8	4.8	2.9	1.3
Norway	2010	358	69%	7.7	0.0	0.2	5.6	11.9	11.6	4.4
Panama	2009	29	69%	0.9	3.0	0.3	0.5	0.7	0.7	1.3
Paraguay	2009	47	87%	0.7	0.7	0.2	0.3	0.6	2.1	1.4
Philippines	2008	212	68%	0.2	0.4	0.2	0.1	0.2	0.3	0.7
Poland	2010	1,539	83%	4.0	0.2	0.2	0.9	4.0	7.8	3.5
Portugal	2010	47	60%	0.4	0.2	0.0	0.0	0.6	0.3	1.0
Republic of Korea (South)	2010	224	77%	0.5	0.1	0.0	0.1	0.3	0.6	1.5
Romania	2010	1,092	72%	5.1	1.6	0.8	1.4	3.3	9.0	9.9
Russian Federation	2010	34,518	77%	24.2	2.3	1.2	7.4	31.5	39.0	20.4
Serbia	2010	76	72%	1.0	0.0	0.0	0.8	1.6	0.8	1.6
Slovakia	2010	128	76%	2.3	0.0	0.2	0.4	2.3	4.8	2.3
Slovenia	2010	66	77%	3.3	0.0	0.0	0.4	5.4	4.1	2.7
South Africa	2009	826	58%	1.7	9.8	0.2	0.4	0.9	1.4	2.5
Spain	2010	722	75%	1.6	0.0	0.0	0.6	2.3	1.5	2.0
Sweden	2010	398	75%	4.2	0.0	0.0	3.1	5.4	6.9	3.5
Switzerland	2007	208	73%	2.8	0.3	0.0	2.6	5.8	2.3	0.7
Ukraine	2010	6,635	79%	14.6	2.0	0.4	4.0	16.0	26.9	12.0
United Kingdom	2010	1,912	69%	3.1	0.1	0.0	1.9	5.6	4.0	1.6
United States	2008	31,116	66%	10.2	0.2	0.1	7.3	16.4	16.6	3.4

Source: National Safety Council tabulations of World Health Organization (WHO) data.
[a]Population estimates based on data from WHO and the U.S. Census Bureau (International Data Base).

International Fall Injury-Related Deaths and Death Rates

"Accidental falls" are identified by codes W00-W19 in the 10th revision of the International Classification of Diseases (ICD) system.

Unintentional fall injury-related deaths and death rates by age group, latest year available

Name	Year	Deaths Total	% male	Deaths per 100,000 population[a] All ages	0 to 4	5 to 14	15 to 24	25 to 44	45 to 64	65 and older
Argentina	2010	337	63%	0.8	0.2	0.1	0.2	0.4	0.9	4.1
Austria	2010	878	54%	10.5	0.8	0.1	0.8	1.4	5.2	48.2
Belarus	2009	1,124	78%	11.6	0.2	0.2	4.4	9.0	19.1	22.5
Brazil	2010	10,426	63%	5.3	0.7	0.3	0.8	2.2	6.2	47.6
Canada	2009	3,589	48%	10.7	0.3	0.1	0.6	0.8	3.5	62.0
Chile	2009	735	52%	4.4	0.5	0.1	0.7	1.3	3.5	35.7
Colombia	2009	1,279	77%	2.9	0.8	0.4	1.0	1.9	4.3	21.5
Costa Rica	2009	81	90%	1.8	0.0	0.3	0.6	1.2	3.7	10.5
Croatia	2010	1,058	42%	23.6	0.0	0.2	0.7	1.5	8.3	123.0
Cuba	2010	2,003	45%	18.0	0.2	0.2	0.6	1.2	5.1	143.3
Cyprus	2010	23	65%	2.1	0.0	0.0	0.5	0.8	1.9	12.5
Czech Republic	2010	1,370	52%	13.4	0.4	0.1	1.8	2.5	8.0	64.3
Egypt	2010	926	75%	1.2	2.2	0.8	1.1	1.0	1.3	2.4
El Salvador	2009	385	66%	6.4	1.5	0.3	2.1	3.4	6.9	62.7
Estonia	2010	92	68%	6.9	1.3	0.0	0.5	4.0	6.6	22.8
Finland	2010	1,185	53%	22.5	0.0	0.0	0.2	2.5	12.4	106.1
France	2009	5,909	49%	9.1	0.5	0.1	0.7	1.1	4.5	45.5
Germany	2010	9,479	46%	11.6	0.4	0.1	0.4	1.0	3.8	49.4
Guatemala	2009	14	93%	0.1	0.0	0.0	0.1	0.2	0.3	0.2
Hong Kong SAR	2009	197	59%	2.8	0.4	0.0	0.1	0.7	1.6	16.5
Hungary	2009	2,013	51%	20.1	0.2	0.0	0.5	2.3	14.3	94.3
Iraq	2008	260	72%	0.9	1.4	0.4	0.8	1.0	1.4	1.4
Ireland	2010	224	51%	4.8	0.0	0.0	0.2	1.2	5.9	27.5
Israel	2009	111	49%	1.5	0.3	0.0	0.3	0.6	1.3	10.8
Italy	2009	3,241	55%	5.4	0.3	0.1	0.5	1.0	2.4	21.8
Japan	2010	7,517	58%	5.9	0.4	0.2	0.7	0.8	2.7	21.3
Kazakhstan	2009	471	76%	3.0	1.8	0.7	2.2	3.6	4.1	5.3
Kyrgyzstan	2009	77	79%	1.5	0.9	0.3	0.8	1.5	3.9	3.2
Latvia	2010	140	70%	6.3	0.0	0.0	0.6	2.3	8.7	19.1
Lithuania	2010	305	73%	8.6	0.6	0.3	1.2	4.3	12.9	23.0
Mexico	2010	2,180	79%	1.9	0.8	0.3	0.8	1.3	3.3	11.3
Netherlands	2010	1,624	44%	9.8	0.3	0.1	0.4	0.4	3.0	56.6
New Zealand	2008	474	46%	11.1	0.7	0.2	2.1	0.8	3.3	77.9
Norway	2010	438	46%	9.4	0.0	0.0	1.1	1.2	2.5	52.9
Panama	2009	87	76%	2.6	0.6	0.6	1.4	2.2	2.8	15.2
Paraguay	2009	69	80%	1.1	0.7	0.2	0.5	0.9	1.7	6.6
Philippines	2008	1,901	67%	2.0	0.6	0.6	0.7	1.2	3.9	19.7
Poland	2010	3,755	55%	9.8	0.2	0.1	1.3	2.4	7.7	49.7
Portugal	2010	344	63%	3.2	0.4	0.1	0.2	1.0	2.8	12.2
Republic of Korea (South)	2010	2,128	76%	4.4	1.2	0.2	0.4	2.0	6.4	17.2
Romania	2010	1,417	79%	6.6	1.4	0.2	1.3	3.7	10.4	17.6
Russian Federation	2010	9,716	72%	6.8	1.7	0.6	3.2	5.9	8.7	15.3
Serbia	2010	317	64%	4.3	1.2	0.0	0.6	0.8	3.6	17.8
Slovakia	2010	460	71%	8.4	0.7	0.2	1.6	3.7	11.3	31.4
Slovenia	2010	525	49%	26.2	1.1	0.6	0.9	3.0	11.7	130.7
South Africa	2009	125	68%	0.3	0.1	0.0	0.1	0.2	0.5	1.6
Spain	2010	1,982	54%	4.3	0.6	0.0	0.4	1.1	2.5	19.0
Sweden	2010	875	55%	9.3	0.0	0.0	0.3	0.3	2.7	46.6
Switzerland	2007	1,308	46%	17.3	0.3	0.2	1.9	1.8	5.3	92.7
Ukraine	2010	2,288	78%	5.0	1.6	0.4	1.5	4.2	7.3	9.6
United Kingdom	2010	4,496	49%	7.2	0.2	0.0	0.4	1.2	3.3	36.7
United States	2008	24,013	51%	7.9	0.3	0.1	0.5	1.0	4.0	50.9

Source: National Safety Council tabulations of WHO data.
[a]Population estimates based on data from WHO and the U.S. Census Bureau (International Data Base).

The International Classification of Diseases (ICD) system identifies drowning by codes W65-W74, which include cases of
unintentional drowning and submersion while in or following
a fall in a bathtub, swimming pool, or natural body of water.
Other specified and unspecified cases of drowning and submersion also are included.

Unintentional drowning injury-related deaths and death rates by age group, latest year available

Name	Year	Deaths		Deaths per 100,000 population[a]						
		Total	% male	All ages	0 to 4	5 to 14	15 to 24	25 to 44	45 to 64	65 and older
Argentina	2010	566	82%	1.4	2.7	1.1	2.0	1.0	1.1	1.2
Austria	2010	43	70%	0.5	0.8	0.0	0.6	0.3	0.4	1.2
Belarus	2009	837	86%	8.7	2.8	4.9	7.9	10.1	10.1	8.4
Brazil	2010	5,548	87%	2.8	2.7	2.2	3.5	2.9	2.8	2.9
Canada	2009	237	82%	0.7	0.9	0.4	0.8	0.6	0.9	0.7
Chile	2009	447	88%	2.7	3.3	0.9	2.8	2.6	3.4	3.9
Colombia	2009	926	81%	2.1	4.4	2.0	2.8	1.6	1.2	2.3
Costa Rica	2009	91	84%	2.0	1.4	1.7	2.2	2.4	2.1	1.5
Croatia	2010	115	79%	2.6	0.0	0.6	1.5	1.1	3.8	5.7
Cuba	2010	224	92%	2.0	1.6	1.2	2.2	2.0	2.4	2.1
Cyprus	2010	27	74%	2.4	0.0	0.0	0.5	2.2	1.9	11.6
Czech Republic	2010	226	74%	2.2	1.3	0.5	1.5	1.8	3.0	3.4
Egypt	2010	1,233	83%	1.6	2.3	1.7	2.5	0.9	0.8	0.6
El Salvador	2009	223	81%	3.7	2.6	1.6	4.8	5.6	3.1	2.7
Estonia	2010	90	80%	6.7	3.9	3.1	4.9	5.8	9.2	8.8
Finland	2010	147	80%	2.8	1.5	0.7	0.6	1.5	4.2	5.6
France	2009	970	73%	1.5	1.2	0.3	0.8	0.9	2.0	3.2
Germany	2010	393	72%	0.5	0.8	0.3	0.3	0.2	0.4	1.0
Guatemala	2009	280	79%	2.1	2.3	0.8	2.3	2.8	2.4	4.2
Hong Kong SAR	2009	40	75%	0.6	0.0	0.3	0.3	0.5	0.5	1.5
Hungary	2009	177	79%	1.8	0.4	0.8	1.8	1.4	2.4	2.4
Iraq	2008	430	78%	1.5	2.9	1.3	2.0	0.8	1.1	1.3
Ireland	2010	31	84%	0.7	0.3	0.0	0.7	0.3	1.4	1.1
Israel	2009	35	71%	0.5	0.1	0.2	0.9	0.3	0.9	0.4
Italy	2009	399	80%	0.7	0.2	0.3	0.6	0.5	0.6	1.2
Japan	2010	6,948	54%	5.4	0.7	0.6	0.8	0.8	2.7	19.0
Kazakhstan	2009	861	82%	5.4	7.7	4.1	4.6	6.2	5.5	3.4
Kyrgyzstan	2009	243	74%	4.7	11.9	1.5	2.6	4.8	6.2	5.7
Latvia	2010	233	85%	10.5	5.7	4.2	10.1	8.9	15.4	10.6
Lithuania	2010	319	82%	9.0	4.4	3.9	5.0	7.6	15.2	9.3
Mexico	2010	2,424	85%	2.2	2.8	1.2	2.8	2.0	2.0	3.4
Netherlands	2010	80	81%	0.5	0.9	0.2	0.5	0.3	0.5	0.9
New Zealand	2008	58	76%	1.4	2.7	0.3	1.6	1.2	1.7	1.1
Norway	2010	50	84%	1.1	0.0	0.7	1.5	1.0	1.1	1.5
Panama	2009	124	90%	3.7	3.9	2.6	6.4	2.6	3.7	3.9
Paraguay	2009	182	86%	2.9	3.8	2.0	4.5	2.3	3.1	1.4
Philippines	2008	3,451	75%	3.6	4.3	3.6	2.9	3.0	4.2	6.6
Poland	2010	977	85%	2.5	0.9	0.8	2.6	2.3	3.8	2.3
Portugal	2010	72	81%	0.7	0.7	0.4	0.7	0.6	0.7	0.9
Republic of Korea (South)	2010	638	78%	1.3	0.3	0.7	1.0	0.8	1.6	3.5
Romania	2010	960	77%	4.5	2.5	3.6	4.0	3.1	6.0	6.6
Russian Federation	2010	11,981	85%	8.4	2.8	4.2	7.0	11.0	10.2	5.5
Serbia	2010	89	84%	1.2	0.3	1.3	1.0	0.7	1.8	1.5
Slovakia	2010	156	85%	2.9	2.4	1.1	2.1	2.2	4.5	3.5
Slovenia	2010	28	79%	1.4	0.0	0.6	0.9	1.0	1.9	2.4
South Africa	2009	1,412	78%	2.9	4.7	3.4	2.1	2.5	2.6	3.9
Spain	2010	432	77%	0.9	0.8	0.3	0.8	0.6	0.9	2.1
Sweden	2010	64	72%	0.7	0.5	0.3	0.5	0.3	0.5	1.9
Switzerland	2007	51	71%	0.7	1.1	0.4	0.8	0.4	0.6	1.2
Ukraine	2010	3,211	84%	7.1	3.5	4.4	6.7	8.5	8.4	5.1
United Kingdom	2010	264	80%	0.4	0.4	0.2	0.5	0.4	0.4	0.6
United States	2008	3,548	77%	1.2	2.4	0.6	1.3	1.0	1.1	1.4

Source: National Safety Council tabulations of World Health Organization (WHO) data.
[a]*Population estimates based on data from WHO and the U.S. Census Bureau (International Data Base).*

Counts and rates of fatal work-related injuries are shown on this page and the next. Comparisons between countries should be made with caution and take into account the differences in sources, coverage, and kinds of cases included.

Occupational deaths by country, 2004-2008

Country	Deaths 2004	2005	2006	2007	2008	Source of data	Maximum period[a]	Worker types[b]	% of total employment[c]	Economic activities excluded
Injuries only – compensated cases										
France	626	474	537	622	569	IR	varies	E	75	P
Injuries only – reported cases										
Austria	132	124	107	108	115	IR	none	E, SE	71	none
Azerbaijan	72	54	81	128	72	LR	–	E	–	–
Belarus	248	235	228	214	185	C	same year	E	–	none
Cyprus	(See: Injuries and commuting incidents)				12	LR	none	E	74	none
Czech Republic	185	163	152	188	174	AR	none	E, SE	95	AF, Pol
Hungary	160	125	123	118	116	LR	90 days	E, SE	98	none
Ireland	50	74	51	67	57	LR	none	E, SE	100	none
Japan	1,620	1,514	1,472	1,357	1,268	LR	–	E	–	C
Latvia	61	56	53	58	43	S, LR[d]	none	E	–	none
Norway	38	48	31	38	51	LR	none	E	100	none
Poland	490	468	493	479	520	LR	6 months	E, SE	76	Agr
Portugal	306	300	306	276	–	IR	1 year	E, SE	67	PA, AF
Singapore	51	44	61	63	67	AR	none	E	33	none
Slovakia	79	76	95	97	80	C	none	IE	98	none
Spain	695	662	682	572	530	IR	none	I	85	PA, AF
Sweden	57	67	68	75	68	IR	none	E, SE	97	none
Ukraine	1,068	989	972	1,069	927	LR	4 months	E	71	AF
United Kingdom	179	173	220	–	–	LR	1 year	E, SE	92	SF, AT
United States[e]	5,764	5,734	5,840	5,657	5,214	C	none	E, SE	100	none
Injuries and commuting incidents – compensated cases										
Croatia	38	62	76	73	79	IR	immediate	E, SE	84	none
Germany	949	863	941	812	765	IR	none	E, SE	100	none
Italy	930	918	987	847	780	IR	none	I	76	none
Injuries and commuting incidents – reported cases										
Cyprus	14	13	18	15	–	LR	none	E	74	none
Hong Kong, China	187	187	187	172	181	LR	none	E	77	none
Lithuania	94	118	108	101	77	LR	none	E, SE	64	AF
Macau, China	2	15	6	14	14	LR	none	E	56	P
Romania	432	531	423	485	497	LR	same year	E, SE	61	AF, P
Russian Federation	3,290	3,090	2,900	2,990	2,550	S	none	E	5	low rates
Slovenia	21	21	31	43	–	LR	1 month	I	85	none
Injuries and diseases – compensated cases										
Australia[f]	178	182	192	193	207	IR	3 years	E	83	AF
Canada	458	491	442	392	465	IR	none	E, SE	85	AF
Malta	12	6	8	7	3	IR	–	E, SE	–	none
Switzerland	67	45	51	59	42	IR	same year	IE	88	none
Injuries and diseases – reported cases										
Iceland	2	3	6	–	–	AR	–	E	–	none
Kazakhstan	345	357	414	341	341	LR	varies	E,SE	54	none
Sri Lanka	42	52	84	77	49	LR	1 year	E	35	M, E, TSC, C
Turkey	(See: Injuries, diseases, and commuting incidents)				866	IR	–	IE	25	none
Injuries, diseases, and commuting incidents – compensated cases										
Estonia	34	24	28	21	21	IR	1 year	I	100	AF, Pol
Israel	109	102	102	98	103	IR	same year	E, SE	100	none
Korea, Republic of[g]	1,417	1,288	1,238	1,267	1,332	IR	–	I	45	none
Thailand	861	1,444	808	741	–	IR	–	I	16	none
Injuries, diseases, and commuting incidents – reported cases										
Bahrain	14	29	25	22	23	IR	none	E, SE	100	none
Bulgaria	130	130	169	179	180	AR	–	E, SE	35	none
Jordan	52	63	87	–	–	IR	none	E	–	AF
Kyrgyzstan	41	24	22	23	23	LR	none	E	33	none
Mauritius	7	4	1	1	3	IR	30 days	E	75	P
Mexico	1,364	1,367	1,328	1,279	1,412	IR	none	IE	32	none
New Zealand	84	109	98	86	90	IR	1 year	E, SE	100	none
Turkey	843	1,096	1,601	1,044	–	IR	–	IE	25	none

Source: International Labour Organization, Department of Statistics, accessed Sept. 21, 2012, from http://laborsta.ilo.org.
Note: Dash (–) means data not available. See footnotes on page 195.

Source of data:
AR = Administrative reports
C = Census
IR = Insurance records
LR = Labor inspectorate records
S = Survey

Economic activites:
AF = Armed forces
Agr = Agriculture
ASO = Air, sea, offshore incidents
AT = Air transport
C = Construction
E = Electricity, gas, and water
Low = Activities with low rates of injuries

M = Manufacturing
P = Public sector
PA = Public administration
Pol = Police
SF = Sea fishing
TSC = Transport, storage, and communication

Worker types:
E = Employees
I = Insured persons
IE = Insured employees
SE = Self-employed

The International Labour Organization estimates that each year, about 2.34 million people die from work-related incidents and diseases, including about 321,000 fatal incidents and an estimated 2.02 million fatal work-related diseases. The total equates to about 6,300 worker deaths per day due to an incident or disease from their work.

Source: International Labour Organization. (2011). XIX World Congress on Safety and Health at Work – ILO Introductory Report: Global Trends and Challenges on Occupational Safety and Health. Accessed Sept. 24, 2012 from www.ilo.org/safework/info/publications/WCMS_162662/lang--en/index.htm.

Occupational death rates by country, 2004-2008

Country	Coverage[i]	2004	2005	2006	2007	2008
Deaths per 100,000 employees						
Injuries only						
Austria	RC	5	4.6	3.9	3.9	4.1
Belarus	RC	6.4	6.1	5.8	5.4	5.1
Cyprus	RC	(See: Injuries and commuting incidents)				3.9
Hungary	RC	4.1	3.2	3.13	3.01	2.99
Ireland	RC	2.5	3.3	2.2	2.8	2.5
Moldova, Republic of	RC	4.9	6.4	4.7	7.1	5.3
Myanmar[h]	RC	3	2	—	7	8.6
Norway	RC	1.7	2.1	1.3	1.6	2
Poland	RC	4.7	4.4	4.6	4.3	4.5
Sweden	RC	1.4	1.6	1.6	1.7	1.5
Ukraine	RC	8.9	8.4	8.3	9.3	8
United Kingdom	RC	0.7	0.6	0.72	—	—
United States[e]	RC	4	4	4	4	3.7
Injuries and commuting incidents						
Croatia	CC	2.7	4.3	5	4.7	5.2
Cyprus	RC	5.4	5	6	5	—
Germany	CC	2.57	2.38	2.54	2.16	2.04
Hong Kong, China	RC	7.7	7.5	7.3	6.6	6.8
Lithuania	RC	9	10.9	9.6	8.7	6.6
Macau, China	RC	—	—	—	4.66	4.33
Romania	RC	7	9	7	8	9
Russian Federation	RC	12.9	12.4	11.9	12.4	10.9
Injuries and diseases						
Australia[f]	CC	2.1	2	2.1	2	2.1
Canada	CC	2.9	3	2.7	2.3	2.7
Kazakhstan	RC	10.4	10.3	11.3	8.7	8.2
Malta	CC	8.1	4	5.2	4.5	1.9
Injuries, diseases, and commuting incidents						
Bahrain	RC	5	10	8	7	5
Israel	CC	3.3	3	3	2.6	—
Kyrgyzstan	RC	8	5	5	5	5
Deaths per 100,000 workers insured						
Injuries only						
Czech Republic	RC	4.2	3.7	3.4	4.1	3.8
France	CC	3.5	2.65	3.02	3.4	2
Portugal	RC	7	7	6	6.3	—
Slovakia	RC	3.91	3.72	4.6	4.1	4.2
Spain	RC	4.89	4.5	4.4	3.6	3.3
Injuries and commuting incidents						
Italy	CC	5	5	5	4	4
Slovenia	RC	2.6	2.6	3.8	5	—
Injuries and diseases						
Switzerland	CC	1.9	1.3	1.4	1.6	1.1
Turkey	RC	(See: Injuries, diseases, and commuting incidents)				9.8
Zimbabwe	RC	—	6.2	7.5	6.3	—
Injuries, diseases, and commuting incidents						
Bulgaria	RC	6	5.8	7.2	7.1	6.4
Estonia	CC	5.71	3.95	4.3	3.2	3.2
Mexico	RC	11	11	10	9	10
Thailand	CC	11.66	18.7	10.1	9.1	—
Turkey	RC	13.6	15.8	20.5	12.3	—
Deaths per 1,000,000 hours worked						
Injuries only						
Japan	RC	0.01	0.01	0.01	0.01	0
Injuries and diseases						
Sri Lanka	RC	0.007	0.009	0.0135	0.012	0.008
Injuries, diseases, and commuting incidents						
Jordan	RC	0.039	0.025	0.055	—	—
Korea, Republic of[g]	CC	0.06	0.05	0.05	0.04	0.05

See source and limitations of data on page 194.
Note: Dash (–) indicates data not available.
[a]*Maximum period between incident and death for death to be counted.*
[b]*Types of workers included in the data.*
[c]*Workers covered by the statistics as a percentage of total employment; latest year available.*
[d]*Survey for 2004-2006, labor inspectorate records for 2007-2008.*

[e]*Excludes farms with fewer than 11 employees.*
[f]*Excluding Victoria and Australian Capital Territory.*
[g]*Establishments with 10 or more workers.*
[h]*Establishments with 10 or more workers and using power, and those with 20 or more workers and without power.*
[i]*Includes reported cases (RC) and compensated cases (CC) of occupational fatalities.*

- Technical Appendix
- Other Sources
- Glossary
- Index

INJURY FACTS® 2013

This appendix gives a brief explanation of some of the sources and methods used by the National Safety Council Statistics Department in preparing the estimates of deaths, injuries, and costs presented in this book. Because many of the estimates depend on death certificate data provided by the states or the National Center for Health Statistics (NCHS), it begins with a brief introduction to the certification and classification of deaths.

Certification and classification. The medical certification of death involves entering information on the death certificate about the disease or condition directly leading to death, antecedent causes, and other significant conditions. The death certificate is then registered with the appropriate authority and a code is assigned for the underlying cause of death. The underlying cause is defined as "(a) the disease or injury which initiated the train of morbid events leading directly to death, or (b) the circumstances of the accident or violence which produced the fatal injury" (World Health Organization [WHO], 1992). Deaths are classified and coded on the basis of a WHO standard, the *International Statistical Classification of Diseases and Related Health Problems*, commonly known as the International Classification of Diseases or ICD (WHO, 1992). For deaths due to injury and poisoning, the ICD provides a system of "external cause" codes to which the underlying cause of death is assigned. (See pages 20-21 of *Injury Facts* for a condensed list of external cause codes.)

Comparability across ICD revisions. The ICD is revised periodically and these revisions can affect comparability from year to year. The sixth revision (1948) substantially expanded the list of external causes and provided for classifying the place of occurrence. Changes in the classification procedures for the sixth revision as well as the seventh (1958) and eighth (1968) revisions classified as diseases some deaths previously classified as injuries. The eighth revision also expanded and reorganized some external cause sections. The ninth revision (1979), provided more detail on the agency involved, the victims' activity, and the place of occurrence. The tenth revision, which was adopted in the United States effective with 1999 data, completely revised the transportation-related categories. Specific external cause categories affected by the revisions are noted in the historical tables.

The table at the end of this appendix (page 202) shows the ICD-9 codes, the ICD-10 codes, and a comparability ratio for each of the principal causes of unintentional-injury death. The comparability ratio represents the net effect of the new revision on statistics for the cause of death. The comparability ratio was obtained by classifying a sample of death certificates under both ICD-9 and ICD-10 and then dividing the number of deaths for a selected cause classified under ICD-10 by the number classified to the most nearly comparable ICD-9 cause. A comparability ratio of 1.00 indicates no net change due to the new classification scheme. A ratio less than 1.00 indicates fewer deaths assigned to a cause under ICD-10 than under ICD-9. A ratio greater than 1.00 indicates an increase in assignment of deaths to a cause under ICD-10 compared to ICD-9.

The broad category of "accidents" or "unintentional injuries" under ICD-9 included complications and misadventures of surgical and medical care (E870-E879) and adverse effects of drugs in therapeutic use (E930-E949). These categories are not included in "accidents" or "unintentional injuries" under ICD-10. In 1998, deaths in these two categories numbered 3,228 and 276, respectively.

Under ICD-9, the code range for falls (E880-E888) included a code for "fracture, cause unspecified" (E887). A similar code does not appear in ICD-10 (W00-W19), which probably accounts for the low comparability ratio (0.8409). In 1998, deaths in code E887 numbered 3,679.

Beginning with 1970 data, tabulations published by NCHS no longer include deaths of nonresident aliens. In 2009, there were 771 such unintentional deaths, of which 257 were motor vehicle related.

Fatality estimates. The Council uses four classes and three venues to categorize unintentional injuries. The four classes are Motor Vehicle, Work, Home, and Public. Each class represents an environment and an intervention route for injury prevention through a responsible authority such as a police department, an employer, a home owner, or public health department. The three venues are Transportation, Work, and Home and Community.

Motor vehicle. The Motor Vehicle class can be identified by the underlying cause of death (see the table on page 202).

Work. The National Safety Council adopted the Bureau of Labor Statistics' Census of Fatal Occupational Injuries (CFOI) figure, beginning with the 1992 data year, as the authoritative count of unintentional work-related deaths. The CFOI system is described in detail in Toscano and Windau (1994).

The 2-Way Split. After subtracting the Motor Vehicle and Work figures from the unintentional injury total (ICD-10 codes V01-X59, Y85- Y86), the remainder belong to the Home and Public classes. The Home class can be identified by the "place of occurrence" subclassification (code .0) used with most nontransport deaths; the Public class is the remainder. Missing "place of occurrence" information, however, prevents the direct determination of the Home and Public class totals. Because of this, the Council allocates non-motor vehicle, nonwork deaths into the Home and Public classes based on the external cause, age group, and cases with specified "place of occurrence." This procedure, known as the 2-Way Split, uses the most recent death certificate data available from the NCHS and the CFOI data for the same calendar year. For each cause-code group and age group combination, the Motor Vehicle and Work deaths are subtracted and the remainder, including those with "place of occurrence" unspecified, are allocated to Home and Public in the same proportion as those with "place of occurrence" specified.

The table on page 202 shows the ICD-10 cause-codes and CFOI event codes for the most common causes of unintentional-injury death. The CFOI event codes (BLS, 1992) do not match exactly with ICD cause codes, so there is some error in the allocation of deaths among the classes.

State reporting system. The Council operates a reporting system through which participating states send tabulations of unintentional-injury death data by age group, class, and type of event or industry. This is known as the Injury Mortality Tabulation reporting system. These data are used to validate current year estimates based on the most recent 2-Way Split and CFOI data.

Linking up to current year. The benchmark data published by NCHS are usually 2 years old and the final CFOI data are usually 1 year old. Starting with the 2011 edition of *Injury Facts*, an exponential smoothing technique is used to make current year estimates. Exponential smoothing is a statistical technique to make short-term forecasts. In exponential smoothing (as opposed to in moving averages smoothing) older data are given progressively less relative weight (importance) whereas newer data are given progressively greater weight. The results of the exponential smoothing is then compared against the latest reported state data for validation.

Revisions of prior years. When the figures for a given year are published by NCHS, the 2-Way Split based on those figures and the CFOI become the final estimate of unintentional injury deaths by class, age group, and type of event or industry. Subsequent years are revised by repeating the exponential smoothing and state data process described above. For example, in the current edition of *Injury Facts*, the 2009 NCHS and CFOI data were used to produce final estimates using the 2-Way Split, the 2010 estimates were revised, and the new 2011 estimates were made with the state data available in the late summer of 2012 together with 2011 preliminary CFOI data.

Nonfatal injury estimates. Starting with the 2011 edition of *Injury Facts*, the Council adopted the concept of "medically consulted injury" to define the kinds of injuries included in its estimates. Prior editions of *Injury Facts* used the definition of disabling injury. There is no national injury surveillance system that provides injury estimates on a current basis. The National Health Interview System, a household survey conducted by NCHS (see page 25), produces national estimates using its own definition of medically consulted injury (Adams, Heyman, & Vickerie, 2009). A medically consulted injury as defined by NCHS is an injury serious enough that a medical professional was consulted. The Council uses the medically consulted injury estimates from the National Health Interview Survey for its motor vehicle, home, and public injury estimates. In addition, the Occupational Safety and Health Administration (OSHA) defines an injury or illness using criteria includ-

ing "Medical treatment beyond first aid." The Council uses the total recordable case estimate defined by OSHA and published by the Bureau of Labor Statistics (BLS) to estimate the number of workplace injuries. Because BLS's estimate excludes the self-employed, unpaid family workers, and federal government employees, the Council uses total employment estimates, as well as BLS nonfatal estimates, to calculate the total number of nonfatal medically consulted injuries.

Injury-to-death ratios. Because estimates for medically consulted injuries are not available for the current year, the Council uses injury-to-death ratios to estimate nonfatal medically consulted injuries for the current year. Complete documentation of the procedure, effective with the 1993 edition, may be found in Landes, Ginsburg, Hoskin, and Miller (1990). The resulting estimates are not direct measures of nonfatal injuries and should not be compared with prior years.

Population sources. All population figures used in computing rates are estimates taken from various reports published by the Bureau of the Census, U.S. Department of Commerce, on their website (*www.census.gov*). Resident population is used for computing rates.

Costs (pages 6-9). The procedures for estimating the economic losses due to fatal and nonfatal unintentional injuries were extensively revised for the 1993 edition of *Accident Facts*. New components were added, new benchmarks adopted, and a new discount rate assumed. All of these changes resulted in significantly higher cost estimates. For this reason, it must be re-emphasized that the cost estimates should not be compared to those in earlier editions of the book.

The Council's general philosophy underlying its cost estimates is that the figures represent income not received or expenses incurred because of fatal and nonfatal unintentional injuries. Stated this way, the Council's cost estimates are a measure of the economic impact of unintentional injuries and may be compared to other economic measures such as gross domestic product, per capita income, or personal consumption expenditures. (See page 109 and "lost quality of life" [page 201] for a discussion of injury costs for cost-benefit analysis.)

The general approach followed was to identify a benchmark unit cost for each component, adjust the benchmark to the current year using an appropriate inflator, estimate the number of cases to which the component applied, and compute the product. Where possible, benchmarks were obtained for each class: Motor Vehicle, Work, Home, and Public.

Wage and productivity losses include the value of wages, fringe benefits, and household production for all classes, and travel delay for the Motor Vehicle class.

For fatalities, the present value of after-tax wages, fringe benefits, and household production was computed using the human capital method. The procedure incorporates data on life expectancy from the NCHS life tables, employment likelihood from the Bureau of Labor Statistics household survey, and mean earnings from the Bureau of the Census money income survey. The discount rate used was 4%, reduced from 6% used in earlier years. The present value obtained is highly sensitive to the discount rate; the lower the rate, the greater the present value.

For permanent partial disabilities, an average of 17% of earning power is lost (Berkowitz & Burton, 1987). The incidence of permanent disabilities, adjusted to remove intentional injuries, was computed from data on hospitalized cases from the National Hospital Discharge Survey (NHDS) and nonhospitalized cases from the National Health Interview Survey (NHIS) and National Council on Compensation Insurance data on probabilities of disability by nature of injury and part of body injured.

For temporary disabilities, an average daily wage, fringe benefit, and household production loss was calculated and this was multiplied by the number of days of restricted activity from the NHIS.

Travel delay costs were obtained from the Council's estimates of the number of fatal, injury, and property damage crashes and an average delay cost per crash from Miller et al. (1991).

Medical expenses, including ambulance and helicopter transport costs, were estimated for fatalities, hospitalized cases, and nonhospitalized cases in each class.

The incidence of hospitalized cases was derived from the NHDS data adjusted to eliminate intentional injuries. Average length of stay was benchmarked from Miller, Pindus, Douglass, and Rossman (1993b) and adjusted to estimate lifetime length of stay. The cost per hospital day was benchmarked to the National Medical Expenditure Survey (NMES).

Nonhospitalized cases were estimated by taking the difference between total NHIS injuries and hospitalized cases. Average cost per case was based on NMES data adjusted for inflation and lifetime costs.

Medical cost of fatalities was benchmarked to data from the National Council on Compensation Insurance (1989) to which was added the cost of a premature funeral and coroner costs (Miller et al., 1991).

Cost per ambulance transport was benchmarked to NMES data and cost per helicopter transport was benchmarked to data in Miller et al. (1993a). The number of cases transported was based on data from Rice and MacKenzie (1989) and the National Electronic Injury Surveillance System.

Administrative expenses include the administrative cost of private and public insurance, which represents the cost of having insurance, and police and legal costs.

The administrative cost of motor vehicle insurance was the difference between premiums earned (adjusted to remove fire, theft, and casualty premiums) and pure losses incurred, based on data from A. M. Best. Workers' compensation insurance administration was based on A. M. Best data for private carriers and regression estimates using Social Security Administration data for state funds and the self-insured. Administrative costs of public insurance (mainly Medicaid and Medicare) amount

to about 4% of the medical expenses paid by public insurance, which were determined from Rice and MacKenzie (1989) and Hensler et al. (1991).

Average police costs for motor vehicle crashes were taken from Miller et al. (1991) and multiplied by the Council's estimates of the number of fatal, injury, and property damage crashes.

Legal expenses include court costs, and plaintiff's and defendant's time and expenses. Hensler et al. (1991) provided data on the proportion of injured persons who hire a lawyer, file a claim, and get compensation. Kakalik and Pace (1986) provided data on costs per case.

Fire losses were based on data published by the National Fire Protection Association in the NFPA Journal. The allocation into the classes was based on the property use for structure fires and other NFPA data for nonstructure fires.

Motor vehicle damage costs were benchmarked to Blincoe and Faigin (1992) and multiplied by the Council's estimates of crash incidence.

Employer costs for work injuries is an estimate of the productivity costs incurred by employers. It assumes each fatality or permanent injury resulted in four person-months of disruption, serious injuries one person-month, and minor to moderate injuries two person-days. All injuries to nonworkers were assumed to involve two days of worker productivity loss. Average hourly earnings for supervisors and nonsupervisory workers were computed and then multiplied by the incidence and hours lost per case. Property damage and production delays (except motor vehicle related) are not included in the estimates but can be substantial.

Lost quality of life is the difference between the value of a statistical fatality or statistical injury and the value of after-tax wages, fringe benefits, and household production. Because this does not represent real income not received or expenses incurred, it is not included in the total economic cost figure. If included, the resulting *comprehensive costs* can be used in cost-benefit analysis because the total costs then represent the maximum amount society should spend to prevent a statistical death or injury.

Work deaths and injuries (page 58). The method for estimating total work-related deaths and injuries is discussed above. The breakdown of deaths by industry division for the current year is obtained from CFOI. The estimate of nonfatal medically consulted injuries by industry division is made using the Survey of Occupational Injury and Illness' estimate of total recordable injury and illness after correcting for the exclusion of self-employed, unpaid family workers, and federal government employees.

Employment. The employment estimates for 1992 to the present were changed for the 1998 edition. Estimates for these years in prior editions are not comparable. The total employment figure used by the Council represents the number of persons in the civilian labor force, aged 16 and older, who were wage or salary workers, self-employed, or unpaid family workers, plus active duty military personnel resident in the United States. The total employment estimate is a combination of three figures –total civilian employment from the Current Population Survey (CPS) as published in *Employment and Earnings*, plus the difference between total resident population and total civilian population, which represents active duty military personnel.

Employment by industry is obtained from an unpublished Bureau of Labor Statistics table titled "Employed and experience unemployed persons by detailed industry and class of worker, Annual Average [year] (based on CPS)."

Time lost (page 62) is the product of the number of cases and the average time lost per case. Deaths average 150 workdays lost in the current year and 5,850 in future years; permanent disabilities involve 75 and 565 days lost in current and future years, respectively; temporary disabilities involve 17 days lost in the current year only. Off-the-job injuries to workers are assumed to result in similar lost time.

Off-the-job (page 63) deaths and injuries are estimated by assuming that employed persons incur injuries at the same rate as the entire population.

Motor vehicle (pages 104-139). Estimates of miles traveled, registered vehicles and licensed drivers are published by the Federal Highway Administration in *Highway Statistics and Traffic Volume Trends*.

Selected unintentional-injury-related code groupings

Manner of injury	ICD-9 codes[a]	ICD-10 codes[b]	Comparability ratio[c]	OI&ICM[d] event codes
Unintentional injuries	E800-E869, E880-E929[e]	V01-X59, Y85-Y86	1.0305 (1.0278-1.0333)[f]	00-60, 63-9999
Railway accident	E800-E807	V05, V15, V80.6, V81(.2-.9)	n/a	44
Motor vehicle accident	E810-E825	V02-V04, V09.0, V09.2, V12-V14, V19.0-V19.2, V19.4-V19.6, V20-V79, V80.3-V80.5, V81.0-V81.1, V82.0-V82.1, V83-V86, V87.0-V87.8, V88.0-V88.8, V89.0, V89.2	0.9754 (0.9742-0.9766)	41, 42, 43 with source = 82, 83
Water transport accident	E830-E838	V90-V94	n/a	45
Air transport accident	E840-E845	V95-V97	n/a	46
Poisoning by solids or liquids	E850-58, E860-66	X40-X49	n/a	344
Poisoning by gases or vapors	E867-E869			341
Falls	E880-E888	W00-W19	0.8409 (0.8313-0.8505)	1
Fires or burns	E890-E899	X00-X09	0.9743 (0.9568-0.9918)	51
Drowning[g]	E910	W65-W74	0.9965 (0.9716-1.0213)	381
Choking[h]	E911-E912	W78-W80	n/a	382
Mechanical suffocation	E913	W75-W77, W81-W84	n/a	383, 384, 389
Firearms	E922	W32-W34	1.0579 (1.0331-1.0828)	0220, 0222, 0229 with source = 911[i]

Source: National Safety Council.
Note: n/a means comparability ratio not calculated or does not meet standards of reliability or precision.
[a]*WHO (1977).*
[b]*WHO (1992).*
[c]*Hoyert, A.S., et al. (2001). Table III.*
[d]*Bureau of Labor Statistics (1992).*
[e]*The National Safety Council has used E800-E949 for unintentional injuries. The code group in the table omits complications and misadventures of surgical and medical care (E870-E879) and adverse effects of drugs in therapeutic use (E930-E949).*
[f]*Figures in parentheses are the 95% confidence interval for the comparability ratio.*
[g]*Excludes transport.*
[h]*Suffocation by ingestion or inhalation.*
[i]*Struck by flying object where the source of injury was a bullet.*

Berkowitz, M., & Burton, J.F., Jr. (1987). *Permanent Disability Benefits in Workers' Compensation*. Kalamazoo, MI: W.E. Upjohn Institute for Employment Research.

Blincoe, L.J., & Faigin, B.M. (1992). *Economic Cost of Motor Vehicle Crashes, 1990*. Springfield, VA: National Technical Information Service.

Bureau of Labor Statistics [BLS]. (1992). *Occupational Injury & Illness Classification Manual*. Washington, DC: Author.

Bureau of Labor Statistics [BLS]. (2012, October 25). *Workplace Injuries and Illnesses* in 2011. Press release USDL-12-2121.

Hensler, D.R., Marquis, M.S., Abrahamse, A.F., Berry, S.H., Ebener, P.A., Lewis, E.D., Lind, E.A., MacCoun, R.J., Manning, W.G., Rogowski, J.A., & Vaiana, M.E. (1991). *Compensation for Accidental Injuries* in the United States. Santa Monica, CA: The RAND Corporation.

Hoyert, D.L., Arias, E., Smith, B.L., Murphy, S.L., & Kochanek, K.D. (2001). Deaths: final data for 1999. *National Vital Statistics Reports, 49*(8).

Kakalik, J.S., & Pace, N. (1986). *Costs and Compensation Paid in Tort Litigation*. R-3391-ICJ. Santa Monica, CA: The RAND Corporation.

Landes, S.R., Ginsburg, K.M., Hoskin, A.F., & Miller, T.A. (1990). *Estimating Nonfatal Injuries*. Itasca, IL: Statistics Department, National Safety Council.

Miller, T., Viner, J., Rossman, S., Pindus, N., Gellert, W., Douglass, J., Dillingham, A., & Blomquist, G.. (1991). *The Costs of Highway Crashes*. Springfield, VA: National Technical Information Service.

Miller, T.R., Brigham, P.A., Cohen, M.A., Douglass, J.B., Galbraith, M.S., Lestina, D.C., Nelkin. V.S., Pindus, N.M., & Smith-Regojo. P. (1993a). Estimating the costs to society of cigarette fire injuries. *Report to Congress in Response to the Fire Safe Cigarette Act of 1990*. Washington, DC: U.S. Consumer Product Safety Commission.

Miller, T.R., Pindus, N.M., Douglass, J.B., & Rossman, S.B. (1993b). *Nonfatal Injury Incidence, Costs, and Consequences: A Data Book*. Washington, DC: The Urban Institute Press.

Occupational Safety and Health Administration (2005). OSHA recordkeeping handbook. OSHA 3245-01R.

Rice, D.P., & MacKenzie, E.J. (1989). *Cost of Injury in the United States: A Report to Congress*. Atlanta, GA: Centers for Disease Control and Prevention.

Adams, P.F., Heyman, K.M., & Vickerie, J.L. (2009). Summary health statistics for the U.S. population: National health interview survey, 2008. *Vital and Health Statistics, Series 10, No. 243*. Hyattsville, MD: National Center for Health Statistics.

Toscano, G., & Windau, J. (1994). The changing character of fatal work injuries. *Monthly Labor Review, 117*(10), 17-28.

World Health Organization. (1977). *Manual of the International Statistical Classification of Diseases, Injuries, and Causes of Death*. Geneva, Switzerland: Author.

World Health Organization. (1992). *International Statistical Classification of Diseases and Related Health Problems – Tenth Revision*. Geneva, Switzerland: Author.

The following organizations may be useful for obtaining more current data or more detailed information on various subjects in *Injury Facts*.

American Association of Poison Control Centers
(703) 894-1858
www.aapcc.org, info@aapcc.org

Bureau of Labor Statistics
U.S. Department of Labor
(202) 691-5200
www.bls.gov
blsdata_staff@bls.gov

Bureau of the Census
U.S. Department of Commerce
(800) 923-8282
www.census.gov

Centers for Disease Control and Prevention
(800) 232-4636
www.cdc.gov, cdcinfo@cdc.gov

Federal Aviation Administration
U.S. Department of Transportation
(866) 835-5322
www.faa.gov

Federal Highway Administration
U.S. Department of Transportation
(202) 366-4000
www.fhwa.dot.gov
execsecretariat.fhwa@fhwa.dot.gov

Federal Motor Carrier Safety Administration
U.S. Department of Transportation
(800) 832-5660
www.fmcsa.dot.gov

Federal Railroad Administration
U.S. Department of Transportation
(202) 493-6065
www.fra.dot.gov

International Labour Organization
Phone: +41-22-799-6111
Fax: +41-22-798-8685
www.ilo.org, ilo@ilo.org

Mine Safety and Health Administration
(202) 693-9400
www.msha.gov

National Center for Health Statistics
(800) 232-4636
www.cdc.gov/nchs

National Center for Statistics and Analysis
(202) 366-4198 or (800) 934-8517
www.nhtsa.dot.gov
NCSAweb@nhtsa.dot.gov

National Climatic Data Center
(828) 271-4800
www.ncdc.noaa.gov/oa/ncdc.html
ncdc.info@noaa.gov

National Collegiate Athletic Association
(317) 917-6222
www.ncaa.org

National Council on Compensation Insurance
(566) 893-1000
www.ncci.com

National Fire Protection Association
(617) 770-3000 or (800) 344-3555
www.nfpa.org
custserv@nfpa.org

National Highway Traffic Safety Administration
U.S. Department of Transportation
www.nhtsa.gov
(800) 877-8339

National Sporting Goods Association
(800) 815-5422
www.nsga.org
info@nsga.org

Occupational Safety and Health Administration
U.S. Department of Labor
(800) 321-OSHA (6742)
www.osha.gov

Substance Abuse and Mental Health Services Administration
(877) 726-4727
www.samhsa.gov

Transportation Research Board
(202) 334-2934
http://gulliver.trb.org

U.S. Coast Guard
(800) 368-5647
www.uscgboating.org
uscginfoline@gcrm.com

U.S. Consumer Product Safety Commission
(301) 504-7923
www.cpsc.gov
clearinghouse@cpsc.gov

World Health Organization
Phone: +41-22-791-2111
www.who.int
info@who.int

Accident is that occurrence in a sequence of events that produces unintended injury, death, or property damage. Accident refers to the event, not the result of the event (see Unintentional injury). The term "accident" has largely been replaced in the public health community with the term "incident."

Death from incident is a death that occurs within one year of the incident.

Disabling injury is an injury causing death, permanent disability, or any degree of temporary total disability beyond the day of the injury. Starting with the 2012 edition of *Injury Facts*, the definition of disabling injury was replaced by medically consulted injury for all non-fatal injury estimates.

Fatal incident is an incident that results in one or more deaths within one year.

Home is a dwelling and its premises within the property lines including single family dwellings and apartment houses, duplex dwellings, boarding and rooming houses, and seasonal cottages. Excluded from home are barracks, dormitories, and resident institutions.

Incidence rate, as defined by OSHA, is the number of occupational injuries and/or illnesses or lost workdays per 100 full-time employees (see formula on page 74).

Incident is the preferred term for "accident" in the public health community. It refers to the occurrence in a sequence of events that produces unintended injury, death, or property damage. Incident refers to the event, not the result of the event (see Unintentional injury).

Injury is physical harm or damage to the body resulting from an exchange, usually acute, of mechanical, chemical, thermal, or other environmental energy that exceeds the body's tolerance.

Medically consulted injury is an injury serious enough that a medical professional was consulted. For the motor vehicle, home and public venues, the National Safety Council uses the medically consulted injury estimates from the National Health Interview survey. The Council uses the total recordable case estimate, using OSHA's definition, published by the Bureau of Labor Statistics (BLS) to estimate the number of workplace injuries. Because the BLS estimate excludes self-employed, unpaid family workers, and federal government employees, the Council extrapolates the BLS estimate to reflect the total worker population.

Motor vehicle is any mechanically or electrically powered device not operated on rails, upon which or by which any person or property may be transported upon a land highway. The load on a motor vehicle or trailer attached to it is considered part of the vehicle. Tractors and motorized machinery are included while self-propelled in transit or used for transportation. Non-motor vehicle is any road vehicle other than a motor vehicle, such as a bicycle or animal-drawn vehicle, except a coaster wagon, child's sled, child's tricycle, child's carriage, and similar means of transportation; persons using these latter means of transportation are considered pedestrians.

Motor vehicle incident is an unstabilized situation that includes at least one harmful event (injury or property damage) involving a motor vehicle in transport (in motion, in readiness for motion, or on a roadway but not parked in a designated parking area) that does not result from discharge of a firearm or explosive device and does not directly result from a cataclysm. [See Committee on Motor Vehicle Traffic Accident Classification (1997), *Manual on Classification of Motor Vehicle Traffic Accidents,* ANSI D16.1-1996, Itasca, IL: National Safety Council.]

Motor vehicle traffic incident is a motor vehicle incident that occurs on a trafficway – a way or place, any part of which is open to the use of the public for the purposes of vehicular traffic. A motor vehicle nontraffic incident is any motor vehicle incident that occurs entirely in any place other than a trafficway.

Nonfatal injury incident is an incident in which at least one person is injured and no injury results in death.

Occupational illness is any abnormal condition or disorder other than one resulting from an occupational injury caused by exposure to environmental factors associated with employment. It includes acute and chronic illnesses or diseases that may be caused by inhalation, absorption, ingestion, or direct contact (see also pages 79 and 101).

Occupational injury is any injury such as a cut, fracture, sprain, amputation, etc., that results from a work incident or from a single instantaneous exposure in the work environment (see also page 79).

Pedalcycle is a vehicle propelled by human power and operated solely by pedals; excludes mopeds.

Pedestrian is any person involved in a motor vehicle incident who is not in or upon a motor vehicle or non-motor vehicle. Includes persons injured while using a coaster wagon, child's tricycle, roller skates, etc. Excludes persons boarding, alighting, jumping, or falling from a motor vehicle in transport who are considered occupants of the vehicle.

Permanent disability (or permanent impairment) includes any degree of permanent nonfatal injury. It includes any injury that results in the loss or complete loss of use of any part of the body or in any permanent impairment of functions of the body or a part thereof.

Property damage incident is an incident that results in property damage but in which no person is injured.

Public incident is any incident other than motor vehicle that occurs in the public use of any premises. Includes deaths in recreation (swimming, hunting, etc.), in transportation except motor vehicle, public buildings, etc., and from widespread natural disasters even though some may have happened on home premises. Excludes incidents to people in the course of gainful employment.

Source of injury is the principal object such as tool, machine, or equipment involved in the incident and is usually the object inflicting injury or property damage. Also called agency or agent.

Temporary total disability is an injury that does not result in death or permanent disability but that renders the injured person unable to perform regular duties or activities on one or more full calendar days after the day of the injury.

Total cases include all work-related deaths and illnesses and those work-related injuries that result in loss of consciousness, restriction of work or motion, or transfer to another job, or require medical treatment other than first aid.

Unintentional injury is the preferred term for accidental injury in the public health community. It refers to the result of an incident.

Work hours are the total number of hours worked by all employees. They are usually compiled for various levels, such as an establishment, a company, or an industry. A work hour is the equivalent of one employee working one hour.

Work injuries (including occupational illnesses) are those that arise out of and in the course of gainful employment regardless of where the accident or exposure occurs. Excluded are work injuries to private household workers and injuries occurring in connection with farm chores that are classified as home injuries.

Workers are all persons gainfully employed, including owners, managers, other paid employees, the self-employed, and unpaid family workers but excluding private household workers.

Work/motor vehicle duplication includes work injuries that occur in motor vehicle incidents (see Work injuries and Motor vehicle incident).